The Air Pilot's **Ma**

Volume 6

Human Performance & Limitations and Operational Procedures

'Recommended reading'
Civil Aviation Authority

POOLEY'S
Air Pilot Publishing

Copyright © 2017 Pooleys-Air Pilot Publishing

ISBN 978-1-84336-234-0

First Edition published 1994
Reprinted 1995
Reprinted 1997
Second Edition 1997
Reprinted 1998, 1999
Reprinted with revisions 2001
Reprinted 2002
Reprinted with revisions 2003
Third Edition 2004
Reprinted with revisions and colour illustrations 2006
Reprinted with revisions 2009
Fourth Edition 2011
Fifth Edition 2013
New Combined Edition 2015
Second Combined Edition 2017

Origination by Pooleys-Air Pilot Publishing Limited.

Printed in England by Portland Print, Kettering NN16 8UN.

Published by Pooleys-Air Pilot Publishing Ltd
Elstree Aerodrome, Elstree, Hertfordshire, WD6 3AW. UK.
Tel: +44(0)208 207 3749
Web: www.pooleys.com
Email: sales@pooleys.com

The Air Pilot's **Manual**

Volume 6 Combined Edition

Contents

Human Performance & Limitations

Introduction _____ vii

Section One – Human Performance and Limitations
1. Human Physiology and High Altitudes _____ 3
2. Eyesight and Visual Illusions _____ 23
3. Hearing and Balance _____ 49
4. Am I Fit to Fly? _____ 65
5. Stress Management, Fatigue and Sleep _____ 73
6. Information Processing _____ 105
7. Judgement and Decision-Making _____ 129
8. Airmanship and Threat and Error Management _____ 141
9. The Flight Deck _____ 151

Section Two – Safety, First Aid and Survival
10. Safety and Care of Passengers _____ 193
11. First Aid _____ 207
12. Survival _____ 215

Index _____ 241

Editorial Team

Dorothy Saul-Pooley LLB(Hons) FRAeS

Dorothy holds an ATPL (A) and a CPL (H), and is both an instructor and examiner on aeroplanes and an instructor on helicopters. She is Head of Training for a school dedicated to running Flight Instructor courses at Shoreham. She is also a CAA Flight Instructor Examiner. In addition, having qualified as a solicitor in 1982, Dorothy acted for many years as a consultant specialising in aviation and insurance liability issues, and has lectured widely on air law and aviation insurance. This highly unusual combination of qualifications led to her appointment as Honorary Solicitor to the Guild of Air Pilots and Navigators (GAPAN).

Dorothy is a Fellow of the Royal Aeronautical Society, Past Chairman of the GAPAN Instructor Committee of which she was a founding member and the prime instigator of the Guild's Joint Forum with Central Flying School at RAF Cranwell for Senior Flying Instructors. She is a Past Chairman of the Education & Training Committee. After serving as a Warden on the Court of GAPAN for three years, she was appointed Master for the year 2014-2015 of the newly renamed Honourable Company of Air Pilots. She is also Chairman of the Professional Flying Instructors Association.

In 2003 Dorothy was awarded the Jean Lennox Bird Trophy for her contribution to aviation and support of Women in Aviation and the BWPA (British Women Pilots Association). In 2013, Dorothy received the prestigious award of a Master Air Pilots Certificate from GAPAN. In 2015 she was awarded the Brabazon Cup by the BWPA for her outstanding achievement in aviation. A regular contributor to seminars and conferences, Dorothy is the author and editor of a large number of flying training books and has published articles in legal and insurance journals and many in aviation magazines.

Gary Hutchinson

Gary caught the aviation 'bug ' at an early age, since plane-spotting at London Gatwick as a boy. He has since held a variety of aviation roles, from airport check-in desks and passenger profiling to operational roles in air cargo involving Health and Safety improvements. He has also travelled extensively worldwide using his airline staff travel privileges.

After gaining a CPL (A) Multi IR, and operating local charters and calibration flights, he won a GAPAN Flight Instructor Scholarship and now instructs at Shoreham.

He studied Psychology at London University, including Ergonomics and Cockpit Resource Management (CRM). As a member of the British Psychological Society, GAPAN and the Air League, he has been published in Psychological journals and since then has sought to combine these interests into a career as a 'Human Factors in Aviation' specialist. His aim is to increase safety, quality and efficiency in aviation, primarily through reducing human error and improving decision making.

He loves flying and would ultimately like to be an airline training captain/ Human Factors Psychologist.

On a lighter note, he dreams of one day flying a P 51 Mustang, but at 6'10" fears his height may preclude this!

Jenny Dodman

Jenny inherited her passion for aviation from her father and happy childhood memories of being in and around aircraft at Nottingham Airport. She studied medicine at the University of St Andrews, where she gained a BSc in Medical Science in 2003, followed by clinical training and medical degree from the University of Manchester in 2006.

After junior rotations in acute medicine, surgery, general practice and A+E, followed by a brief dabble in orthopaedic surgery; Jenny was appointed as the only Academic Clinical Fellow in Occupational Medicine in the UK, in 2009. During this 3 year post, she undertook specialist training in Occupational Medicine, alongside study for the MSc in Occupational Medicine and research work into safety critical work at the Centre for Occupational and Environmental Health at The University of Manchester.

Jenny completed the Basic Aviation Medicine Course at King's College, London, in 2008, followed by the Advanced Course in 2011, which was funded by the Mobbs Travelling Fellowship Award from Corporate Health and The Faculty of Occupational Medicine. She aims to complete specialist training in Occupational Medicine and to apply to become appointed as an Aviation Medical Examiner in due course, as well as to further her research work and clinical practice in Occupational and Aviation Medicine.

Jenny was awarded a Swire Charitable Trust Flying Scholarship (Air League) in 2005, which funded some flying while at University, and went on to complete a PPL in 2009. She has a share in a PA28 with her father and enjoys flying this regularly. She was awarded a Flying Bursary from the Air League in 2011; funded by the British Women Pilots' Association. This enabled her to undertake aerobatic training; She wanted to gain an appreciation for the effect of G on the human body, but it also started a new obsession!

She enjoys teaching and has taught undergraduate students as well as MSc level Toxicology. She hopes to extend this to flying instruction and intend to gain an FI rating in the future. She is passionate about improving, promoting and maintaining safety in aviation and hopes that her clinical training, academic work and flight training will enable her to achieve this. She is keen member of the BWPA, 99's and Women in Aviation and supporting the advancement of women in all sections of aviation, around the world.

Acknowledgements

The Civil Aviation Authority, British Aerospace, Boeing and McDonnell Douglas; Graeme Dennerstein, Daryl Guest, Frank Horwill, Michael Leahy and Peter Loughnan for medical comments; Robert Seaman, Captain R. W. K. Snell, Ian Swan, Thomas Syburra, Simon Ferrari, Joe Harper, Assen Assenov, Fabio Tozzi & Robert Pooley.

A Condensed History of the Air Pilot Manuals

For over 25 years the Air Pilot Manuals have led the academic training of pilots in the United Kingdom and in many countries around the world.

I first met Trevor Thom, a professional pilot and natural teacher, in Melbourne during a visit to Australia in January 1985. He already had his series of PPL Manuals for the Australian market and I asked him to produce a series for the New Zealand market where we had a small aviation business. Having completed this task, Trevor immediately began writing the first of the Air Pilot Manuals for the United Kingdom market and this project began in earnest on 5th December 1985.

Both Trevor Thom and Robert Johnson commenced the task in my office at Feldon. By the end of the following year, all four volumes were complete and were published in February 1987. At that time, we estimated that 95% of all the UK Flying Schools were using our manuals. Volumes 5, 6 and 7 followed, so completing the full series.

Unfortunately, Trevor Thom had a serious accident at home which prevented him from continuing with the editing of the manuals. His rights were eventually sold to David Robson, another experienced pilot and natural teacher, who progressively improved the drawings and brought colour into the manuals for the first time.

Over the years there have been many assistant editors, in particular Peter Godwin, whose help I first asked for in the very early days with Trevor Thom and which continued until quite recently. The rights in the Air Pilot Manuals are now vested with the Pooley family and they continue to be edited and published from our offices and the school at Shoreham Airport.

The Air Pilot Manuals have an outstanding reputation for accuracy and are continuously updated. They are recommended CAA reading material and are referred to extensively in the CAA examination answer booklet.

Robert Pooley
CStJ FRIN FRAeS

Introduction

Human Performance & Limitations

The **human factor** is the most important factor in aviation. Human skills have led to the design of very fine aircraft, and human factors (i.e. the performance of the ground engineer, the air traffic controller, and the pilot) play a major role in safe operation of these aircraft during every flight.

The human factor is vital.

Human factors not only play a major role in the *safe* operation of aircraft – they also play a major role in *unsafe* operation, leading to incidents and accidents. On a less dramatic note, less-than-optimal operation of an aircraft is inefficient – costing time, money and stress – and is best avoided. Always aim for optimum performance, and learn from each flight so that the next one can be even better.

What is the Human Factor?

The human factor is the performance and behaviour of the individual, and of the group. It involves internal psychological and physical aspects of the individual, as well as interaction with other people, with the machine and the equipment in use, and with the operating environment.

There are other terms in common usage with a similar meaning to *human factors,* such as *human aspects* and *human elements,* as well as *ergonomics,* which is the study of the efficiency of people in their operating environment.

Optimising Human Performance

The Human Factor **SHELL** approach involves viewing Human beings as the central 'components' in the complex operation of a flight and considering their strengths/weaknesses both in isolation and in relation to other 'components'. In essence, it is a framework enabling us to consider and optimise the many aspects of a pilot's behaviour and performance. This is illustrated below.

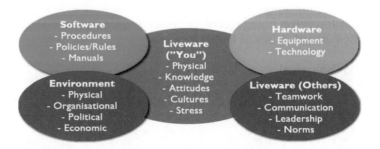

or use;

NOTE that the edges of the 'components' are jagged, to illustrate that the interactions between them are variable.

Components

S = Software
Rules/procedures and their design – Manuals, charts, flying orders book, PA28, C152 checklist etc.

H = Hardware
The design of the aircraft itself and includes controls, displays and systems.

E = Environment
Where the Liveware operates, the situation where the components operate.

L= Liveware
The Human component, the 'hub' of the model, the most critical part. It involves both psychological (pilots' mental processes) and physiological (physical health) aspects.

Psychological
- Perception.
- Developing flying skills, knowledge and attitudes.

- Thinking ability cognition applied through judgement and decision making.
- Demonstrating leadership, communication skills.

Physiological
- Sensory perception.
- Personal fitness and wellbeing.

L= Liveware
A second human component, to illustrate the interaction and *co-ordination* between the human elements - eg. other pilots, ATC, re-fuellers, engineers, flying club management etc.

Minimising Human Error
Consider that whilst mechanical causes of aircraft accidents have been vastly reduced in recent years, human error still accounts for 70% of the cause of all accidents. But it is not enough merely to 'label' a human error, we need guidance as to WHY it occurred in order to prevent re-occurrence. Human error can be minimised by:
- good selection of people (in a professional environment);
- good training;
- good design – matching the machine, controls, displays and operating procedures to human characteristics (physical and psychological);
- providing a good working environment (low noise level, comfortable temperature, no vibration); and
- good operating procedures – such as good cockpit checklists, and cross-checking and crew cooperation in two-pilot cockpits.

Therefore, knowledge of the human element can be viewed as *the* most important factor for pilots ie. to know the predictable capabilities and limitations of both themselves and others involved in the flight. But historically most student pilots place most emphasis on the 'aircraft handling' part of the syllabus, when really they should realise the scope that *they* have to play, the key role in flight safety and that human factors are the 'glue' that holds the rest of the flight together. When considering their own performance, both physically and psychologically, pilots should always strive to demonstrate Airmanship and good threat and error management.

Airmanship is the 'consistent use of good judgement and well developed knowledge, skills and attitudes to accomplish flight objectives' EASA Part-FCL (CAP 804). Threat and Error Management is described in detail in chapter 8.

The Aim of this Book

This book concentrates on the performance and the behaviour of the individual pilot (and of the crew as a unit, in larger aircraft), with the aim being to enable the pilot to practise airmanship through:

- safety and efficiency of the operation; and
- well-being of the individual.

It will also enable the reader to pass the relevant CAA *Human Performance and Limitations* examinations.

Safety, First Aid and Survival

The second section in the book supplies a good working knowledge of this important area of flight operations.

Also, those planning a trip over water or through remote areas of the world, particularly in a light aircraft, need to prepare for survival in a hostile environment. This section will help give an understanding of the factors involved, and enable an evaluation of the appropriate safety equipment that should be carried.

Section **One**

Human Performance and Limitations

Chapter 1

Human Physiology and High Altitudes 3

Chapter 2

Eyesight and Visual Illusions 23

Chapter 3

Hearing and Balance 49

Chapter 4

Am I Fit to Fly? 65

Chapter 5

Stress Management, Fatigue and Sleep 73

Chapter 6

Information Processing 105

Chapter 7

Judgement and Decision-Making 129

Chapter 8

Airmanship and Threat and Error Management ... 141

Chapter 9

The Flight Deck 151

Human Physiology and High Altitudes

As pilots, we need a basic understanding of the effect of flight on the human body and the human factors that may influence flight. It is therefore necessary to understand how the human body operates, in order to appreciate our limitations in the aviation environment. Identifying and managing the demands and influences that flying places on us is necessary in order to maintain our own safety and that of the flight.

The Nervous System

Information is carried, from one part of the body to another by the nervous system, in the form of nervous impulses. These impulses are transmitted along nerves and co-ordination of these by the nervous system is what produces bodily activity.

The nervous system is made up of two parts, which are connected:

1. **The central nervous system**, which comprises the brain and spinal cord. It processes information that it receives from all parts of the body and co-ordinates this into activity.

2. **The peripheral nervous system**, which comprises all of the vast networks of nerves and ganglia (relays) that lie outside the brain and spinal cord.

The peripheral nervous system can be further divided in to:

(a) The autonomic nervous system, which controls organs, systems and bodily functions that are not primarily* under voluntary control; e.g. Control of the heart beat, intestinal movements, sweating and salivation. (*this will be touched upon in later chapters).

(b) The sensory-somatic nervous system, which is involved with movement that is under voluntary control, using skeletal muscle; e.g. Picking up a cup, walking and flying an aeroplane! Training and experience can reduce the amount of effort required to undertake conscious activity, such as driving a car or flying an aircraft, but this will never be entirely automatic.

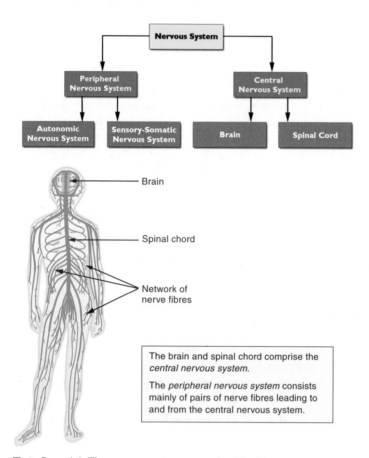

■ ✎ Figure 1-1 **The nervous system controls all bodily activity**

The Brain

The brain has central control of the nervous system. It is constantly sending and receiving nervous impulses (electrical signals) from all over the body and processing and co-ordinating these into voluntary and non-voluntary activity. These nervous impulses are carried along nerves from one part of the body to the brain, and from the brain back again. This allows the human being constantly to respond to the surrounding environment.

The brain controls the body.

Each muscle, organ or sense within the body has nerves connecting it to the brain.

EXAMPLE 1; *a finger may send a message that it is in contact with a hot metal plate, to which the brain responds by sending messages to various muscles telling them to contract, thereby withdrawing the finger from the plate.*

EXAMPLE 2; *a sudden and unexpected noise may cause fright, to which the brain responds by quickly preparing the body for action – electrical signals are transmitted to appropriate muscles, and certain chemicals are released (adrenalin, for instance) to speed up the rate of metabolism and prepare the body to 'fight or flee'. The constant interplay of transmitted signals and reception of feedback signals is a never-ending activity of the brain right throughout life, even when we are asleep.*

The brain is involved in:

- The autonomic (non-voluntary) control of processes such as control of lungs, heart, other organs, body temperature and control of the release of some hormones;
- The co-ordination and response to sensory information from e.g. the eyes, nose, ears, skin, tongue;
- The co-ordination of voluntary muscle activity.
- Information processing and decision making – more about this in chapters 6 and 7.

The Cardiovascular System (or Circulatory System)

The cardiovascular system is made up of the heart, blood vessels (cardio = heart, vascular = blood vessels), and blood.

The circulatory system moves blood around the body.

The heart is a muscle which pumps blood.

The Heart

Is a muscular structure, about the size of a clenched fist. It is divided up into two sides, each of which is divided into two chambers that are connected to each other and the blood vessels, by one way valves. It acts as a central pump that drives blood out of the heart, into the connecting blood vessels and in this way, around the body. The rate and force at which the heart muscle contracts controls how much and how quickly blood is delivered to the organs and tissues of the body.

Blood Vessels

Are tubular structures that carry blood around the body. The three main types are: arteries, veins and capillaries. Arteries have thicker, elasticated muscular walls and they carry blood away from the heart. Veins have thinner walls and carry blood back to the heart. Capillaries are very small blood vessels that connect the arteries at one end to veins at the other, and they form networks in the bodily tissues. Blood is carried into the capillaries from the arteries, travels through the capillaries, which allow transfer of nutrients from the blood to the tissues and waste from the tissues to the blood, and out of the capillaries into veins.

Blood

Is a fluid that consists of cells that are suspended in fluid called plasma, which is mostly water but also contains protein. Red blood cells contain a pigment called haemoglobin (which is what makes them red, because it contains iron), which binds oxygen and carries it around the body in this way. There are a number of different types of white blood cells; they are part of the immune system, which protects against infection. Some types produce antibodies that attack infection (among other functions).

The functions of the cardiovascular system are:
• To transport nutrients and oxygen to muscles, organs and other body tissues;
• To remove waste products from muscles, organs and other bodily tissues and transport them to be excreted from the body;
• Fighting disease by transporting white blood cells around the body and providing connections (via blood vessels) between organs of the immune system (the liver, spleen and glands);
• The regulation of body temperature;
• Transporting hormones around the body. Hormones are chemical messengers, which may need to be carried from one part of the body to another in order to act. This is done by releasing them into the blood stream.

As mentioned, the heart is separated into two sides, which in turn are each divided into two chambers. The circulation is correspondingly thought of in two sides, these are called the **systemic circulation,** which carries blood from the left side of the heart, through the body tissues and to the right side of the heart, and the **pulmonary circulation**, which carries blood from the right side of the heart, through the blood vessels in the lungs and to the left side of the heart.

The Systemic Circulation
Blood travels out of the lower chamber of the left side of the heart, into a very large artery called the aorta. From here it travels through the arteries and to the body tissues, through the capillary networks in the tissues (including the brain), where it exchanges nutrients and oxygen for waste products (including carbon dioxide) and then into the veins. The veins then carry the blood back to the top chamber of the right side of the heart, and through a one way valve to the bottom chamber. The blood must then be rid of its waste products (including carbon dioxide) and replenished with oxygen before it does a further journey around the body tissues. As the blood travels around the systemic circulation, it receives nutrients that are absorbed from the gut and carries waste products to the liver and kidneys. Via further bodily processes, these waste products are excreted in the urine and faeces.

The Pulmonary Circulation

Blood travels from the bottom chamber of the right side of the heart to the blood vessels of the lungs, where the waste carbon dioxide is removed and the oxygen content is replenished. From here it travels to the top chamber of the left side of the heart and through a one way valve onto the bottom chamber. Here the cycle starts again as it re-enters the systemic circulation.

It is useful to think of the cardiovascular system as a closed system. The **blood pressure** is a measure of the pressure exerted by the blood (and its contents) on the wall of the arteries. This pressure is highest when the heart contracts (called the systolic blood pressure) and pushes the blood into the closed system of blood vessels and is lowest in between beats, when the heart muscle is relaxed and filling with more blood ready for the next beat (called the diastolic blood pressure). The value range for normal blood pressure varies with age but typically it is quoted as being systolic 120mmHg and diastolic 80mmHg (written as 120/80). Blood pressure is essential to maintain pressure in the circulatory system that drives the delivery of oxygen and nutrients.

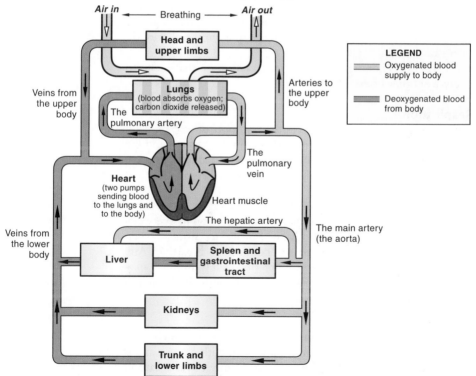

Figure 1-2 *Schematic of the circulatory (or cardiovascular) system*

The Respiratory System

The process of respiration brings oxygen into the body and removes carbon dioxide. The respiratory system is made up of the lungs and the muscles in the chest wall that facilitate the action of breathing.

> The respiratory process supplies energy-giving oxygen to the body, and removes carbon dioxide.

The Lungs

Are organs composed of a network of airways and small air sacs called *alveoli*. The two lungs are the organs in which the waste carbon dioxide in the blood, which is returned from around the body, is exchanged with oxygen brought in by freshly breathed air.

> The lungs absorb oxygen, and expel waste carbon dioxide.

The lungs are housed within the chest cavity, protected by the rib cage, and have a muscular, curved diaphragm beneath them.

The functions of the respiratory system are:

- Gas exchange between the external environment and the circulatory system; removing waste carbon dioxide from the blood and adding oxygen to be taken to the body tissues.
- Immune defence; to help fight infection entering the body through the lungs or causing infection in the lungs.
- Talking! The air that moves into and out of the lungs passes over the vocal cords (in the upper trachea) and this, together with co-ordinated movement of the pharynx and mouth, creates speech.
- Release of chemicals, proteins and enzymes that help to control other body systems.

> A high level of waste carbon dioxide in the lungs causes an increased breathing rate.

Respiration

The process of respiration involves the transport of oxygen from the outside environment into the cells within the tissues, and the removal and excretion of carbon dioxide. This happens in three stages: external respiration (ventilation), internal respiration and cellular respiration.

The body has a constant requirement for oxygen; it is used in the energy-producing 'burning' process that goes on in every cell of the body tissues. The body is unable to store oxygen permanently – hence the need for continuous breathing. Any interruption to breathing lasting more than a few minutes may lead to permanent physical damage, especially of the brain, and to possible death.

External Respiration

Is sometimes called **ventilation**. It is the process by which air is drawn into the lungs, in order to supply them with oxygen and is then expelled from the lungs in order to remove waste carbon dioxide. As we breathe in, the diaphragm flattens by contraction of the muscles, which expands the chest cavity, and draws fresh air in down the pressure gradient through the mouth and/or nose. This function is normally controlled by the autonomic nervous system without our conscious intervention, although we can consciously increase the rate and depth of our breathing if we want to.

The lowered pressure in the chest cavity draws the air down through the trachea, which divides into two tubes (right and left main bronchi), one going to each lung. The two tubes divide into smaller and smaller tubes, ending in millions of small sacs with very thin walls known as *alveoli,* which are surrounded by blood capillaries.

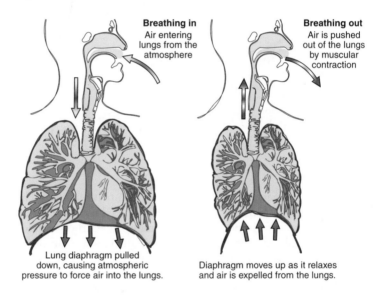

■ ✎ Figure 1-3 **Expanding the chest cavity draws air into the lungs.**

Internal Respiration

Is the exchange of gases in the lungs and the body tissues. In the lungs, oxygen diffuses from the air in the lungs into the blood, and carbon dioxide diffuses from the blood into the air in the lungs. When the blood reaches the body tissues, oxygen diffuses from the blood into the cells and carbon dioxide diffuses from the cells into the blood.

Oxygen molecules diffuse through the walls of the alveoli sacs and into the bloodstream, attach themselves to the *haemoglobin* in the red blood cells, which have an affinity for oxygen, and are transported to the body tissues requiring oxygen. The oxygen attached to the haemoglobin causes the blood to look very red, whereas the oxygen-deficient blood returning through the veins looks somewhat bluer.

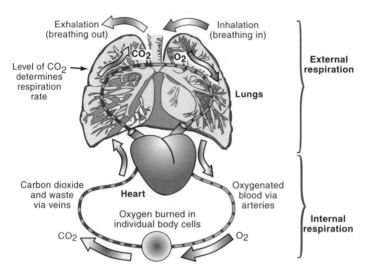

■ ✎ Figure 1-4 **The two-stage respiration process**

Cellular Respiration

occurs inside the cells of the body tissues and is the process whereby oxygen is used in biochemical pathways to produce energy.

Breathing Rate

This is sometimes called respiratory or ventilation rate. The autonomic nervous system detects both the need for more blood to certain parts of the body, and the amount of carbon dioxide (CO_2) in the blood. The carbon dioxide in the blood returning to the heart, and then to the lungs, is a waste product from the consumption of oxygen (O_2) in the tissues to produce energy.

A higher than normal amount of carbon dioxide means that a lot of oxygen has been burned, and therefore there is a need for more replacement oxygen around the body. As a result of a high carbon dioxide content in the blood, the breathing rate is automatically increased to bring more oxygen into the lungs for the bloodstream to absorb.

Chemical sensors in the lungs detect the level of waste carbon dioxide and, to a lesser extent the level of oxygen, and send messages to the brain. A high level of carbon dioxide (or a low level of oxygen) returning to the lungs in the blood is interpreted automatically by the brain as a need for more oxygen. A lot of carbon dioxide means that a lot of oxygen has been burned in the body tissues. The brain then responds automatically by speeding up the respiration rate to increase the supply of oxygen.

Each breath when we are resting is about one-half litre – only one-tenth of the lung capacity of five litres. This means that a lot of used air remains in the lungs. With the constant transfer of oxygen into the bloodstream and the addition of carbon dioxide out of the bloodstream, the air in the lungs will have a much higher concentration of carbon dioxide than the surrounding atmospheric air, and a lower concentration of oxygen. This is increasingly the case as altitude is gained. The air in the lungs is also saturated with water vapour (as witnessed by the fog it forms when we breathe out on a cold day).

Flying at Altitude

The human body is designed to function normally in the lower levels of the atmosphere, where the air is fairly dense. Aircraft, however, operate above sea level, often at quite high altitudes where the air density is very low, exposing the pilot to possible lower than normal pressures of oxygen, which can lead to low oxygen in the tissues and other problems such as low ambient temperatures.

The Composition of Air

Air is a mixture of various gases that is held to the earth by the force of gravity. The main gases are oxygen (21%), nitrogen (78%), with small quantities of carbon dioxide (0.03%) and ozone, and an extremely variable percentage of water vapour (which is not considered to be a component of the atmosphere).

COMPOSITION OF AIR	
Gas	*Volume (%)*
Nitrogen	78%
Oxygen	21%
Other gases (argon, carbon dioxide, neon, helium, etc.)	1%
Total	100%

The natural oxygen supply decreases with altitude.

THE ATMOSPHERE is held to the earth by the force of gravity and, because air is compressible, it packs in around the earth's surface. As altitude is gained, the air thins out, with fewer and fewer molecules in the same volume, but the percentage composition of the air does not change. Total air pressure falls with altitude, as does the partial pressure of each of the gases in the air. (Total air pressure is a sum of all of the partial pressures.)

OXYGEN (O_2) is a product of photo-synthesis which is the main source in the atmosphere. This uses carbon dioxide and water for the purposes of the plant – one of the resulting products being oxygen, which is needed by animals for their purposes. In this way, the plant world supports the animal world, providing it with oxygen, as well as being a source of food.

Oxygen is use in biochemical processes in the body, to produce energy. An oxygen deficiency can have a devastating effect on a person, therefore the supply of oxygen to a pilot, in the form of fresh air of a suitable density, or supplemented by an additional supply of oxygen, is of critical importance.

The body and brain need oxygen.

NITROGEN (N_2) is the most plentiful gas in air, but it is not directly used by the body in the respiration process. It is found in amino acids, which are the building blocks of proteins and DNA. It is used in the building of cells in both plants and animals, and saturates the body cells and tissues. Excess nitrogen in the tissues can cause problems, however, as any diver who has suffered *the bends* can tell you.

CARBON DIOXIDE (CO_2) is produced in the burning process, when oxygen combines with carbon, and forms about 0.03% of the atmosphere. Since the Industrial Revolution the wide-spread combustion of fossil fuels (oil, diesel and petrol) has led to a significant increase in the amount of carbon dioxide present in the atmosphere. This is a major contributor to global warming.

Carbon dioxide is also produced when oxygen is burned in the body tissues, and is carried to the lungs in the bloodstream through the veins and expelled in the breath. The human body is much more sensitive to changes in carbon dioxide levels than to changes in oxygen levels. In a normal healthy person, respiratory rate is regulated by CO_2 levels.

WATER VAPOUR, whilst not considered to be a component of the atmosphere, is carried in the air and plays a very important role in the weather. When the saturation point for water is reached, the water vapour condenses out as liquid water droplets and forms cloud, fog, rain, or dew.

The percentage of water vapour in the air varies from almost none over dry, desert areas to about 5% in warm, humid air. At high altitudes, above the level where clouds form, there is little water vapour.

OZONE is a molecule containing three oxygen atoms (O_3), whereas normal oxygen contains two (O_2). It is formed when air or oxygen is subjected to electrical discharges, and is poisonous if breathed in large amounts. It is found in the stratosphere, and prevents a lot of the sun's damaging ultraviolet radiation from reaching the earth's surface (hence the concern about holes in the ozone layer). The presence of ozone in the earth's atmosphere is a consideration when flying at extremely high altitudes for long periods.

Hypoxia

A lack of sufficient oxygen to the body tissues including the brain is called **hypoxia**.

Air pressure and density decrease with altitude. As an aeroplane climbs, the density of the air in which it is flying gradually reduces. The less dense the air, the lower the mass of oxygen taken into the lungs in each breath. Also, because of the lower partial pressure of oxygen at altitude (i.e. fewer molecules), less oxygen will diffuse across the alveoli membranes in the lungs into the bloodstream.

A high cabin altitude, therefore, means that less oxygen will be transported into and around the body, and less energy will be generated (including in the brain). In this oxygen-deficient condition, a pilot is less able to think clearly and less able to perform physically.

Above about 8,000 feet cabin altitude, the effects of oxygen deprivation may start to become apparent in some pilots, especially if the pilot is active or under stress. At 10,000 feet, most people can still cope with the diminished oxygen supply, but above 10,000 feet supplementary oxygen is required (i.e. oxygen supplied through a mask), if a marked deterioration in performance is not to occur. The effects of oxygen deprivation are very personal in that they may differ from person to person, and become apparent at different cabin altitudes. In some people, night vision, for instance, might start to deteriorate at 4,000 feet cabin altitude – in others it might start to deteriorate at a higher cabin altitude. The effects of oxygen deprivation will eventually be the same, but some people are more resilient than others. In general terms, 10,000 feet cabin altitude is considered to be the critical cabin altitude above which flight crew should wear an oxygen mask.

A lack of oxygen (hypoxia) leads to poor performance, even unconsciousness.

At 14,000 feet without supplementary oxygen, performance will be very poor, and at 18,000 feet the pilot may become unconscious; this will occur at lower altitudes if the pilot is a smoker, or is unfit or fatigued. Rapid rates of ascent can allow higher altitudes to be reached before severe symptoms occur. In these circumstances, unconsciousness may occur before any or many of the symptoms of hypoxia appear. At 18,000 feet the partial pressure of oxygen in the air is about *half* that at sea level.

The initial symptoms of hypoxia may hardly be noticeable to the sufferer, and in fact they often include feelings of *euphoria*. The brain is affected quite early, so a false sense of security and well-being may be present. Physical movements will become clumsy, but the pilot may not notice this.

Difficulty in concentrating, faulty judgement, moodiness, drowsiness, indecision, giddiness, physical clumsiness, a headache, deterioration of vision, a high pulse rate, blue lips and blue fingernails (cyanosis), and tingling of the skin may all follow, ending in loss of consciousness. Throughout all of this pilots will probably feel euphoric and as if doing a great job. Hypoxia is subtle and it sneaks up on you!

A pilot may not notice hypoxia (a lack of oxygen).

Chances of hypoxia is increased by anything which reduces the oxygen available to the brain, such as a high cabin altitude (of course), high or low temperatures, illness, stress, fatigue, physical activity, or smoke in the cockpit.

Very high positive g-loadings, say when pulling a high-speed acrobatic aircraft quickly out of a steep dive and experiencing 5g, will force the blood into the legs and lower regions of the body, and temporarily starve the brain of oxygen. This could lead to a *greyout* (when vision is affected) or a *blackout* or loss of consciousness (G-Loc). Such g-loadings, however, are not achievable in typical light aircraft. (See *Sensing Acceleration* on page 53.)

Pressurised Cabins

Pressurised cabins can lead to hypoxia if they depressurise.

Advanced aeroplanes have pressurised cabins which allow the cabin to hold air at a higher pressure than in the outside atmosphere. For instance, an aeroplane flying at 35,000 feet may have a cabin that is pressurised *(pumped up)* to the same pressure level found at 5,000 feet in the outside atmosphere, eliminating the need for the pilot and passengers to be wearing oxygen masks – a significant improvement in comfort and convenience.

Pressurised cabins improve the oxygen supply at altitude.

The situation, of course, changes if the aeroplane depressurises at high altitudes for some reason and the cabin air escapes, reducing the partial pressure of oxygen in the air available to the pilot. The suddenly lower pressure surrounding the body in a rapid depressurisation causes a sudden exhalation of breath (as the air pressure in the lungs tries to equalise with the external air pressure). The same volume in the lungs will now contain fewer oxygen molecules. Supplementary oxygen then becomes vital, and it is usually obtained through a mask until the pilot descends to a lower altitude (below 10,000 feet), where there is sufficient oxygen available and the mask can be removed.

If a cabin depressurises, supplemental oxygen may be required.

Time of Useful Consciousness

If a person is suddenly deprived of an adequate supply of oxygen, unconsciousness will follow unless they receive supplemental oxygen. This is a very important consideration for a high-flying pressurised aircraft that suffers depressurisation.

The cells of the brain are particularly sensitive to a lack of oxygen. Total cessation of the oxygen supply to the brain results in unconsciousness in 6 to 8 seconds and irreversible damage ensues if the oxygen supply is not restored within 4 minutes.

The time available for pilots to perform useful tasks *without* a supplementary oxygen supply, and before severe hypoxia sets in, is known as the **time of useful consciousness (TUC),** which gets shorter and shorter the higher the altitude. The pilots *must* get the masks on and receive oxygen well within this period, if flight safety is to be preserved.

TIME OF USEFUL CONSCIOUSNESS		
Altitude above sea level	Sudden failure of oxygen supply	
	Moderate activity	Minimal activity
22,000 feet	5 minutes	10 minutes
25,000 feet	2 minutes	3 minutes
28,000 feet	1 minute	$1\frac{1}{2}$ minutes
30,000 feet	45 seconds	$1\frac{1}{4}$ minutes
35,000 feet	30 seconds	45 seconds
40,000 feet	12 seconds	15 seconds

Remaining conscious is paramount for the pilot, even if the passengers become unconscious for a short period. You must think of yourself first, since the safety of all on board depends upon your well-being.

How To Avoid Hypoxia

To avoid hypoxia it is best to be reasonably fit, to have no cigarette smoke in the cockpit, and to ensure that oxygen is used at the higher cabin altitudes, and definitely above 10,000 feet. Remember that lack of oxygen can lead to a feeling of euphoria and a lack of judgement (a similar effect perhaps to alcohol). Self-discipline must be imposed and the oxygen mask donned when the altitude approaches 10,000 feet.

Types of Hypoxia

Hypoxia caused by a lack of oxygen taken into the body (e.g. by decreased partial pressure in the air) is called *hypoxic hypoxia.*

Hypoxia caused by an inability of the blood to carry oxygen is called *anaemic hypoxia,* and may be due to a medical condition (anaemia) or to carbon monoxide poisoning in the blood (from a faulty engine exhaust system or from smoking).

The reduction of the oxygen-carrying capacity of the blood by smoking has the same effect as increasing the cabin altitude by 4,000 to 5,000 feet; the effect on you will worsen as the aeroplane climbs to higher altitudes. Hypoxia can also result following a loss of blood – for instance, after a person has made a blood donation.

Hyperventilation

Hyperventilation can occur when the body 'over-breathes' as a result of some psychological distress such as fear or anxiety. It is a self-perpetuating cycle, in which a feeling of breathlessness develops – one is unable to 'catch one's breath' – and continues even if the triggering influence is removed. Even though the person is now over-breathing, he or she still feels breathless, which tends to add to the anxiety and so promote the over-breathing.

Hyperventilation is 'over-breathing.'

Hyperventilation flushes the carbon dioxide out of the blood which causes chemical imbalance; this produces symptoms of numbness and tingling in the lips, fingertips and toes. The further effects may include palpitations, an increased pulse rate, sweating, chest pain, blurred vision, dizziness, fainting and ringing in the ears, muscle spasms, drowsiness, and unconsciousness.

Hyperventilation is too little CO_2 in the blood.

Donning an oxygen mask will not help treat hyperventilation.

Dealing with Hyperventilation

In working out how to treat a person experiencing breathing difficulties, it is necessary first to establish whether the problem is hyperventilation (over-breathing) or hypoxia (too little oxygen). This may be difficult to differentiate - note how similar some of the symptoms are. **Hypoxia is the more urgent situation to treat.** If in doubt, try oxygen first, if above 10,000 feet. Hypoxia is <u>urgent</u>. If there is no rapid improvement, remove oxygen and treat as hyperventilation.

The best procedure to deal with hyperventilation is to try and calm the person, both by being calm yourself and by talking normally to them. Allocating simple distracting tasks in the cockpit may also help the person to take it easy.

Hyperventilation can affect anyone (including the pilot).

- **Hyperventilation can be remedied** by consciously slowing down the breathing rate (talking is a good way of doing this).
- **A suggested direct remedy** for hyperventilation is to breathe into and out of a bag to increase the carbon dioxide level in the blood.
- **If recovery is not evident,** then assume that hypoxia rather than hyperventilation is the problem.

NOTE If you have a passenger who is breathing abnormally and experiencing symptoms that could be caused by either hypoxia or hyperventilation, but you have a low cabin altitude (say below 10,000 feet) where hypoxia is not a consideration, assume that hyperventilation is the cause and apply the appropriate remedy.

Decompression Sickness

Decompression sickness can follow scuba diving. Scuba diving and flying do not mix.

Do not mix deep scuba diving with flying.

When the body is deep under water it is subjected to strong pressures, and certain gases, such as nitrogen, are absorbed into the blood. The deeper and longer the dive, the more this absorption occurs. If the pressure on the body is then reduced – for example, by returning to the surface from a great depth or, even worse, by flying in an aeroplane at high cabin altitudes – the gases (especially nitrogen) may form bubbles in the bloodstream. (You can see the same effect caused by a suddenly reduced pressure when the top is removed from gaseous drinks and bubbles of gas come out of solution.)

Gas bubbles in the blood will cause great pain and some immobilisation in the shoulders, arms and joints. This serious complaint is called **decompression sickness** or *the bends*. The remedy is to return the body to a region of high pressure for a lengthy period of time (say in a decompression chamber), and then gradually return it to normal lower pressures over a period of hours or days.

In an aircraft, the best you can do if *the bends* is suspected is to descend to a low altitude, where air pressure is greater. Even landing may not provide a sufficient pressure increase to remedy the problem, in which case seek medical assistance without delay.

■ ✎ Figure 1-5 **Scuba diving just prior to flying can have serious consequences**

As a guide, do not fly within 12 hours of any scuba diving where compressed air was used to breathe, even if only to shallow depths. Scuba diving at depths below approximately 30 feet for long periods should *not* be considered in the 24 hours prior to flying! Snorkelling will not cause decompression sickness, only the underwater breathing associated with scuba or deep-sea diving.

The risk of suffering decompression sickness increases with the depth to which you dive, the rate at which you resurface, how soon and how high you fly, how quickly the cabin altitude increases, age, obesity, fatigue, and re-exposure to decompression within 24 hours.

Carbon Monoxide Poisoning

Carbon monoxide is produced during the combustion of fuel in the engine. It is present in engine exhaust gases and in cigarette smoke, both of which can sometimes be found in the cockpit.

Carbon monoxide is poison.

Susceptibility to carbon monoxide poisoning increases as the cabin altitude increases.

Carbon monoxide is a colourless, odourless and tasteless gas for which haemoglobin in the blood has a greater affinity for carbon monoxide than for oxygen. Haemoglobin is found in red blood cells and its prime function is to transport oxygen from the lungs throughout the body to act as 'fuel'.

Haemoglobin in the blood prefers carbon monoxide to oxygen.

If carbon monoxide molecules are present in the air inhaled into the lungs, then the haemoglobin will transport them in preference to oxygen, causing the body and the brain to suffer oxygen starvation, even though oxygen is present in the air. Haemoglobin shows a far greater affinity for carbon monoxide (poisonous, and just what we do not need) than for oxygen (which we do need).

The performance of a pilot in an environment contaminated by carbon monoxide will be seriously impaired. Recovery, even on pure oxygen, may take several days. **Carbon monoxide poisoning is serious and can be fatal!**

Do not breathe carbon monoxide.

Many cabin heating systems use warm air from around the engine and exhaust manifold as their source of heat. Any leaks in the engine exhaust system can allow carbon monoxide to enter the cabin in the heating air and possibly through open windows and cracks. To minimise the effect of any carbon monoxide that enters the cockpit in this way, fresh air should always be used in conjunction with cabin heat.

Regular checks and maintenance of the aircraft are essential. Even though carbon monoxide is odourless, it may be associated with other exhaust gases that do have an odour. Engine smells in the cabin are a warning that carbon monoxide may be present.

Symptoms of Carbon Monoxide Poisoning:

- headache, dizziness and nausea;
- deterioration in vision;
- impaired judgement;
- personality change;
- impaired memory;
- slower breathing rate;
- loss of muscular power;
- convulsions;
- coma, and eventually death.

If Carbon Monoxide Is Suspected in the Cabin:
* shut off the cabin heat;
* stop all smoking;
* increase the supply of fresh air through vents and windows; and
* land as soon as possible.

Many operators place carbon monoxide detectors in the cockpit. The most common type contains crystals that change colour when carbon monoxide is present. These detectors only cost a few pounds and are a wise investment, but they do have a limited life, so check the expiry date. If the detector is date-expired it may not indicate the presence of carbon monoxide, and so may lull you into a false sense of security.

Barotrauma

As cabin altitude increases, gases in the body expand.

Another effect of increasing cabin altitude is that gases trapped in parts of your body – such as the stomach, intestines, sinuses, middle ear, or in a decaying tooth – will want to expand as external pressure decreases. Either they will be able to escape to the atmosphere, or they may be trapped and possibly cause pain, known as *barotrauma*.

Upper Respiratory Tract Problems

The common cold, hay fever, sinusitis, tonsillitis or any similar condition can lead to blocked ears. This can mean trouble for a pilot because the equalisation of pressure on either side of the eardrum is not possible when the *Eustachian tubes,* which connect the ears and the nasal passages, are blocked by a cold or similar infection. In the training environment, problems are more likely to occur on descent than when climbing, as even low-powered aircraft can change altitude rapidly on descent, giving rise to rapid pressure changes.

Blocked ears can sometimes be cleared by holding your nose and blowing hard (a technique known as the *Valsalva* movement), by chewing, swallowing or yawning. The best advice is, however, if you have a cold, do not fly.

Do not fly with a cold or sinus problem.

Problems can also arise in the sinuses, which are cavities in the head connected by narrow tubes to the nasal/throat passages. Such blockages can cause great pain, especially during descent, so do not fly with sinus problems. This applies to flight in any aircraft; even though pressure changes in a pressurised cabin will be less as the aircraft changes altitude (compared with an unpressurised cabin), there is always the risk of a sudden depressurisation, in which case the pressure changes can be dramatic.

The possible serious effects of upper respiratory tract infections on aviators are covered in more detail in Chapter 3, *Hearing and Balance* and Chapter 4, *Am I Fit to Fly?*

Now complete: **Practice Questions - Human Physiology and High Altitudes**

1. The Peripheral, Central and Autonomic are what type of system in the body?

(a) Circulatory

(b) Nervous

(c) Cardiac

(d) Digestive

2. The System that moves Blood around the body is called the:

(a) Nervous System

(b) Digestive System

(c) Cardiac System

(d) Circulatory System

3. The Respiratory System:

(a) Brings Oxygen into the body and Removes Carbon Dioxide.

(b) Is made up of Muscles in the Chest wall that facilitate Breathing.

(c) Is sometimes called Ventilation.

(d) Is made up of Alveoli.

4. The body not having sufficient Oxygen to meet its requirements is a condition known as:

(a) Hypoxia

(b) Hypoglycaemia

(c) Hypochondria

(d) Hyperventilation

5. The initial signs of the onset of Hypoxia include:

(a) Dizziness and tingling sensation in the fingers.

(b) Euphoria, clumsiness and impaired judgement.

(c) Anxiety and tingling sensation in the fingers.

(d) Clumsiness and hot flushes.

6. To Avoid Hypoxia

(a) *Fly above 10,000 feet often to become acclimatised.*

(b) *Be fit, do not smoke, use oxygen if necessary.*

(c) *It is not necessary to consider Hypoxia until 13,000 feet.*

(d) *Experienced pilots are not affected by Hypoxia.*

Eyesight and Visual Illusions

The eyes provide us with a **visual** image of the environment. Their messages to the brain are backed up by messages from other sensory organs, including the balance mechanisms in the inner ear *(vestibular* inputs), as well as skin and muscular feeling from all over the body ('seat-of-the-pants' inputs, known more technically as *somatosensory* inputs).

Each eye acts as a natural and very sophisticated camera. Its basic function is in collecting light rays coming from an object, using the lens to focus these rays into an image on a screen (the *retina*), and then converting this image into electrical signals which are then sent via the optic nerve to the brain. In this way we 'see'.

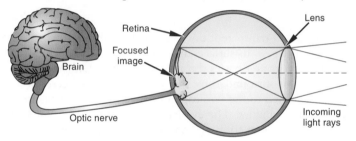

■ ✎ *Figure 2-1* **The basic components of vision**

The connection of the optic nerve to the brain is so close that it is considered to be a part of the central nervous system and integral, and the importance of the messages sent via it to the brain so immense, that the two eyes can almost be considered an extension of the brain.

The Structure of the Eye

The main components of the eye are the cornea and lens, the retina, and the optic nerve.

Light passes into the eye through the cornea and the lens, which focus the light rays onto a screen, the retina, at the back of the eye. The retina converts the image made by the received light into electrical signals which are then sent via the optic nerve to the brain – and so we 'see'.

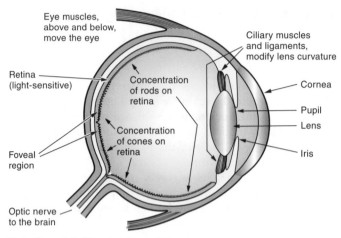

■ ✎ *Figure 2-2* **The structure of the eye**

The Cornea

The cornea is a transparent cap over the lens, through which the light rays first pass. Its surfaces are curved and some refraction of the light occurs as it passes through the cornea. Unlike the lens, whose edge is surrounded by the 'ciliary' muscles, there are no muscles attached to the cornea, and so we cannot alter its shape and refractive abilities. The eye has eyelids which can close over the cornea for protection and to assist in spreading lubrication. Most of the movement comes from a large upper eyelid, and less movement from the smaller and weaker lower eyelid.

The Iris

Between the cornea and the lens is a coloured membrane known as the *iris*. The colour of the iris determines the colour of the eye. At the centre of the iris is a small round aperture known as the *pupil*. The pupil changes its size to restrict the amount of light entering the lens. In very bright light, the pupil becomes quite small; in very dim conditions, the pupil widens to allow more light to enter.

The Lens

The lens, like the cornea, is transparent to light, but we change its shape with the ciliary muscles surrounding it, allowing us to focus the light rays. When the muscles are relaxed, the lens tends to flatten, and the reduced curvature of its surfaces means less refraction of the light rays, i.e. less focusing. The muscles can be used to squeeze the lens, which increases the curvature of the lens surfaces, thereby increasing the amount of refraction and the amount of focusing – the greater the curvature, the greater the focusing. This occurs when you focus on a very near object.

Muscles alter the curvature of the lens to alter focusing.

The ability of an eye to change its focus, e.g. from a far object to a near object, is known as *accommodation*.

The power of the eyes to accommodate varies, especially with tiredness and with age. When a person is fatigued, accommodation diminishes, which may result in blurred images. Also, with increasing age the lens becomes less flexible, and less able to modify its curvature. This reduced focusing capability that is noticed by middle-aged people means that starting to use glasses is usually necessary sometime in the forties.

> *The ability to focus deteriorates with tiredness, and with age.*

The Retina

> *The retina is the 'screen' which collects images.*

The *retina* is a light-sensitive layer located at the back of the eye. It is the screen onto which the lens focuses images, which are converted to electrical signals that pass along the optic nerve to the brain.

The retina contains two types of light-sensitive (or photosensitive) cells: cones and rods.

> *Cones in the central area are sensitive to colours and detail by day.*

CONES are concentrated around the central section of the retina, especially the *foveal* region directly opposite the lens. Cones are sensitive to colour, small details, and distant objects, and are most effective in daylight, and less effective in darkness. They provide the best visual acuity (the ability to resolve fine detail). The foveal region is where we focus most objects and it is this area of the retina which provides our central vision in good light conditions. Objects focused on the foveal region in very dim light (as at night) will not stimulate the cones to transmit a message along the optic nerve, so the image will therefore not be 'seen' by us.

> *Rods in the peripheral area are sensitive to greys and movement.*

RODS are concentrated in a band outside the central foveal area. They are sensitive to movement, but not to detail or colour, and so 'see' only in shades of black, white, and grey, rather than the colours seen by the cones. Rods are effective in both daylight and darkness, and are responsible for our *peripheral* vision (i.e. off-centre vision), which helps our orientation and night vision. Objects in dim light, such as at night, are therefore most easily noticed when their image falls somewhere on the peripheral area of the retina where the rods are concentrated. You can achieve this by looking slightly to the side of an object at night, rather than directly at it as you would during daylight.

Sight Is Very Sensitive

Rods and cones are really the nerve endings of the vital optic nerve. As an extension of the brain, they will be affected by anything that affects the brain. With a shortage of oxygen (hypoxia), or an excess of alcohol, medication, or other drugs, your sight will be one of the first things to suffer. High positive g-loadings, such as in very strenuous acrobatic manoeuvres, will force the blood into the lower regions of the body and temporarily starve the brain of blood, leading to a *greyout* (only black-and-white vision) or even unconsciousness *(blackout)*.

The Eyes Move in their Sockets

The eye is roughly the shape of a ball, hence it is often referred to as an eyeball. Each eye has a series of muscles that can be used to rotate it in its socket, thereby allowing it to follow a moving object without you having to move your whole head. Conversely, it means you can also keep focused on a stationary object even though your head might be moving, for instance in a turn.

To keep tracking a moving object with your two eyes, they need to act in harmony with one another, and this means coordinated control of the two sets of muscles, one set for each eye, by the brain. This coordination sometimes fails, for example, if a person is fatigued, and the result is quite different images from each eye, resulting in *double vision*.

When focusing on very near objects, the visual axis of each eye will be turned-in slightly; when focusing on distant objects, say more than six metres away, the visual axes of your two eyes will be roughly parallel.

■ ✎ *Figure 2-3* **Focusing on a near object, and on a far object**

The natural tendency, when you are *not* trying to focus on any particular object and you are – for instance, just gazing out of the window into an empty blue sky, is for the eyes to focus somewhere in the range of one to two metres. This is referred to as *empty field myopia* (empty field short-sightedness).

A pilot flying visually must continually scan the sky for other aircraft and for obstacles, and then focus on any that are observed. In an empty sky, it requires effort to focus on distant objects, since the eyes tend to focus on a much closer point. It is very important, therefore, that the eyes are fit and healthy, and that you are not fatigued when flying. Scanning is an <u>active</u> process not a passive one.

It requires effort to focus on distant and very close objects.

Binocular Vision

A normal person has two functioning eyes that together provide binocular vision. *Binocular* is the adjective used to describe the use of both eyes, as against *monocular* which describes the use of one eye only. Two eyes are better than one for a number of reasons.

Each eye has a blind spot. One reason is protection against the **blind spot** in each eye. The blind spot is the small area on the retina of the eye where the *nerve fibres* from the light-sensitive cells *(rods* and *cones)* on the retina lead into the optic nerve. There is therefore no space at this spot on the retina for light-sensitive cells, and hence any light falling here will not register, i.e. it is a blind spot.

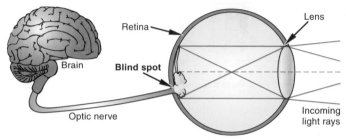

■ ✎ *Figure 2-4* **The blind spot**

Binocular vision eliminates risk from blind spots. It is not possible for an image of an object to fall on the blind spot of *both* eyes simultaneously. Even when an image falls on the blind spot of one eye, and is therefore not registered, the brain will receive a message from the other, and so the object will be seen. People with only one functioning eye, of course, do not have this protection, and run a greater risk of not seeing other aircraft in flight. (More about this later.)

Binocular vision aids depth perception. Another advantage of two eyes is **binocular vision,** which is the ability to focus both eyes on one object at the same time. Light from a particular object, especially a near one, will enter each eye at a slightly different angle, causing the images formed by each eye to be different. The brain uses these two different images as one means of estimating the distance of nearby objects – the difference in the two images being greater for near objects than for far objects.

You can observe this effect by holding a pencil or a finger up against a distant background, closing one eye at a time and viewing it through the other. Each eye will provide a different image – the pencil or finger will be seen from different angles, and its relationship to the background will be different.

Left eye   Right eye

■ ✎ *Figure 2-5* **Binocular vision – different view from left and right eyes**

With normal two-dimensional photographs or films projected onto a screen, each eye receives an identical image, so the impression of depth and reality is lost to some extent. Attempts have been made artificially to replicate binocular vision and its three-dimensional (3-D) effect by using 3-D films and 3-D photographs. This is done, not by presenting a real three-dimensional situation, but by presenting a slightly different two-dimensional picture to each eye, with objects seen from slightly different angles and in slightly different positions relative to the background. The brain then forms a more realistic three-dimensional picture than is possible when each eye receives an identical picture.

The Optic Nerve and the Blind Spot

There is no place for cones or rods on the area of the retina where the nerves bundle together to form the big optic nerve. Any image that falls on this area will therefore not be 'seen' – in other words, there is a *blind spot* on the retina of each eye.

You can observe the existence of the blind spot in each eye by viewing Figure 2-6. Hold the page at arm's length, cover your right eye, and then with your left eye focus on the aeroplane on the right. It will be clearly recognisable as a biplane because it will be focused on your fovea (cone vision). If it were coloured, you would also be able to detect this. The helicopter on the left will be visible in your peripheral vision (rod vision), but it may not be defined clearly enough for you to recognise it as a helicopter, nor will you see its colour. You will, however, be aware that there are two potential collision risks: the aeroplane in focus through the right windscreen, and some other aircraft not clearly defined (because you are not looking directly at it and focusing on it) in the left windscreen.

Now move the page closer to your open left eye, continuing to focus on the aeroplane (right windscreen). At some point, the helicopter will disappear from your peripheral vision, and then come back into view as you bring the page even closer. The time when the image is not seen is when it falls on the optic nerve blind spot on your retina. The lack of rods or cones here means that the image is not detected. The left windscreen at this time appears empty – a dangerous situation which significantly increases the collision risk. Repeat the experiment by concentrating your right eye on the helicopter, in which case the biplane will disappear from view when its image falls on the blind spot of your right eye.

■ ✎ Figure 2-6 **Your blind spot**

Binocular vision protects you from blind spots.

Now repeat the experiment with both eyes open. Both aircraft should remain in view at all times, because the eyes are designed so that the image from a particular object cannot fall on the blind spots of both eyes simultaneously. This is another advantage of binocular vision.

Be careful when you are scanning the sky that another aircraft is not blocked from view by the magnetic compass or some part of the windscreen structure. If it is blocked from the view of both eyes, you will not see it at all; if it is blocked from the view of only one eye, you will lose the blind spot protection provided by binocular vision.

Normal Functions of the Eye

Visual Acuity – The Clarity of What We See

Visual acuity (seeing clearly and sharply) is vital to a pilot.

Visual acuity is the ability of the eye to see clearly and sharply. Perfect visual acuity means that the eye sees the object exactly as it is, clearly and without distortion, no matter how distant the object is. The degree of visual acuity varies between different people and also between the two eyes of any one person, as well as for the single eye at different times. This depends upon whether the person is fatigued, suffering hypoxia (lack of oxygen), or under the influence of alcohol or some other drug.

To describe differences in visual acuity, the standard is considered to be what a 'normal' eye is capable of seeing clearly at a particular distance. The eye test chart usually has lines of letters readable for a normal eye from 36, 24, 18, 12, 9, 6 and 5 metres respectively. (The large letter at the top of eye charts is sized that a person with normal sight can read it from a distance of 60 metres.)

The standard testing distance between the eye and the eye chart is 6 metres; the normal eye is capable of seeing clearly letters of a certain size at this distance. If another eye at 6 metres cannot read the 6-metre line clearly, and can only identify letters on the chart that a normal eye can see clearly at 9 metres, then the 'abnormal' eye is said to have '6/9' vision. This is compared with the '6/6' vision of the so-called normal eye.

 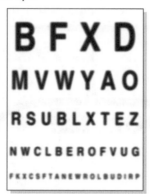

■ ✎ Figure 2-7 **An eye chart seen with 6/6 vision and 6/9 vision**

The best visual acuity within the individual eye occurs when the image is focused sharply by a high-quality cornea and lens onto the central foveal region of a healthy retina, where the cone receptors predominate. The cone receptors are very sensitive to small details and send very sharp, colourful images to the brain.

Light rays that are focused on the retina away from the central foveal region in areas where there are not so many cone receptors, but more rod receptors, will not be seen as clearly, nor will they be in colour. Visual acuity will therefore be less for these images.

To illustrate the difference between central and peripheral vision, look at the words on this page. You must move your eyes so that the image of the word that you want to read falls on the central foveal region. Whilst you can clearly read the word you are looking at right now, you will not be able to read words some distance away from it – up, down, or sideways from it – unless you move your eyeball so that the image of that word falls on the central high-visual-acuity area of the retina.

Glare
When flying at high altitudes, especially above cloud layers or flying into a rising or setting sun, the pilot is exposed to light of very high intensity, possibly coming from all angles.

Whereas the eyes are protected from light coming from above by the forehead, eyebrows, eyelashes, and strong upper eyelid, they are not so well protected from light coming from below. Bright sunlight reflected from cloud tops, for instance, can be particularly bothersome because of this lack of natural protection.

Avoid glare from strong sunlight by wearing sunglasses.

In conditions of glare, it is advisable to protect your eyes by using high-quality sunglasses that reduce glare but not your visual acuity.

The contrast between the glare of a very bright outside environment and the darker cockpit interior may also make it difficult for the eyes to adjust quickly enough to read instruments and charts inside the cockpit.

Effect of Flickering Lights

Helicopter pilots should be aware that bright flickering lights can bring on epileptic-type fits in some people. On the ground this effect can be seen when driving along a sunlit avenue of trees, where areas of light and shade are constantly changing. Common airborne causes are the shadows of rotating helicopter blades or windmilling propellers in bright sunshine. These problems usually occur at 'flash' frequencies of between 5 Hz and 20 Hz. For instance, a 2-bladed helicopter rotor at 240 rpm would give 8 flashes per second.

Common symptoms of this effect are feelings of unease or discomfort. Susceptible passengers should wear sunglasses, cover the window, or close and cover their eyes. People so affected by flickering lights should not operate as helicopter pilots. See AIC 75/2001 (Pink 23).

Depth Perception

Binocular vision aids depth perception.

The eyes and your brain use many clues and memories of past experience to help you in judging distance. Some items are mathematical, such as the relative size of objects – a bigger object appearing to be nearer than a smaller object. Also, binocular vision (the slightly different images of a nearby object relative to its background seen by each eye) assists in depth perception when the object is near.

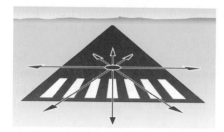

■ Figure 2-8 **Texture moves outward from the aiming point as you approach the runway**

Texture also assists in depth perception: the more visible the texture, the closer the object appears to be. On final approach as you near the runway, its texture will appear to flow outwards in all directions from the point on which you are focused. This is one means by which you can visually maintain a constant approach slope to the aiming point – adjusting descent angle and track so that the point from which the texture appears to be moving outwards remains at the desired aiming point.

Texture aids depth perception.

Texture is also used for the estimation of height – for instance, as you approach flare height for a landing, the actual texture of the runway or the grass passing by the cockpit becomes increasingly noticeable.

Relative motion also aids in depth perception. Near objects generally appear to pass by the windscreen faster than more distant objects. This helps a visual pilot estimate height above the runway before and during the flare – the closer the aeroplane is to the runway, the faster the runway surface and the surrounding environment appears to pass by.

Relative motion aids depth perception.

Depth perception can also be difficult in hazy or misty conditions, where edges are blurred, colours are muted, and light rays may be refracted unusually. This gives the impression of greater distance, an impression reinforced by the fact that we often have to look at distant objects through a smoggy or hazy atmosphere.

In haze or mist, objects may be closer than what they appear to be.

In hazy conditions, the object might be closer than it seems; in very clear conditions, the object might be further away than it seems. On hazy days you might touch down earlier than expected; on very clear nights, you might flare a little too soon.

Colour Vision

Colours are detected in the central foveal region of the retina by the cone receptors, which are only active in fairly bright light. By differentiating between the various wavelengths of light in the visible spectrum (red light with its longer wavelength, through to violet light with its shorter wavelength), the average eye can distinguish over one hundred hues (single wavelength colours) and one thousand shades.

There are some eyes that cannot distinguish any colours at all, even in bright light, but this total colour-blindness is very rare. Males are susceptible to colour blindness, with about 1 in 12 caucasian males having some colour blindness (better called *defective colour vision*), compared with only about 1 in 200 for females.

Defective colour vision shows up as trouble distinguishing between red and green. It may cause problems during night flying, as well as in poor visibility, when the white, red and green navigation lights of other aircraft are used for recognition, and also when visual light signals from the control tower are used in a radio-failure situation instead of radio voice messages (a rare event nowadays).

Adaptation of the Eyes to Darkness

At night, there are some special considerations regarding vision. Since your attention during night flying will be both inside and outside the cockpit, care should be taken to ensure that your eyes can continuously function at near maximum efficiency. It takes the eyes some minutes to adapt to a dark environment, as most of us have experienced when walking into a darkened cinema and stumble across other patrons in an attempt to find an empty seat.

The rate at which *dark adaptation* of the eyes occurs depends to a large extent on the contrast between the brightness of light previously experienced and the degree of darkness of the new environment.

Night adaptation of the eyes takes many minutes.

Whereas the cones, concentrated in the central region of the retina, adjust quickly to variations in light intensity, the rods (which are most important for night vision) take some 30 minutes to adapt fully to darkness. In dim light the cones become less effective, or even totally ineffective, and there is a chemical change in the rods to increase their sensitivity.

Protecting Your Night Vision

Bright light will immediately impair your night adaptation.

To assist in night adaptation, it is good airmanship to **avoid bright white lights** (landing lights, strobes, flashlights, etc.) in the 30 minutes prior to night flight, and also while in flight. Exposure to bright light, even for just a second or two, can cause a loss of night adaptation which will then require many minutes to return.

Since bright lights will impair your outside vision at night, it is good airmanship to keep the cockpit lighting at a reasonably low level, but not so low that you cannot see your charts, or find the fuel selector.

A good oxygen supply is also essential for good night vision, which can begin to deteriorate at cabin altitudes as low as 4,000 feet. At cabin altitudes above 10,000 feet, make sure that you don an oxygen mask and use supplementary oxygen.

Scanning for Other Aircraft by Day

The central (foveal) region of the retina provides the best vision, but only during daylight, and not in darkness. Aeroplanes and other objects are best seen by day if you can focus their image on the foveal region, and you do this by looking directly at them.

■ *Figure 2-9* **Scanning by day**

The most effective method of scanning for other aircraft for collision avoidance during daylight hours is to use a series of short, regularly spaced eye movements to search each 10° sector of the sky. Systematically focusing on different segments of the sky for short intervals is a better technique than continuously sweeping the sky.

Scan carefully for other aircraft, using short eye movements.

You may be on a collision course with another aircraft if there is no apparent relative motion between you and the other aircraft, especially if the other aircraft appears to be getting bigger and bigger in the windscreen. Because of the lack of movement across your windscreen, an aircraft on a collision course with you will be more difficult to spot than one that is not on a collision course. Any relative movement of an object against its background usually makes it easier to notice in your peripheral vision.

The image of the other aircraft may not increase in size much at first, but, shortly before impact, it would rapidly increase in size.

The time available for you to avoid a collision may be quite brief, depending upon when you see the other aircraft and the rate of closure. If you are flying at 100 knots and it is flying at 500 knots in the opposite direction, the rate of closure is 600 knots, i.e. 10 nautical miles per minute.

If you spot the other aircraft at a distance of 1 nm, you only have $1/10$ th of a minute, i.e. 6 seconds, to potential impact. If you are a vigilant pilot, and spot it at 3 nautical miles (nm), you have 18 seconds in which to act. In hazy or low-visibility conditions, your ability to see other aircraft and objects whose edges might be blurred will be diminished and, if you can see them, they may *appear* to be further away than their actual distance, i.e. you might be closer than you think.

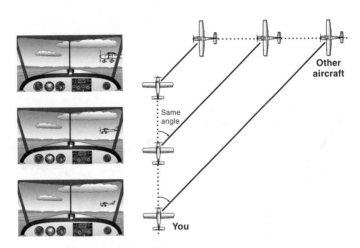

■ ✎ Figure 2-10 **A potential collision**

When trying to search for other aircraft in an empty sky, we often have trouble because of *empty field myopia*, the natural tendency of a resting eye to focus at 1 to 2 metres, and not at infinity as we might think. Consequently, distant aircraft may not be noticed; or sometimes a dust particle, a scratch, or an insect on the windscreen might be mistaken for a distant aeroplane. To avoid this empty-field myopia, you should focus on any available distant object, such as a cloud or a landmark, to lengthen your focus. If the sky is empty of clouds or other objects, then focus briefly on a relatively distant part of the aeroplane like a wingtip as a means of lengthening your focus.

Having spotted an aeroplane in an otherwise empty sky, be aware that it could be closer to you than it appears to be, because you have no other object with which to compare its size.

Scanning for Other Aircraft by Night

Peripheral vision is more effective than central vision at night.

Because the central foveal region of the retina containing mainly cones is *not* effective by night, causing a night blind spot in your central vision, you need to rely to a greater extent on your peripheral vision which is provided by the rods in the outer band of the retina. **An object at night** will be more readily visible when you are looking to the side of it by 10 or 20°, rather than directly at it. Colour will not be perceived by the rods, and so your night vision will be in black, white, and shades of grey, and objects will not be as sharply defined as in daytime central vision.

The most effective way to use your eyes during night flight is to scan small sectors of sky more *slowly* than in daylight, to permit 'off-centre' viewing of objects in your *peripheral vision*. Because you

may not be able to see the aircraft shape at night, you will have to determine its direction of travel making use of its visible lighting:
- **the flashing red beacon;**
- **the red navigation light** on the left wingtip;
- **the green navigation light** on the right wingtip; and
- **a steady white light** on the tail.

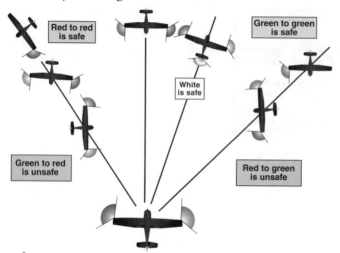

■ ✎ Figure 2-11 **Using navigation lights to evaluate and avoid collisions at night**

Visual Illusions

Sometimes what we 'see' in our brain is not the precise reality because images sent from the eyes can sometimes be misinterpreted by the brain.

Autokinesis

The visual illusion of *autokinesis* (self-motion) can occur at night if you stare continuously at a single light against a generally dark background. It will appear to move, perhaps in an oscillating fashion, after only a few seconds of staring at it, even though in fact it is stationary. You could lose spatial orientation if you use it as your single point of reference. The more you try to concentrate on it, the more it may appear to oscillate.

You can guard against autokinesis at night by maintaining movement of your eyes in normal scanning, and by monitoring the flight instruments frequently to ensure correct attitude.

Keep your eyes moving and check the flight instruments.

Unless you have a distant object in view at night, your eyes will tend to focus at a point about one to two metres ahead of you, especially if you are an older person with 'tired eyes', and you may miss sighting distant objects. This *empty field myopia* or *night myopia* (short-sightedness) can be combated by searching for *distant* lights and focusing briefly on them.

Beware also of false horizons at night (see later in this chapter).

False Expectations

We expect that a pencil will be smaller than a tree, so when we see the image of a pencil beside the image of a tree that is occupying the same angular area on the retina, we assume that the tree is further away. This is usually the case, but need not be, e.g. if the tree is a miniature one.

What we see   What we expect   The reality

■ ✎ *Figure 2-12* **What we 'see' is sometimes not how it really is**

Similarly, a small, dark image formed on the retina could be a distant, but rapidly approaching aircraft, or it could be a speck of dirt or dust, or an insect spot, on the windscreen.

■ ✎ *Figure 2-13* **Is it a distant aircraft, or a speck on the windscreen?**

If we spend most of our time landing on the one runway, we get very used to its width and length, and how it should look on approach. Landing on a different runway, which has a different width and/or length, may present us with quite a different view on approach, even though we are on the correct slope; its appearance at the correct flare height might also be different.

It is quite common for a pilot familiar with a small country airfield to flare too high on the first landing at a large international airport where the runways are usually long and wide.

Interpreting Patterns

The brain often has to make sense of a pattern of lines, and the interpretation may not always be correct, as can be seen from some of the figures which follow.

■ ✎ *Figure 2-14* **Is this a two-bladed propeller on a radial engine, or a Mexican riding a bicycle?**

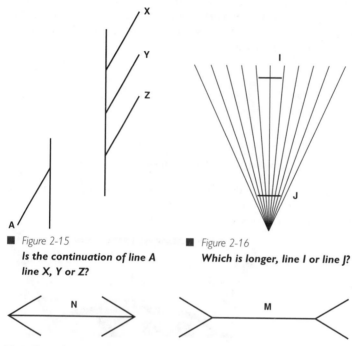

■ *Figure 2-15*

Is the continuation of line A line X, Y or Z?

■ *Figure 2-16*

Which is longer, line I or line J?

■ ✎ *Figure 2-17* **Is line N longer or shorter than line M, or are they the same length?**

Does a stick bend upwards as I put it into a bucket of water? No, it does not, but it certainly looks as though it does because our brain and eyes assume light travels in straight lines, which is not always the case, as we know from an understanding of refraction.

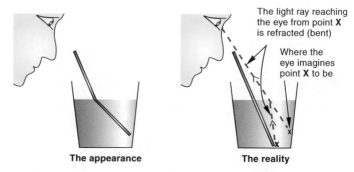

The appearance   **The reality**

■ ✎ *Figure 2-18* **Does a stick bend upwards as I put it into a bucket of water?**

An aeroplane on approach through heavy rain can sometimes experience quite a build-up of water on the windscreen, which refracts the light rays on their way to the pilot's eyes, perhaps causing an illusion like the 'bent stick'. Knowledge of this effect can be some protection for the pilot.

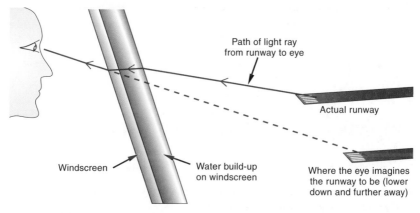

■ ✎ *Figure 2-19* **A visual illusion can be caused by a layer of water on the windscreen**

False Horizons

Sloping cloud layers by day, or angled lines or areas of lights by night, can sometimes present a pilot with a false horizon that can be very misleading. Make use of your flight instruments to confirm your flight attitude.

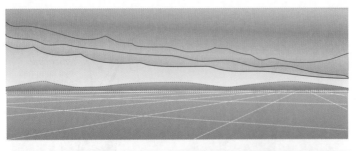

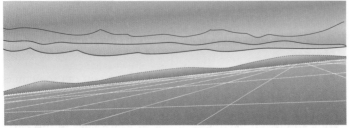

■ ✎ Figure 2-20 **A sloping cloud layer that is more prominent than the horizon can cause a strong visual illusion of a false horizon – check your attitude indicator and balance ball regularly**

■ ✎ Figure 2-21 **A visual illusion of same level due to a sloping cloud layer (do not change level prematurely)**

■ ✎ Figure 2-22 **What the pilot sees through the windscreen; and what might be seen if the pilot had x-ray vision (sloping cloud layer)**

Visual Illusions on Approach

Runway Slope

Most runways are of standard width and on flat ground. On every approach, you should try to achieve the same flightpath angle to the horizontal, and your eyes will become accustomed to this, allowing you to make consistently good approaches along an acceptable approach slope merely by keeping your view of the runway through the windscreen in a standard perspective.

Allow for a different perspective when approaching a sloping runway.

Approaching a **sloping runway,** however, the perspective will be different. A runway that slopes *upwards* will look longer, and you will feel that you are high on slope, when in fact you are right on slope. The tendency will be for you to go lower and make a shallower approach. If you know that the runway does have an upslope, you can avoid this tendency.

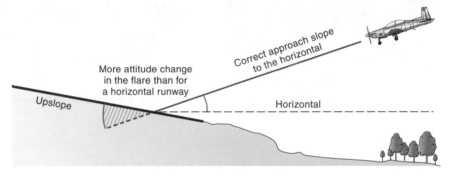

■ ✎ Figure 2-23 **An upward sloping runway creates a 'too-high' illusion**

A runway that slopes *downwards* will look shorter, and you will feel that you are low on slope, when in fact you are on slope. The tendency will be for you to go higher and make a steeper approach. If you know that the runway does have a downslope, you can avoid this tendency.

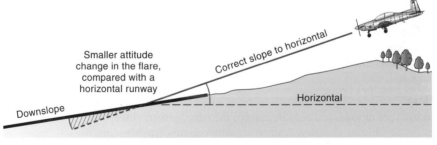

■ ✎ Figure 2-24 **A downward sloping runway creates a 'too-low' illusion**

If you know the runway slope, you can allow for it in your visual estimation of whether you are high or low on slope (Figure 2-25).

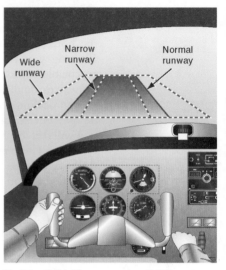

■ *Figure 2-25* **How runways of different slopes should appear at the same point on final approach to land**

■ *Figure 2-26* **How runways of different widths should appear at the same point on final**

Runway Size

A runway that is *larger* than usual will appear to be closer than it really is. Conversely, a runway that is *smaller* than usual will appear to be further away than it really is.

A *wide* runway, because of the angle at which you view it peripherally in the final stages of the approach and landing, will cause an illusion of being too low, and you may flare and hold-off too high as a result. This may lead to 'dropping-in' for a heavy landing. Conversely, a *narrow* runway will cause an illusion of being too high, and you may delay the flare and make contact with the runway earlier (and harder) than expected.

If you know that the runway is wider or narrower than that with which you are familiar, then you can allow for this in your visual judgement of flare height and hold-off prior to touchdown (Figure 2-26).

Haze

In hazy conditions, you may be *closer* to the runway than you appear to be, an illusion that may lead to an unnecessarily hard landing if you are not prepared for the effect of haze on your vision.

The Night Approach

It is preferable to **make a powered approach at night,** rather than a glide approach, providing a normal well-controlled approach at normal speeds. In modern training aircraft, the powered approach is generally used by day also. Power gives the pilot more control, a lower rate of descent and, therefore, a less-steep approach slope. The approach to the aiming point should be stable, using any available aids, such as the runway lighting and a PAPI (precision approach path indicator) if available. The *red-on-white* PAPI is commonly used throughout the world, but there are other types in use also.

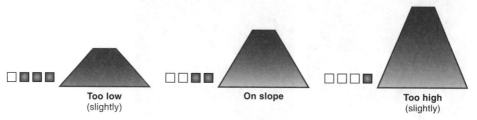

Too low (slightly)　　　On slope　　　Too high (slightly)

■ ✎ *Figure 2-27* **Perspectives on approach using PAPI**

Using the runway edge lighting only, correct tracking and slope is achieved when the runway perspective is the same as in daylight. For correct tracking, the runway should appear symmetrical in the windscreen. Guidance on achieving the correct approach slope is obtained from the apparent spacing between the runway edge lights.

If the aeroplane is below slope, the runway lights will appear to be closer together. If the aeroplane is flying above slope, then the runway lights will appear to be further apart. Attention should also be paid to the airspeed indicator throughout the approach, to ensure that the correct airspeed is being maintained.

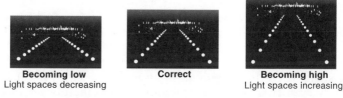

Becoming low
Light spaces decreasing　　　Correct　　　Becoming high
Light spaces increasing

■ ✎ *Figure 2-28* **Perspectives on approach using runway edge lighting**

A VASI will provide correct slope guidance by day or night, but the perspective provided by runway edge lighting may be slightly misleading if you do not allow for any runway slope.

The 'Black-Hole' Approach

Flying an approach to a runway without other visible references can often be difficult. This can occur when approaching a runway on a dark night where the only lights visible are the runway edge lights, with no town lights or street lights to be seen, and no indication of the nature of the surrounding terrain. This is what is known as 'a black-hole approach'.

Black-hole approach   Approach with good
                                          ground reference

■ ✎ Figure 2-29 **Visual information is considerably less in a 'black-hole' situation**

The tendency is to think that you are higher than in fact you are, resulting in an urge to fly down, and fly a lower and flatter approach. Approach aids such as an electronic glideslope (instrument landing system – ILS) or a VASI can help you to resist this unwanted tendency. If these aids are not available, you can resist the temptation to fly too low an approach by monitoring the altimeter and vertical speed indicator (VSI) to ensure that the rate of descent is reasonable for the approach slope that you wish to maintain.

Black-hole approaches are common at night on tropical atolls, at desert airfields, or on approaches to land on runways that are surrounded by water.

Similar situations to a black-hole approach arise in **white-out** conditions where the ground is covered with snow, making it fairly featureless. The lack of features around the runway make depth and slope perception much more difficult. See Figure 2-30.

Obscured approach   **Normal perspective**

■ ✎ Figure 2-30 **Snow considerably restricts the visual perspective information**

Glasses and Contact Lenses

Artificial lenses can compensate for most deficiencies in an eye lens.

Faulty focusing by the eye can result naturally from a lens that has become less flexible with age and cannot be made curved enough to focus nearby objects, or it can result from a lens that is not shaped correctly. In almost all cases, artificial lenses in the form of glasses or contact lenses can be made to correct the specific deficiency and restore clear vision.

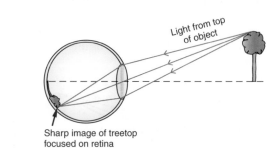

Light from top of object

Sharp image of treetop focused on retina

■ ✎ Figure 2-31 **Normal vision, without the need for correction**

Short-Sightedness (Myopia)

Short-sightedness (myopia) is a common problem. It occurs when the eye is relaxed and the cornea and lens focus the rays from a distant object not on the retina, but in front of it. By the time the light rays reach the retina they have moved apart and are no longer concentrated at a point. The resultant image formed on the retina is therefore out of focus.

A short-sighted person might see near objects clearly, but distant objects (which require less focusing) might be blurred.

Poor distant vision caused by short-sightedness can be corrected by using an artificial concave lens to reduce the overall refraction of the light rays. The light rays will then focus at a greater distance behind the lens, which ideally will be on the retina.

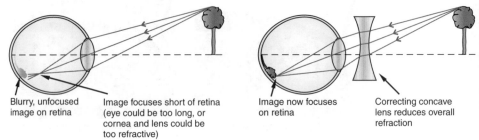

Blurry, unfocused image on retina

Image focuses short of retina (eye could be too long, or cornea and lens could be too refractive)

Image now focuses on retina

Correcting concave lens reduces overall refraction

■ *Figure 2-32* **Short-sightedness (myopia) – image focuses short of the retina**

■ *Figure 2-33* **Short-sightedness corrected using a concave lens**

Long-Sightedness (Hyperopia or Hypermetropia)

Long-sightedness (hyperopia) occurs when the eye is relaxed and the cornea and lens do not focus the rays from an object before they reach the retina. The resulting image formed on the retina will therefore not be in focus. The point of focus for the rays is beyond the retina. A long-sighted person might see distant objects clearly, but near objects that need more focusing might be blurred.

Long-sightedness (hyperopia) can be corrected by a conscious effort to focus the image, or by using an artificial convex lens to increase the overall refraction of the light rays so that they focus earlier, ideally on the retina.

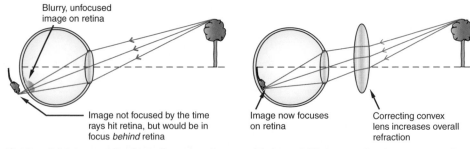

Blurry, unfocused image on retina

Image not focused by the time rays hit retina, but would be in focus *behind* retina

Image now focuses on retina

Correcting convex lens increases overall refraction

■ *Figure 2-34* **Long-sightedness (hyperopia) – image not focused by the time the light rays reach the retina**

■ *Figure 2-35* **Long-sightedness corrected using a convex lens**

A form of long-sightedness that occurs quite naturally in people in their forties or older is *presbyopia*. It is caused by the lens material losing some of its flexibility and so the muscles are less able to increase its curvature. Rays, especially from near objects, will not be focused by the time they reach the retina, i.e. the eyes have lost some of their ability to accommodate for near vision. This is when people say that their arms are not long enough, i.e. not long enough to hold a book or newspaper at a distance where their eyes are capable of focusing the words.

Presbyopic people, with diminished near-vision, may have distant vision that requires no correction. The solution for them, to improve reading vision without affecting distant vision, is to use half-glasses with a half-moon convex lens in the lower half to increase the refraction, and nothing in the upper half.

■ *Figure 2-36*
Half glasses improve near vision without affecting distant vision

Astigmatism

Astigmatism occurs when the curvature of the cornea, and less commonly the curvature of the lens, is not perfectly round, i.e. may be ellipsoid rather than spheroid. This causes uneven refraction of the various light rays passing through the lens, and the formation of distorted images. It can be corrected by a lens which has varying curvature over its surface.

Glasses for Flying

If you are required to wear glasses when flying, you should carry a second pair to guard against loss or damage to the first pair.

Conclusion

A pilot should always handle any vision deficiency and/or correction under the supervision of an expert. For information about vision correction requirements for pilots see EASA Part FCL MED. B.070 and MED. B.075.

Now complete: **Practice Questions - Eyesight & Visual Illusions**

1. With a flight visibility of 3nm, a light aircraft and a military jet have a closing speed of 400 kts. Approximately how much time do the pilots have to avoid a collision if visual contact was made at maximum range?

   (a) Approximately 27 seconds.

   (b) Approximately 33 seconds.

   (c) Approximately 38 seconds.

   (d) Approximately 18 seconds.

2. The Retina:

   (a) Is a light sensitive layer located next to the lens.

   (b) Is made up of "Rod and Cone" light sensitive cells.

   (c) Reflects light as it enters the eye.

   (d) Is made up of ciliary light sensitive cells.

3. Having allowed sufficient time for night vision to develop, when looking at an object beyond the aircraft, the maximum visual acuity is achieved by looking:

   (a) Slightly below the object.

   (b) 45° to the side of the object.

   (c) Directly at the object.

   (d) Slightly off centre by about 10°.

4. If a runway is narrower than expected, a pilot will tend to:

   (a) Fly a lower approach than normal and possibly land short.

   (b) Fly a lower approach than normal and possibly overshoot.

   (c) Fly a higher approach than normal and possibly land short.

   (d) Fly a higher approach than normal and possibly overshoot.

5. The Blind spot:

   (a) Is in the same position in each eye.

   (b) Is protected by closing one eye.

   (c) Is protected by binocular vision.

   (d) Is the position where the incoming light hits the retina.

Answers: 1a, 2b, 3d, 4a, 5c.

Hearing and Balance

The Ears

The ear is a very important organ for two senses – for hearing, and for balance. *Hearing* allows us to perceive sounds and to interpret them; the sense of *balance* lets us know which way is up and whether we are accelerating or not. Balance is the next most important sense for a pilot after vision.

Sound is defined as energy that we can hear with our ears. It is often very useful and pleasant, as with voice messages and music, but excessive sound may be annoying and fatiguing, and can even lead to damage within the ear. Irregular, unwanted, and unpleasant sound is called *noise*, and is best filtered out if we can find a means to do it.

Sound signals are caused by pressure variations travelling through the air as pressure waves, and these cause sensitive membranes like the eardrum to vibrate. The inner ear translates these pressure vibrations into electrical signals which are sent via the auditory nerve to the brain, where they are interpreted.

Similarly, **balance and acceleration signals** from the balance mechanism in the inner ear pass to the brain as electrical signals for interpretation. The interpretation is sometimes tricky in the case of an airborne pilot, since the brain is used to the person generally being upright on the earth's surface.

The ears are used for hearing and for balance.

The Structure of the Ear

The ear is divided into three areas: the outer, middle, and inner ear.

THE OUTER EAR includes:
- **the external ear** (known medically as the *pinna* or *auricle*), which is used as a megaphone to gather the sound signals;
- **the outer canal** through which the pressure waves pass; and
- **the eardrum,** which is caused to vibrate in harmony with the pressure waves.

Any obstruction to the outer canal, such as earplugs or an excess of wax, can reduce the sound pressure waves reaching the eardrum. Similarly a padded cover over the external ear will reduce the sound waves entering the ear, unless the cover is a headset that blocks external noise, but has a small speaker for radio and interphone messages.

THE MIDDLE EAR are is an air-filled cavity containing three small bones, known as *ossicles,* which are forced to move by the vibrating eardrum, converting the pressure wave energy into mechanical energy of motion. The ossicles are arranged like a series of levers to increase the effect of the initial movement. This energy then passes on to the cochlea in the inner ear.

The air in the middle ear is maintained at ambient pressure via the *Eustachian tube,* which connects the interior of the middle ear to the nasal passages. There is (or should be) no leakage of air across the eardrum, and there should be easy passage of air through the Eustachian tube, when needed, to equalise pressures – for instance, when climbing or descending. This is sometimes hindered by swelling and inflammation when a person has a cold, and can lead to serious consequences (explained later) if a person flies with a cold or similar infection.

The Eustachian tubes equalise pressure either side of the eardrums.

Interference to the movement of the three small ossicles or their joints will reduce or distort the sound signal. This can be caused by ear infections, damage to the bones or joints, or a blocked ear with air trapped inside the middle ear *(barotitis).*

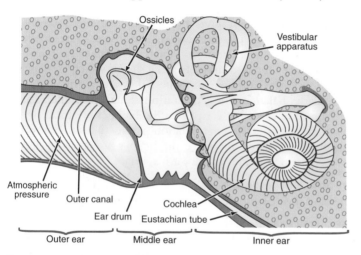

■ ✎ *Figure 3-1* **The structure of the ear**

THE INNER EAR contains two very important pieces of apparatus:
- The *cochlea* for hearing; it converts the mechanical energy from the ossicles into electrical signals which then travel via the auditory nerve to the brain for interpretation.
- The *vestibular apparatus,* consisting of the *static organ* and the *semi-circular canals;* these contain fluid and small hairs that convert gravity and acceleration forces into electrical signals which are sent to the brain for interpretation.

Fluid in the cochlea is moved by the mechanical energy from the ossicles, and this causes a wavy movement of small hairs protruding into the fluid. The movement is converted to electrical signals at the bottom of each hair, and these signals are sent along the *auditory nerve* to the brain.

Excessive noise can lead to damage of the hairs in the cochlea, and infection or injury can damage the auditory nerve, possibly causing ringing in the ears (tinnitus).

The ear is never switched off, and loud noises can stir us from even the deepest sleep. For this reason, a quiet room is best if you want to sleep soundly. It is interesting to note how you can extract messages important for you out of a noisy background – for instance, a radio message directed at you, the sound of your own child on a crowded beach, or your own name mentioned in a distant conversation – known as 'the cocktail party effect'.

The comments that follow apply to the *hearing* aspects of the ear. The *balance* aspects, i.e. the gravity and acceleration signals from the semi-circular canals of the middle ear, will be discussed shortly.

Hearing

What is Sound?

Sound is what we hear, and each sound can be defined by:

- **Frequency or pitch:** the number of pressure waves per second (or hertz, Hz) that the sound source produces. Perfect human hearing is in the range of 20 Hz to 20,000 Hz, and voices use the frequency range 500 Hz to 3,000 Hz.
- **Loudness or intensity:** the strength or amplitude of the pressure waves, measured in decibels (dB), a logarithmic scale where an increase of 20 dB signifies an increase in intensity of 10 times (20 dB is 10 times as loud as 0 dB, the threshold of hearing; 40 dB is 10 times louder again, i.e. 100 times as loud as 0 dB; 60 dB is 1,000 times as loud as 0 dB and 100 times as loud as 20 dB; an increase from 80 dB to 100 dB is an increase in loudness by a factor of 10).
- **Duration:** how long the sound lasts (the longer you are exposed to loud noise, the more damage it can do to your hearing).

Fatigue and Damage From Noise

Loud noise can damage hearing.

Unwanted sound, especially if it is loud and disagreeable, is *noise.* It can be mentally fatiguing through its effect on our ears, but it also affects the rest of our body, especially if it is associated with vibration as is often the case. Noise can interfere with communications, and with our concentration.

Extreme noise levels can also do permanent damage to our ears, with duration of exposure as important as loudness.

NOISE LEVELS OF TYPICAL SOUNDS	
130 dB	*Standing near a jet aircraft (noise becoming painful)*
120 dB	*Standing near a piston-engined aircraft (noise becoming uncomfortable). Several hours per day for 3 months could lead to deafness.*
110 dB	*Maximum recommended for up to 30 minutes' exposure*
100 dB	*Maximum recommended for 2 hours' exposure*
90 dB	*Maximum recommended for 8 hours' exposure (a working day)*
80 dB	*Standing near heavy machinery. Above 80 dB for long periods can lead to temporary or permanent hearing loss.*
60 dB	*Loud street noise, trucks, etc.*
50 dB	*Conversation in a noisy factory*
40 dB	*Office noise*
30 dB	*Quiet conversation*
20 dB	*Whispering*
0 dB	*The threshold of hearing*

Loss of Hearing

A person can experience a temporary hearing loss after exposure to noise. The noise of an engine, for instance, may no longer be heard after a while even though the engine noise is still there. Some factory workers lose the ability to hear frequencies that they are subjected to all day long. A temporary hearing loss may disappear after a few hours or after a few days.

Exposure to high noise levels for long periods can also lead to a *permanent* hearing loss, especially in the high-frequency range. This is a risk area for pilots who are exposed to a noisy work environment for long periods. Put it together with visits to the car races, noisy discotheques, plus a top set of loudspeakers at home, and you are in a high risk environment from the point of view of your hearing. Very, very gradually, and imperceptibly, a person can lose the ability to hear certain sounds clearly, speech becomes more difficult to comprehend, and radio communications become more difficult.

Sudden, unexpected loud noises greater than about 130 dB, such as an explosion or the sound of an impact, can cause damage to hearing, possibly even physical damage to the eardrum or to the small and delicate ossicle bones behind the eardrum.

Hearing loss can also result from:
- **Problems in the conduction** of the sound, through a blocked outer canal (ear wax), fluid or pressure problems in the middle ear (barotrauma caused by a cold, for instance), or faulty ossicle bones and joints – this is known as *conductive* hearing loss.

- **Loss of sensitivity** of the hair cells in the cochlea, through exposure to noise, infection, or age – this is known as a *sensory* or *noise-induced* hearing loss.
- *Presbycusis,* a natural loss of hearing ability with increasing age, especially in the higher frequencies, (down about 5% by age 60 and 10% by age 70).
- **Alcoholism,** or excessive use of medications.

Preventing or Minimising Hearing Loss

A noise-induced hearing loss may develop gradually over a period of years without the person noticing – something which cannot be reversed, hence the need for prevention rather than cure. As pilots, we are lucky in that we have regular audiometry tests which can be monitored over the years to look for any gradual loss of hearing, especially in the higher frequencies.

Wear hearing protection in noisy environments.

Try to wear hearing protection when in noisy areas. A good noise-cancelling **headset** is highly recommended for the cockpit, and earplugs or earmuffs for when you are moving around outside the aircraft. **Earplugs** can reduce noise by about 20 dB, and good earmuffs by about 40 dB.

Headsets protect your hearing and aid radio communications.

The radio headset, especially if it is well sealed, will block out background noise but not affect radio communications. You should use the *squelch* control on the radio, if available, to reduce unwanted background hash, and you should keep the volume turned down as much as possible without disturbing your comprehension of voice messages.

Unprotected exposure to jet-engine noise close up can be hazardous to the sensitive balance mechanism in the ears also – another reason to wear hearing protection outside the aircraft.

Balance

Sensing Acceleration

The human body does not sense motion in a straight line at a steady speed, except by visual means, since muscular sensations and the balance organs of the inner ear do not sense *unaccelerated* motion.

The body can sense accelerations (changes in speed), but not speed itself.

Sometimes, when you are a passenger on one of two trains travelling on parallel tracks, it is difficult to know whether your train is moving, the other train is moving, or both trains are moving – even with your eyes open. A steady speed in a straight line is unaccelerated 1g motion, as is being stationary, and so the muscles and balance organs will not sense motion in this situation at a steady speed.

The human body, with its muscular sensations ('seat-of-the-pants' or 'proprioceptive' sensing) and balance organ of the inner ear, however, *does* react to *acceleration, i.e.* changes in either speed or direction. For instance, as an elevator accelerates upwards, you experience more than 1g and feel heavier than normal, reverting to your normal 'weight' once the elevator has reached a steady speed. As it slows down, you tend to keep on going, experiencing less than 1g and feeling lighter than usual. You revert to normal 1g feeling once the elevator has stopped. Your body also reacts to changes in *angular* speed, i.e. to angular acceleration – for instance, when you roll into a banked turn, or when you spin.

The g-force changes in an elevator are only fractional compared with those experienced by a pilot, especially in aerobatic manoeuvres such as loops and in steep turns. In a 60° banked turn, for instance, you will experience 2g and feel double your weight.

In normal flying, the g-force changes are also only fractional and have no significant effect on the body. In strenuous aerobatics, however, forces of +4g or more for a sustained period, say when pulling out of a steep dive, will have a significant effect. The blood will be forced towards the lower extremities and away from the brain, causing a loss of vision due to the lack of oxygen, leading to *greyout* and, eventually, *blackout*.

If *negative* g-forces are experienced – for instance, if the control column is suddenly pushed forward and held there – the blood rushes to the head. In an extreme case of negative g, the lower eyelids will move up and cover the eyes, giving an impression of *red-out*.

How the Balance Mechanism Works
Sensing Angular Accelerations
The inner ear contains a balance organ consisting of three **semicircular canals** connected at a sac. They contain fluid which can flow in the canal, and move gelatinous material into which hairs from the base of the canal protrude. Any movement of the fluid will move the gelatinous material and the hairs. Small nerve cells at the base of each hair convert this movement into an electrical signal which is sent to the brain for interpretation.

The three semicircular canals are at right angles to each other, like the pitch–roll–yaw planes of an aeroplane, and can detect angular accelerations (in pitch, roll and yaw).

During angular acceleration, the relevant semicircular canal accelerates away from the fluid, which is 'left behind'. This causes the fluid to flow in the semicircular canal in a direction opposite to the angular acceleration, and bend the sensory hairs, which send an angular acceleration message to the brain.

Three semicircular canals in the inner ear sense angular accelerations in the three planes.

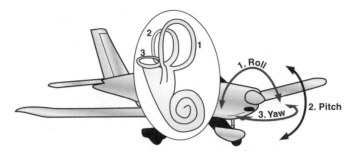

■ ✎ *Figure 3-2* **The semicircular canals for roll, pitch and yaw**

Once the angular acceleration has ceased, and a steady angular speed is maintained, the fluid ends up moving with the canal, i.e. there is no longer any relative motion between the fluid and the canal, and so the sensory hairs on the canal wall no longer bend. The semicircular canals no longer sense any turning motion because there is no angular acceleration, even though a steady turn is continuing.

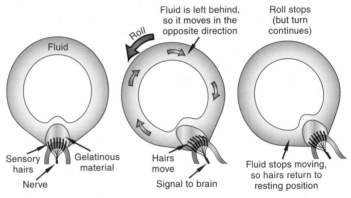

■ ✎ *Figure 3-3* **Angular acceleration**

Sensing Gravity and Linear Accelerations

Gravity and linear accelerations or decelerations are detected in a similar fashion by sensory hairs in the sac, which is sometimes known as the **static organ**. The hairs protrude into a gelatinous material called the *cupula* containing small crystals called *otoliths*.

The cupula has a resting position when the head is upright, and the brain interprets the message sent from the small hairs at this time as 'up', i.e. the cupula is supported by a 1g force directly upwards. If the head is tilted to one side, or forward or back, then the cupula moves under the force of gravity and takes up a new position, bending the hairs, which then send a different signal to the brain.

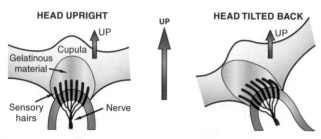

■ ✎ Figure 3-4 **The cupula sends a message as to which way is 'up'**

The cupula detects the direction of g-forces, but cannot distinguish their origin – the force of gravity, or a centripetal force, which will not be vertical, pulling you into a coordinated turn. We must remember that the body was designed for fairly slow motion on the face of the earth, with a basic 1g force of gravity exerted on it, and not really for the three-dimensional forces we experience in flight.

For instance, sitting firmly in your seat in a perfectly coordinated 60° banked turn, you will experience a 2g force exerted by the seat on your body at an angle of 60° to the vertical. With your eyes closed, you might feel that you are still sitting upright with respect to the vertical which, in fact, is not the case. It is sometimes difficult to know if you are level or in a banked turn, hence the need to use your eyes to look outside or at the flight instruments to confirm your actual attitude.

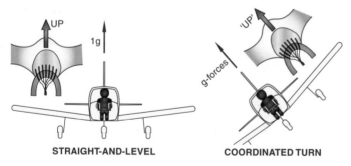

■ ✎ Figure 3-5 **'Up' is the direction of the g-forces exerted on your body, according to your static organ**

The cupula in the static organ also detects linear accelerations. During a linear acceleration, the body accelerates away from it and the cupula is temporarily 'left behind', causing the hairs to bend and send a new signal to the brain. They will return to their normal position once the body is no longer accelerating and is moving at a steady speed (which may be zero).

The static organ in the inner ear senses gravity (weight) and linear accelerations.

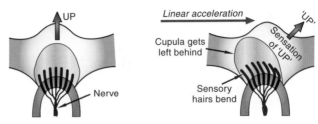

■ ✎ *Figure 3-6* **The cupula detects linear accelerations**

NOTE If you compare Figure 3-6 with the one regarding 'which way is up' (Figure 3-4), you will see that the relative position of the cupula during a linear acceleration is similar to that when the head is tilted back; this can lead to an illusion of tumbling backwards, when in fact you are accelerating.

Orientation

Orientation – the ability to determine your position in space – is usually achieved by some combination of three senses:
- **vision** – the most powerful sense of all;
- **balance** – the vestibular sense (gravity, acceleration, and angular acceleration); and
- **'seat-of-the-pants'** (bodily feel or the *proprioceptive* sense).

Vision is your most powerful sense.

In most situations, each of the three senses reinforces the others, but this is not always the case in flight. Each of these senses can sometimes have its messages misinterpreted by the brain, and you must guard against this. Not knowing your attitude in space (i.e. which way is up) is called *spatial disorientation*. Usually, the most reliable sense is vision! Hence the need to rely on your flight instruments.

Vestibular Illusions Involving Rolling
The Illusion of Level Flight While In a Steady Turn

The semicircular canals can send good signals to the brain whilst the aircraft is rolling at a reasonable rate into or out of a turn, i.e. during any angular acceleration, but once in a steady turn the fluid motion stops and the signals cease. The sensation of rolling ceases. The static organ senses the direction of the g-forces, not only gravity, and the brain interprets this direction as 'up', which it may not be. Therefore, in a steady turn, your vestibular apparatus might indicate a false 'up'. You are now in a steady turn, but receiving no vestibular signals that a turn is occurring.

Sight is more reliable than balance.

To avoid this illusion, **use your eyes,** either to refer to the natural horizon, or to the flight instruments (which may be difficult to interpret for an untrained instrument pilot).

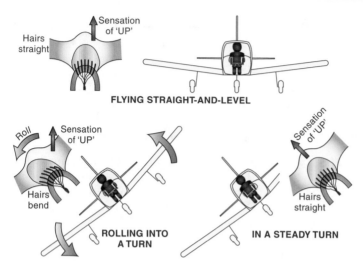

FLYING STRAIGHT-AND-LEVEL

ROLLING INTO A TURN

IN A STEADY TURN

■ ✎ Figure 3-7 **An illusion of level flight while in a steady turn**

The Illusion of being in Level Flight While Slowly Banking into a Shallow Turn

Another illusion of level flight can occur when the aeroplane banks over very slowly, perhaps while the pilot is distracted reading the navigation chart. The rate of roll is insufficient to cause any movement of fluid in the semicircular canals, hence there is no impression of angular acceleration and no impression of either entering or being in a turn. Once again, the solution is to use your eyes and the natural or artificial horizon to return to wings level.

Your balance mechanism may not sense slow banking.

The 'Leans'

The 'leans' is the illusion of the aeroplane being banked when in fact the wings are level. The leans will be accentuated if the pilot has no visual references, and, once again, can occur in the following manner.

An aeroplane has been in a steady turn for 15 seconds, time enough for the initial movement of fluid in the semicircular canals to have ceased and the vestibular apparatus to have forgotten that it is in a turn, or maybe the aeroplane has banked gently unbeknown to the pilot. Anyway, the situation is that the aeroplane is in a turn, but the vestibular apparatus is not sending any signals to the brain to indicate this – the vestibular apparatus senses wings-level even though the aeroplane is banked, say to the left.

In a lengthy, steady banked turn, your balance mechanism senses 'wings-level.'

The pilot now rolls right to level the wings. The vestibular apparatus registers this roll to the right, but it does so from what it sensed as a wings-level situation rather than the left turn that in reality it was. It now senses the situation as a right banked turn, even though the wings in reality are level – this is an illusion.

After rolling out to wings-level after a lengthy, steady banked turn, your balance mechanism senses a 'lean' in the direction of roll.

The tendency is for the pilot to feel as if he is leaning into an unwanted turn to the right, and to roll back in the other direction to what felt like wings-level, i.e. into the original left turn. If things get out of hand, a 'graveyard spiral' in the original direction of turn could be the undesired result. Once again, your eyes should come to your rescue! Check the natural horizon or the artificial horizon on the attitude indicator.

STEADY TURN

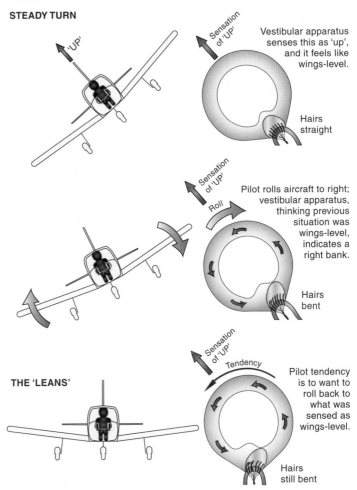

'UP'

Sensation of 'UP'

Vestibular apparatus senses this as 'up', and it feels like wings-level.

Hairs straight

Sensation of 'UP'

Roll

Pilot rolls aircraft to right; vestibular apparatus, thinking previous situation was wings-level, indicates a right bank.

Hairs bent

Sensation of 'UP'

Tendency

THE 'LEANS'

Pilot tendency is to want to roll back to what was sensed as wings-level.

Hairs still bent

■ ✎ *Figure 3-8* **The 'leans' after rolling wings-level from a steady turn**

You can expect two illusions in every normal steady turn:
- **first of all,** the illusion, once you have settled into the turn for 10 or 15 seconds, that the wings are level when they are not; and then

- **a second illusion,** after you have rolled out of the turn to wings-level, of turning in the opposite direction, with a tendency to want to roll back out of the imagined turn.

Figure 3-8 illustrates the situation. You can overcome this illusion by using your eyes to look at the real or artificial horizon.

Keep Your Head Upright

The illusions caused by shifting the semicircular canals out of their normal plane of rotation are known as *Coriolis* illusions. The means of avoiding any Coriolis illusion is to hold your head in a steady upright position relative to your body and minimise its movement, and keep all turns coordinated (ball in the centre).

We have discussed here the situation regarding rolling into and out of a turn – the same situation applies to changes in pitch and in yaw using the semicircular canals relative to those axes.

Vertigo

Vertigo is generally experienced as a feeling of rotation, when in fact no rotation is actually occurring (or vice versa). It can be caused by:

- **disease;**
- **accelerations** that disturb the delicate balance mechanisms in the inner ear; and
- **sudden pressure changes** in the inner ear; strong blowing of the nose or sneezing can do this quite violently, and bring on a spell of dizziness.

Vertigo can also be brought on by a flashing light, such as a strobe light or sunlight reflecting off rotating propeller blades (especially in the case of helicopter rotor blades) – this is known as **flicker vertigo.** If you wish to experience vertigo on the ground, you can bring it on by spinning around about 20 times with your head held low, and then stand up and try to walk in a straight line.

Avoid flashing lights.

Similar forces on your body occur when an aeroplane is manoeuvring, especially when high g-loadings are pulled in steep turns, spins, spiral dives, etc., and vertigo can occur, especially if there is no visual reference to the horizon. This is the reason why non-instrument-rated (i.e. VFR) pilots are asking for trouble if they enter cloud and lose the advantage of visual reference to the horizon!

Check your flight instruments.

A form of vertigo known as **pressure vertigo** can result from the effect on the balance apparatus following inwards failure of the eardrums because of blocked Eustachian tubes. This could occur, in an extreme case, if flying with a cold or other similar infection, when pressure changes outside the ear while descending at a high rate or from a great height cannot be equalised inside the ear.

Do not fly with a cold.

Vestibular and 'Seat-of-the-Pants' Illusions Caused by Accelerations and g-forces

The Illusion of Climbing When In a Turn

In a turn, the body experiences a force on the seat-of-the-pants greater than 1g normally exerted on it by the seat in straight-and-level flight, the same feeling as if the aeroplane was being pulled up from straight-and-level into a climb.

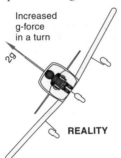 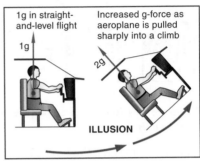

■ ✎ Figure 3-9 **The illusion of climbing when in a turn**

<table>
<tr><td>*Turns can feel like climbs.*</td><td>The pilot must avoid the tendency to push the control column forward to stop the imagined climb – it will only send the aeroplane into a descending turn. (The semicircular canal fluid may have settled down and stopped indicating a roll, so you will not be getting any sense of a turn from the vestibular apparatus.)</td></tr>
</table>

The Illusion of Descending after being in a Turn

Rolling out of a lengthy turn can feel like a descent.

After being in a steady turn for some time, the body gradually gets used to the increased g-forces. Immediately after rolling back to wings-level, and reducing the g-forces to just 1g, the body feels this reduced g-force as less than 1g, the same effect as pushing the nose over into a descent. Use your eyes to check the horizon or the flight instruments to avoid making incorrect inputs on the controls.

The Tumbling-Backwards Illusion Caused by Strong Linear Acceleration

In a state of rest or steady velocity (i.e. no acceleration), the body experiences an upward force from the seat. If you now accelerate strongly, there is a further force from the back of the seat accelerating you forwards, and your vestibular apparatus, as well as the seat-of-your-pants, interprets this as a g-force angled forwards.

Accelerating forward may feel like tumbling backwards.

Since you are used to g-forces always being 'up', you interpret the tilted direction of the new g-force as being 'up'; in other words, you must have tumbled backwards. This is known as the *oculogravic* illusion or the *somatogravic* illusion. The tendency is, as a result of this illusion of tumbling backwards during strong accelerations, to want to push the nose of the aeroplane down – a tendency which you can avoid if you use your eyes.

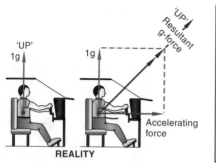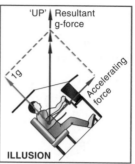

■ ✎ Figure 3-10 **Rapid acceleration creates the illusion of tumbling backwards**

Similarly, pushing the nose forward strongly, to level off from a climb or enter a descent from straight-and-level, will also exert a force on your back, which may create the illusion of tumbling backwards.

The Illusion of Pitching Forwards Caused by Strong Linear Deceleration

The converse happens when you are travelling fast, and then decelerate rapidly. The seat–belt now exerts a force on you, and the resultant g-force from this and the force of gravity is now angled backwards. You sense this direction as 'up', so you imagine that you must have pitched forward. The tendency is to pull the control column back, which you can resist if you use your eyes.

Slowing down may feel like tumbling forwards.

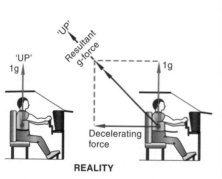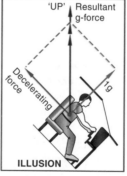

■ ✎ Figure 3-11 **Rapid deceleration creates the illusion of pitching forwards**

Motion Sickness

Motion sickness, also called airsickness, is often caused by the balance mechanisms of the inner ear continually being over-stimulated by accelerations. This can be caused by turbulence, or manoeuvres such as steep turns or spins, in which forces other than the normal 1g that the body is used to will be experienced. A hot, smelly cockpit does not help!

Psychological aspects can also play a role in the onset of motion sickness – for instance, a fear of flying or apprehension at seeing the horizon at different angles.

Motion sickness can also be caused by a mis-matching of balance signals from the ears and visual signals from the eyes. For example, an experienced pilot practising instrument flying in a fixed-base (non-moving) simulator may experience motion sickness because the visual sense (what is seen on the flight instruments, which may be a steep bank) is different from the vestibular signals being received from the ears (1g straight-and-level).

Many pilots have experienced airsickness, especially early in their training when stress levels are higher than normal, and slightly unusual attitudes and g-forces are encountered perhaps for the first time, so do not be discouraged if you experience it occasionally.

To avoid airsickness:
• **fly the aeroplane smoothly** and in a coordinated manner;
• **avoid manoeuvres** involving unusual g-forces;
• **avoid areas of turbulence;**
• **ventilate** the cabin with a good supply of fresh air;
• **involve a potentially airsick passenger** in the operation of the flight, especially if this involves looking outside the aeroplane and into the distance (e.g. to help identify ground references);
• **as a last resort,** recline the airsick passenger's seat to reduce the effect of the vertical accelerations and keep an airsickness bag handy; and
• **land** as soon as is reasonably possible (if necessary).

Now complete: **Practice Questions - Hearing and Balance**

1. The Eustachian tube serves what purpose?

   (a) It allows the middle ear to drain.

   (b) It allows pressure in the middle ear to equalise with ambient pressure.

   (c) It allows pressure in the outer ear to equalise with ambient pressure.

   (d) It allows pressure in the sinus to equalise with ambient pressure.

2. The cause of motion sickness:

   (a) The movement of fluid in the inner ear.

   (b) Too many visual clues.

   (c) Eating shortly before flight.

   (d) A mismatch between signal from the eyes and the inner ear.

3. Pilots who are aware they are experiencing spatial disorientation should:

   (a) Briefly close their eyes.

   (b) Concentrate on and trust the aircraft instruments.

   (c) Rely on external exterior clues.

   (d) Rely on somatosensory (seat of pants) information.

4. Why should you not fly when suffering from a cold?

   (a) The pressure between the inner ear and the middle ear may not be equalised.

   (b) The pressure between the inner ear and atmospheric may not be equalised.

   (c) The pressure between the middle ear and atmospheric may not be equalised.

   (d) The pressure between the middle ear and the outer ear may not be equalised.

5. The human auditory range is:

   (a) 20-20,000 Hz.

   (b) 20-200,000 Hz.

   (c) 200-20,000 Hz.

   (d) 200-200,000 Hz.

Answers: 1b, 2d, 3b, 4c, 5a.

Am I Fit to Fly?

Before each flight you must ask yourself, "Am I fit to fly? Do I feel well? Am I able to perform the physical and mental tasks that may be required of me as pilot-in-command?"

During the course of your training, you should read this chapter through several times but, right at this early stage, it will suffice if you just note the paragraph headings, and then read those paragraphs relevant to you.

Physical Fitness

As a pilot, you should maintain a reasonable degree of physical fitness. It allows better physical and mental performance during flight and in the long term, and quite apart from flying, improves your chances of a long and healthy life.

Keep physically fit.

Keeping fit takes some effort, and this effort must be continuous for fitness to be retained; but it can also be good fun and very recreational. Walking, jogging, digging in the garden, cycling, swimming – in fact anything that steadily raises your pulse rate will improve your fitness.

If you are grossly unfit or obese, then allow yourself several diet-conscious months with moderate exercise that is gradually increased, and consider medical supervision. It might seem like a long haul, but the quality of life and your self-perception will improve together with your fitness. Physical activity also promotes a hunger for healthy foods as well as encouraging good sleeping patterns.

Physical fitness helps pilots cope better with stress, tiredness, fatigue and the reduced availability of oxygen at higher levels in the atmosphere.

Mental Fitness

Keep mentally fit.

Flying an aeroplane involves physical activity but the main workload on a pilot is intellectual. Mental fitness is vital to safe flying, but it can be degraded by:

- medication;
- drugs, including alcohol and cigarettes;
- stress;
- personal or family problems;
- lack of sleep or poor eating habits; and
- fatigue or allowing oneself to become over-tired.

Illness and Drugs (including alcohol and smoking)

A reasonably innocuous complaint on the ground (such as the common cold) may have serious effects under the stress of flying and high altitudes.

Medical drugs taken to combat an illness may impair flying abilities and physical comfort in flight. 'Recreational drugs' such as alcohol, marijuana, LSD, etc. must **never** be mixed with flying and a person dependent upon these may not be fit to hold a pilot's licence.

Be careful with medicines and drugs.

Smoking also significantly decreases a pilot's capacity to perform by reducing the amount of oxygen carried in the blood, replacing it with the useless and potentially poisonous by-products of cigarette smoke. A pilot does not have to be the active smoker to suffer the effects; smoke from any person in the cockpit (or anywhere in the aircraft, if it is small) will affect everyone.

Medical Checks

Regular checks by an Aviation Medical Examiner are required to monitor your general health, both physical and mental. Major items in the medical test include checks of the central nervous system (including eyesight), the cardiovascular system (including heart and blood pressure), the kidneys (using a urine test), hearing ability, and the respiratory system (ears, nose, throat and lungs), especially the Eustachian tubes for their ability to allow pressure to equalise either side of the eardrums.

Regular medical checks verify your general health and fitness, but occasional bouts of sickness or injury may make you temporarily unfit to fly, particularly if medication is involved. If in doubt consult an Aviation Medical Examiner.

If you are travelling to tropical countries, seek medical advice about taking precautions against malaria. Not many people are aware that over 2,000 cases are reported in the UK annually, and in 1991, twelve of these patients died. AIC 97/00 (Pink 10) contains details on malaria prevention.

Do not assume that because you have a disability you may not be able to hold a pilot's licence. There are many people with disabilities who are permitted to fly. Check with an Aviation Medical Examiner.

Pilots carry a heavy responsibility to themselves and to the general community, and so medical fitness in general, and on the day of flight in particular, is most important.

Medication

Until cleared by a doctor, it is safest to assume that *any* drug or medication will temporarily ground you.

A list of common medications considered incompatible with flying includes:

- **antibiotics** (e.g. penicillin) used to combat infection;
- **tranquillisers,** antidepressants and sedatives;
- **stimulants** (caffeine, amphetamines) used to maintain wakefulness or suppress appetite;
- **antihistamines,** often used to combat colds and hay fever;
- **drugs for the relief** of high blood pressure;
- **analgesics** to relieve pain;
- **anaesthetics** (used for local, general or dental purposes) usually require about 24 hours before returning to flight.

BLOOD AND BONE MARROW DONATION. Blood donation is a safe procedure for aircrew, provided that a suitable time is allowed after the donation before flight. In some cases there is a slight risk of fainting after donation. If you do donate blood, do not fly for at least 24 hours afterwards. In the case of bone marrow donation you should not fly for at least 48 hours afterwards, because a general anaesthetic is involved. See AIC 97/2004 (Pink 70).

Alcohol

A pilot who has 'had a drink' is obliged not to fly if under the influence of alcohol or any drug which will impair the ability to perform pilot duties. **Alcohol and flying should never be mixed!**

■ ✎ Figure 4-1 **Alcohol is dangerous when associated with flying**

Alcohol impairs performance.

Even *small* quantities of alcohol in the blood can impair one's performance, with the added danger of relieving anxiety so that the person thinks he is performing marvellously. Alcohol severely affects a person's judgment and abilities. High altitudes, where there is less oxygen, worsens the effect.

Alcohol disturbs sleep.

It takes time for the body to remove alcohol and, as a general rule, a pilot should not fly for at least 8 hours after drinking small quantities of alcohol and increase this time if greater quantities are consumed. After heavy drinking, alcohol may still be in the blood 30 hours later. Sleep will *not* speed up the removal process; in fact it slows the body processes down and the elimination of alcohol may take even longer.

NOTE The average time required to eliminate one unit of alcohol from the blood is one hour.

People who are dependent upon alcohol (alcoholics) should not hold a pilot's licence.

A drunk person should not be permitted on board an aeroplane.

Upper Respiratory Tract Problems

Each eardrum has ambient pressure from the outer ear on one side and air pressure in the middle ear on the other. The middle ear is connected to the nose and throat via the Eustachian tube, whose function it is to equalise the pressure in the middle ear with ambient pressure outside.

At rest, the Eustachian tube lies closed; it opens naturally when the pressure in the middle ear is higher than that outside. As you climb in an aircraft the ambient pressure decreases; therefore, the relative pressure in the middle ear is higher and the Eustachian tube opens, allowing the pressure inside the middle ear to equalise with that outside.

If for any reason the Eustachian tube is blocked and not functioning correctly (for example because of congestion caused by a common cold), the pressure cannot equalise and it remains higher inside the middle ear than outside. When the pressure becomes too high, it has the potential to cause damage (barotrauma) and can also affect hearing by preventing sound waves from transmitting normally through the ear.

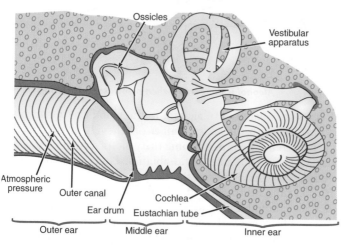

■ ✎ *Figure 4-2* **The Eustachian tube equalises pressure either side of the eardrum**

As atmospheric pressure on the outer parts of the body increases during a descent, it pushes the eardrums in. Ideally, some air will flow from the throat and nasal passages via each Eustachian

Flying with a cold can cause problems, especially on descent.

tube into the middle ear and equalise the pressure. However, the nature of the Eustachian tubes is such that air will not move into them from the nasal passages as readily as it moves out, and so any swelling or blocking can lead to problems. High rates of descent worsen the situation.

Flying with a common cold or other upper respiratory tract infection can be problematic. The **blocked Eustachian tubes** which can accompany such a complaint will lead to problems with pressure equalisation, especially on descent (when ambient pressure changes can be high even in low-performance aircraft).

- **Pain in the ears** could be severe, which is very distracting.
- **There is a danger of the eardrums collapsing** inwards as the external pressure builds up, giving rise to a loss of hearing which may or may not be permanent.
- **The balance mechanisms** could be affected.

Blocked ears can sometimes be cleared by holding the nose and blowing hard (a technique known as the *Valsalva* movement), by chewing, swallowing or yawning. The best advice is, however, **if you have a cold, do not fly.**

Problems can also arise in the sinuses, which are cavities in the head connected by narrow tubes to the nasal/throat passages. Blockages can cause great pain, especially during descent. For this reason, do not fly with sinus problems, or any problems to do with your upper respiratory tract. This applies to flight in any aircraft – pressurised or unpressurised.

Carbon Monoxide Poisoning

Exhaust fumes are poison.

As mentioned in Chapter 1, *Human Physiology and High Altitudes*, carbon monoxide poisoning can occur if engine exhaust fumes or excessive cigarette smoke is inhaled.

Food Poisoning

Food poisoning can kill.

Food poisoning may result from an improperly prepared meal and its onset may be almost immediate following consumption of the food, or it may not become evident for some hours, but, even then, its onset may be very sudden. The stomach pains, nausea, diarrhoea, vomiting, etc., that accompany food poisoning can make it physically impossible to perform pilot duties.

It is a good practice, for the half day prior to flight, to avoid foods that are often associated with food poisoning, including shellfish, fish, mayonnaise, creams, over-ripe and thin-skinned fruits, uncooked foods such as salads and raw foods, and old food (e.g. food that has been cooked and stored for some time). If you suspect that some effects of food poisoning are imminent from something bad that you have eaten, **do not fly!**

Glasses and Contact Lenses

If you are required by the Aviation Medical Examiner to wear glasses to correct your sight, then you must wear them as required. It is also compulsory to carry a spare pair of glasses whenever you are flying.

If you wear glasses or contact lenses, you must carry a spare pair of glasses when flying.

Before your Medical Certificate can be endorsed to approve the wearing of contact lenses you must provide a report from an ophthalmologist including details of your field of vision, unaided and corrected visual acuity, corrective lenses prescription, and confirmation that the contact lenses have been worn constantly and successfully for over 8 hours a day for at least one month.

If your Certificate is endorsed to permit the use of contact lenses for flying you must carry a pair of ordinary spectacles at all times while exercising the privileges of the licence.

Bifocal contact lenses for the correction of presbyopia are unsuitable for use in flying. Any near-vision correction must be provided by 'look over' spectacles. In such cases, therefore, suitable bifocal spectacles should be carried for emergency use.

Pilots considering refractive surgery for vision correction should refer to the CAA Medical Division before undertaking the procedure.

For more information about vision correction requirements for pilots see EASA Part-MED.

If flying in bright sunlight, especially above clouds, it is good practice to wear a high-quality set of sunglasses.

Smoking

Smoking is detrimental to good health, both in the short term and in the long term.

In the short term – carbon monoxide, which is present in cigarette smoke, is absorbed into the blood in preference to oxygen. This reduces the body's ability to produce energy (including in the brain). The diminished supply of oxygen to the body and brain becomes very noticeable at higher altitudes where cigarette smoke in the cabin can significantly decrease the pilot's performance (even if not actually smoking the cigarette!).

In the long term – it is generally accepted that cigarette smoking plays a significant role in cardiovascular (heart) and other diseases. If you want to live a long and healthy life, then you should not smoke.

Incidentally, smoking in the cockpit is banned by almost all airlines, and, in most countries, smoking by everyone, including passengers, is banned in aircraft and airports.

Smoking is bad.

Fatigue and Sleep Deprivation

Do not fly when fatigued.

Fatigue, tiredness and sleep deprivation can lower a pilot's mental and physical capacity quite dramatically. The nature of flying is such that moderate levels of these complaints are involved. As a pilot, you must train yourself to cope with them, and to recognise when your **personal limits** are being approached. However, a deeply tired or fatigued pilot should not be flying!

Fatigue can become deep-seated and chronic if personal, psychological or emotional problems are not solved, preventing deep rest and good sleep over a prolonged period. Chronic fatigue will be cured when the problems are solved, or at least being coped with, and the person can relax and unstress. As a pilot, you should prohibit yourself from flying until this is the case.

Short-term fatigue can be caused by overwork, mental stress, an uncomfortable body position, a recent lack of sleep, *living it up* a bit too much, lack of oxygen or lack of food. Sleep and rest are essential!

To guard against fatigue that is detrimental to flight safety, you should:

- **have your psychological** and emotional life under control;
- **be reasonably fit;**
- **eat regularly;**
- **ensure that you are not deprived** of having adequate and effective sleep;
- **ensure that cockpit comfort** is optimised and that energy foods and drink are available on long flights; and
- **exercise your limbs** occasionally and, if practicable, land to stretch your legs at least every four hours.

Now complete: **Practice Questions - Am I Fit to Fly?**

1. A pilot suffering from gastro-enteritis is?
   (a) Probably fit to fly.
   (b) Fit to fly with medication.
   (c) Unfit to fly for more than one hour.
   (d) Unfit to fly.

2. Assume one unit is half a pint of beer, a standard glass of wine, or a single measure of spirit. Approximately how long will it take to eliminate one unit of alcohol from the blood?
   (a) 1 hour.
   (b) 30 minutes.
   (c) 2 hours.
   (d) 3 hours.

3. A pilot intending to self medicate using a preparation that does not require a doctor's prescription should:
   (a) Check that the side effects have been evaluated and are minor.
   (b) See if the drugs have any side effects before flying.
   (c) Seek professional advice from a CAA AME.
   (d) Be aware of any likely performance reducing side effects.

4. When fatigued:
   (a) You can fly as long as you take regular breaks.
   (b) You can fly as long as you drink energy drinks.
   (c) Observe your personal limitations when fatigued.
   (d) Do not fly when deeply tired or fatigued.

5. If required to wear spectacles:
   (a) You can wear contact lenses as an alternative.
   (b) If you wear contact lenses you must have spare contact lenses with you.
   (c) You must have a spare pair of spectacles with you.
   (d) Bifocal contact lenses are approved for use in aeroplanes.

Answers: 1d, 2a, 3c, 4d, 5c.

Stress Management, Fatigue and Sleep

Stress Management

Stress

In the course of normal activity we respond to stimuli, or demands, placed on us in response to our actions and by our environment. These demands can be mental or physical, and if they create a pressure overload, we are *adversely affected* and stress results. The cause of the stress is called a **stressor**.

Just as an airframe undergoes mechanical stress and tension, in humans this takes the form of nervous and mental strain. However, whilst aircraft stress limits are known, human stress levels are more complex and uncertain, each individual can have a different perception and personal definition of stress.

Just as aircraft stress can rupture a fuel tank, similarly human stress can deplete a pilot's energy reserves. Hence like fuel management, stress management is vital for safe flight operation.

Exposure to constant stress can bring about changes in the balance of hormones in the body, which threatens the health. Also, the existence of one form of stress tends to diminish the resistance to other forms.

Stressors cause stress.

A potential stressor can be *acute* in the sense that it is immediate and disappears after a short time; another can be *chronic,* long lasting, and fatiguing. It is important for general health, and for longevity, that all pressures and demands are managed so as not to be stressful for us as much as possible.

Stress management is a vital skill for the modern pilot to develop. It requires learning how to deal with pressure and disallow it from:

- **overwhelming** the ability to respond properly; and/or
- **disrupting** the ability to operate smoothly, correctly and efficiently in the cockpit and on the ground in the course of conducting a flight.

Stress accumulates.

Any individual demand on ourselves is a potential stressor if not managed properly. Also, combinations of demands which are individually small can be potentially overloading. For example, radio calls coming in to a pilot who is making a difficult crosswind approach, say in turbulent conditions in poor visibility or at night. A system malfunction at this time would further increase the load.

A small amount of pressure can raise our arousal level into the optimum area and can actually improve our performance by making us more alert. An overload of pressure, however, can move us beyond this, maybe into the 'panic' area, and affect us adversely, causing poor performance.

Some stress is good.

The aim when flying is for the load to be kept at a manageable level, well below the overload level (but not so low that we are not stimulated or alert).

Responding to Demands and Stimuli

Every person functions under some form of pressure, which serves as a stimulus to act. The person responds to 'demands'. For a pilot, these demands are many and varied and will include feedback on how well the desired flightpath and airspeed are being maintained, cockpit procedures, navigation requirements, radio procedures, and so on, often happening almost simultaneously.

How well a person handles these demands varies with the person's ability or capacity to respond, and this may depend on:
- **general health;**
- **personality,** and how at ease the person feels;
- **having a happy** and organised personal life;
- **sufficient rest** having been taken;
- **the degree of preparation** for the task; and
- **the person's intelligence** and aptitude for the activity.

A particular situation can cause differing degrees of difficulty for different people, and in the same person under different circumstances. The situation can be a stressor for one person and 'normal life' for another. For instance, a strong crosswind on final approach will be more demanding for a beginning pilot than for an experienced one. However, if the experienced pilot was tired or fatigued, concerned about family life, and trying to cope with an emergency, then the stress level might also be high during the crosswind approach.

Overload

If the demands become too much, the person becomes overloaded, and performance usually drops. This can have serious consequences in aviation.

Different people can cope with different levels of pressure. Each one of us, though, has probably been overloaded at one time or another. It is important then that we develop a strategy to prevent overloads, or to cope with them if they occur.

Family and social life should be under control. If not, this can cause a high level of stress. Generally good health and fitness is also important.

| Being fit, rested, and experienced reduces stress. |

Always be well rested and well prepared, so that you can approach the task in a responsible, but natural and easy manner. Knowledge, experience and flight proficiency will allow you to keep stress levels manageable, and make correct decisions quickly and efficiently. This requires effort during your training and prior to every flight.

Perceived Pressures

Stress is the adverse effect on the mind and body of an overload of pressure. When we react to perceived pressures, a response is usually demanded from the brain. These perceived pressures may not, in fact, be real pressures – something which is very important for us to appreciate when we find ourselves having to deal with a potential overload.

The first question to ask, once you decide that you want to reduce the level of stress, is: "Does the stressor – the item causing the stress – really exist?" For instance, a slamming door may cause your body to react in the same way as an explosion since, in each case, the body receives a shock, even though in the case of the slamming door there is no danger. The same applies to perceived emotional stresses, many of which turn out to be imaginary. Once you realise that the danger does not exist in reality, the stress gradually dissipates.

Tolerance to pressure demands varies a lot between individuals, with some people being able to tolerate a much higher level than others. The tolerance to new stress also varies within the one individual, depending upon the current level of stress, and the time of day (according to the personal body clock). Increasing age may also lead to a decrease in tolerance to stress, something older pilots and their younger colleagues need to be aware of.

Physical Stress – Fight or Flight?

A sudden fright, like the perception of physical danger, causes your brain to prepare rapidly for action. The adrenal gland sends out the hormone *adrenalin* which stimulates your body physically to meet the threat – to fight or to flee. You have no doubt experienced the sudden rush of adrenalin on occasions. The heart rate increases quickly, certain blood vessels constrict to divert blood to where it is most needed for physical action, and many other changes occur in the body.

Your performance will, most probably, be enhanced, within the limits of your experience and training. Your responses may be quick and exact – the well-practised ones may even be automatic – and you will be very sensitive to your surroundings. In cases like this the stimuli can enhance the level at which you function.

Whether you 'fight or flee' depends on many things, including personality and aptitude (or suitability) for the job, and the level of perceived danger.

Non-Physical Stress

Some stressful situations arise, not from a perceived physical threat, but from intellectual, psychological and emotional causes. These could be the pressure of time (too much to do in too little time), difficult decisions to be made (to continue into deteriorating weather ahead or to divert to an alternate aerodrome), a lack of self-confidence, a strained personal relationship, or an emotional overload.

Emotional overload will cause stress.

Some psychological or emotional demands, such as a failing personal relationship, can be debilitating on a long-term or chronic basis, whereas some intellectual pressure can prepare you for quick mental activity. Some stimuli can be performance-enhancing; other types can inhibit your performance.

Arousal

How well you can handle a task depends to a large extent on your state of arousal. Many types of stimuli increase your arousal level – for instance, a fright – whereas other types decrease your arousal level, such as fatigue.

A *low* level of arousal is associated with deep sleep, fatigue, sleep deprivation, a lack of motivation, and low body temperature, which will occur naturally when internal body temperature is at a low point in its daily circadian rhythm.

A *high* level of arousal is associated with fear, panic, and under-confidence.

Being under-aroused – for instance, overly casual or apathetic – may lead to poor performance of a task; being over-aroused – for instance, highly keyed up and tense – may also lead to poor performance.

Between these two extremes, however, there is a region of *optimum* arousal leading to optimum performance of the task. The measure of your performance may be the speed with which you respond to the situation, the intensity and accuracy of your response, how well you are coordinated in your response, and how quickly you react in modifying your response as the situation changes. Your response to the situation will be best in the region of optimum arousal, between low and high arousal.

Optimum arousal facilitates optimum performance.

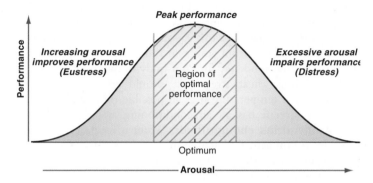

■ ✎ Figure 5-1 **Optimum arousal facilitates optimum performance**

Poor performance will be the result at both extremes of the arousal scale; good performance will be the result in the central region where arousal is optimum. This connection between state of arousal and level of performance can be shown graphically (Figure 5-1).

For peak performance during take-off, landing and emergencies, you should be in the intermediate area of arousal – aroused, but not over-aroused.

For satisfactory performance in the relatively low workload period of a long-haul cruise, a moderate level of arousal is adequate (but not under-arousal where you might miss important things such as a reporting point and heading change, or a developing emergency).

Stressors

An experience causing stress is known as a **stressor.** Stressors can be divided into two classes:

- **environmental or physical stressors** – these include such items as noise and physical contact; and
- **intellectual, psychological, and emotional stressors** – these are often related to problems at home and at work.

Environmental or Physical Stressors

Keep the working environment comfortable.

If you are working in an environment that differs from the ideal environment for man – for instance in an environment which is excessively hot, cold, noisy, damp, dry, turbulent, vibrating, dark, light, smelly, or lacking in oxygen – you can become tired and stressed more quickly than otherwise.

STRESS CAUSED BY HEAT (HYPERTHERMIA). In very high environmental temperatures, say 35°C and above, the body struggles to keep its internal temperature at just under 37°C and prevent itself from overheating (known as *hyperthermia*). The perspiration rate, heart rate and blood pressure all increase. In a humid atmosphere, as opposed to a dry atmosphere, your perspiration will tend *not* to evaporate, hence no latent heat is absorbed into the air from your skin and the underlying blood, so there is a greater tendency for your body to overheat.

To minimise heat stress you should try to control the environmental temperature if at all possible (but, unfortunately, not every aircraft has an air-conditioning system), and, most importantly, **drink enough fluids.** Water is ideal. Try to take a drink *before* you actually become thirsty, since thirst is a sign that you are already on the way to becoming dehydrated.

Remember that tasks outside the cockpit prior to flight, such as loading the aircraft or flight planning, or even just standing or sitting in high temperatures, may cause your body to overheat and/or dehydrate. Take appropriate measures by drinking fluids, staying under shade, and not rushing.

STRESS CAUSED BY COLD (HYPOTHERMIA). In a cold environment, the body automatically sends more blood to the body core, rather than to the extremities. This is an attempt to keep the internal temperature at about 37°C by minimising heat loss from the skin. Heat loss can occur by:

- **radiation** from exposed areas of skin, especially from your head which has many blood vessels near the surface of your scalp;
- **conduction** as wind flows across your skin and carries heat away, which is known as the *wind chill factor*; and
- **evaporation** of perspiration or other moisture from your skin, which causes cooling by absorbing heat from the skin and underlying blood vessels, and using it to change the state of the moisture from liquid to vapour (latent heat).

In low temperatures, your toes and fingers may feel cold, your muscles might feel stiff and weak, you may feel tired and drowsy, and you might start to shiver – this is an attempt by your body to generate warmth by muscle activity. It is said that "if your hands and feet feel comfortable, then all is well".

STRESS CAUSED BY VIBRATION. Vibrations transmitted to the body from the aircraft via the seat, seat-belts and the floor can make you feel uncomfortable, distract you from your main tasks, and lead to fatigue.

A vibrating instrument panel may make the instruments difficult to read. Severe vibration may even cause your eyeballs to vibrate, making it almost impossible to read your flight instruments or your navigation charts, or to scan for other aircraft. Even though it might be impossible to reduce the vibration from the aircraft itself, the vibration reaching your body can be reduced by well-mounted and well-cushioned seats.

STRESS CAUSED BY TURBULENCE. Turbulence will cause irregular movements of the aircraft, varying from fairly small movements when flying through slight turbulence to unbelievably strong movements associated with severe turbulence that may even damage the aircraft. Turbulence can cause discomfort to the pilot and passengers by shaking them around, exerting unusual g-forces on them, and perhaps causing motion sickness. It may cause the instrument panel to vibrate or the eyeballs to judder, making it difficult to read the instruments, and it may make the aircraft very difficult to control.

STRESS CAUSED BY NOISE. Excessive noise in the cockpit, especially if it is high-pitched and loud, can cause stress and fatigue. An industry limit for continuous noise is 85 dB (decibels), with ear protection required above this level. Noise levels in a typical cockpit are in the range 75–80 dB, but this is only background noise, with noise from radio messages superimposed on it. Noise above about 90 dB will cause stress that raises your arousal into the poor performance area, making you irritable, and leading to fatigue. Above about 80 dB, you should wear protection to avoid stress damage to your ears.

Use a high-quality headset.

Stress can also be caused by having to strain to understand radio messages against a high background noise level. With your ears protected from background engine and air noise by a high-quality headset, you should be able to hear radio messages even when the volume is quite low.

STRESS CAUSED BY BEING UNCOMFORTABLE. The nature of our job as pilots is that we are confined to sitting in small cockpits for long periods of time. The stress of sitting in a noisy, vibrating aircraft for long periods, and having to cope with the usual problems of flight, such as turbulence, navigation, radio calls, and so on, can lead to an accumulation of stress and fatigue.

The best means of combating this form of stress is to keep yourself fit, be well rested prior to flight, maintain a good posture with your tail tucked well back into the seat and your lower back well supported, and exercise periodically by wriggling your toes and feet and stretching your arms.

It is also important to be appropriately dressed for the job. Wearing too much or too little clothing will make you uncomfortable and is thus distracting. You should also make sure that your clothes fit well. There are few things worse than a tight shirt collar, tight trousers, or tight shoes.

STRESS CAUSED BY FEELING UNWELL. If feeling unwell, you may
be easily overloaded and prone to becoming fatigued. Your body
will be using up a lot of your energy to combat the illness, and so
you will have less energy available for other tasks. Your general
performance will be much lower than normal.

Keep fit and well.

If you have a headache, an upper respiratory tract infection
(such as a cold), a sporting and other injury, a stomach upset, or a
sneezing attack, you should consider whether it is a responsible
decision to commence your flight. If you feel unwell in flight,
then you should consider landing and resting.

Motion sickness (feeling airsick) can make a person feel very
low and uninterested in events. It is not confined to new student
pilots and passengers – on rare occasions even experienced pilots
feel airsick. Their knowledge that it might cause them to feel
apathetic, however, is protection to some extent against lowered
performance.

A pilot will also be subject to stress unnecessarily if not eating
regularly or eating well, the result possibly being *hypoglycemia*, a
low blood sugar level. Its symptoms are headache, stomach pain,
lack of energy, nervousness and shaking, and can be relieved in the
short term by eating a snack.

STRESS CAUSED BY EYE STRAIN. Eye strain because of impaired
vision or poor lighting can cause stress. Impaired vision can be
remedied with glasses or contact lenses. The solution to bad
lighting is obvious – turn the lights up! This need not mean that
the whole cockpit should be brightly lit when all you need to see
are the instruments and your charts – simply turn the instrument
lights up and use a small spotlight, if available, for your charts. If
the main cabin lights are turned up too bright at night, you may
have to strain your eyes to scan outside for other aircraft and
weather.

STRESS CAUSED BY FLASHING LIGHTS. A flashing light is designed
to attract attention, usually to other vehicles or aircraft. Seeing a
flashing light will raise your level of alertness. If, however, the
warning does not apply to you, the flashing light may be very
distracting and even fatiguing. For instance, a flashing amber light
from a fuel truck parked right in front of your cockpit at night can
be very distracting if you are trying to complete your flight
preparation tasks – ask the driver to move a little! Reflected light
from your own strobe lights when flying in cloud at night can be
highly distracting, so turn the strobes off temporarily – other
aircraft will not be able to see them while you are in cloud anyway.

Avoid flashing lights.

STRESS CAUSED BY CONCENTRATION. Skill stress which leads to
fatigue can result if you have to maintain a high level of

performance for an extended period – for instance, hand-flying on instruments in turbulent IFR conditions, or even just straight-and-level visual flying for a student pilot.

Rest properly.

STRESS CAUSED BY LACK OF SLEEP. A lack of restful sleep leaves a pilot fatigued, and needing to struggle to stay awake to handle the demands of flying. The pilot has to fight off sleep, and really force concentration, leading to a high stress level and even deeper fatigue. It is a vicious circle. The solution to this is, of course, not to fly unless well rested.

Psychological and Emotional Stressors

Psychological or emotional stress can arise from a number of sources. It could be work-related (a difficult flight about to begin, or a strained relationship with management or colleagues), or it could have a domestic cause (marital or financial problems).

The result of psychological stress is that a pilot may be over-aroused and move into the area of poor performance:

- **concentrating on a single problem** and not maintaining a good overview of the flight;
- **exhibiting poor judgement;**
- **becoming disoriented** quite easily;
- **being distracted** from prime tasks;
- **taking a resigned attitude** to problems that arise ("why does this always happen to me?"); and
- **becoming fatigued** at an early stage.

WORK-RELATED PSYCHOLOGICAL STRESS. Most pilots experience a certain amount of apprehension regarding a forthcoming flight, but this is quite normal and can raise the level of arousal into the optimum area for good performance. A pilot who is stressed and over-anxious, however, may be too highly aroused to perform well – a common situation with inexperienced student pilots, and in many experienced pilots who are facing a demanding flight.

PSYCHOLOGICAL & EMOTIONAL STRESS. Psychological   and emotional stress can be caused by problems at home. Domestic-related stress can be very damaging to a pilot. If distracted by emotional problems during highly charged periods such as following the death of a spouse or child, a divorce, or when experiencing severe financial difficulties, a responsible pilot should consider grounding himself. Domestic-related problems can lead to lack of sleep, chronic fatigue, emotional instability, and a dangerous flight operation.

Anxiety

Anxiety is the extreme worry that results when a person is overloaded, particularly for prolonged periods. It is a state of being uneasy, apprehensive or worried about what may happen, and experiencing a generalised pervasive fear.

An anxious person will probably perform poorly – the condition is often apparent to a sensitive observer (such as a flying instructor or cockpit colleague) by signs of:

- **physical discomfort,** such as perspiring, nervous twitching, a dry mouth, breathing difficulties, panting, increased heart rate;
- **inappropriate behaviour,** such as laughing or singing at inappropriate times, painstaking self-control, extreme over-cooperation, rapid changes in emotion, impulsiveness or extreme passivity;
- **mood changes,** perhaps from extreme light-heartedness to depression;
- **unreasonable behaviour** towards other people, unnecessary anger, impatient and rude behaviour, etc.;
- **fatigue** – the extreme and deep tiredness that can result from being under pressure for too long;
- **incorrect thought processes,** poor concentration, or concentrating on one point to the exclusion of others, an inability to set reasonable priorities, forgetting important items such as the use of flaps for take-off or on final approach, or failing to read a checklist.

A person suffering from a *chronic stress overload* may show a personality change, behave poorly and erratically towards others, perform at a low level, become ill with stomach pains or headaches, drink, smoke or eat excessively, and may well become accident-prone.

Anxiety is a dangerous condition for a pilot to be suffering from, and top priority should be given to reducing the anxiety level before making a flight. It may be advisable to seek medical attention, but certainly the best antidote is to remove the cause (if it can be identified) as much as possible and give yourself plenty of deep rest.

Over-anxiousness causes poor performance.

Handling Pressure

Some pressure or stimulus is needed to alert you and to enhance your performance. The risk is, not the activity itself, but an *overload* of it, and an inability to cope with the demands.

The best way to handle pressure is to be physically and psychologically well prepared. This means being fit, well rested, on top of your job, on top of your life, and ready to face challenges. It is also sensible to reduce the level of unwanted stress if you can, giving you a greater capacity to handle any new

Reduce unnecessary risks.

situations that might arise. This can be achieved by resolving emotional problems at least to a point where they do not interfere with your work.

Manage your time.

Knowledge is also important, such as knowing the emergency procedures for your aeroplane so that you can cope with basic emergencies. You must also learn to manage your time efficiently so that you are never rushed. Stress can also be reduced if you control your environment as much as possible, keeping unwanted noise and vibration to a minimum, for instance, and maintaining a comfortable ambient temperature.

Prepare Yourself Physically

- **Keep fit** and well-exercised.
- **Eat well** and eat regularly.
- **Sleep well** and go flying with plenty of sleep-hours in credit.
- **Take time out** to relax.
- **Manage your time** so that you do not have to rush.
- **Control your physical environment** (noise, temperature, humidity).

Prepare Yourself Psychologically

- **Be well prepared** regarding knowledge, skills, and standard operating procedures.
- **Have well-placed confidence** in your ability but be aware of your limitations and do not operate outside them.
- **Have a structured approach** to working through and evaluating problems in order to gain knowledge, experience and confidence from unexpected or challenging events.
- **Leave your domestic and financial worries at home** – preferably arrange your life so that you have these matters well under control – have a well-rounded social and/or family life.
- **Do not procrastinate** – tackle your problems and solve them, or at least have a timetable for attempting to solve them.
- **Do not be afraid to discuss** your doubts and worries with appropriate people, with an aim to removing or minimising any unnecessary stress or anxiety.
- **Do not allow yourself to become over-excited** about non-events, or to become resigned and pessimistic unnecessarily – control your psychological environment.

Techniques of Stress Management

You will have prepared yourself in general terms to manage the normal demands of life, as suggested above, by the way you think and behave (cognitive/behavioural techniques), relaxation, and by managing your time. But sometimes you find yourself in one of those situations that arise where, even though you are generally in control of your life, the current situation seems about to get out of hand. You need to recognise this, and take appropriate action.

Recognise a Potential Overload
The first step in coping with a potential overload is to recognise its presence. As we have seen, a certain amount of pressure is essential if we are to live a normal life and handle everyday problems, both at home and in our workplace, but an overload can drastically reduce our performance and our happiness.

Remember that we respond to perceived pressures (rather than actual pressures), and to our perceived ability to handle these pressures (rather than our actual ability). After consideration, you might find that the excessive pressures are not there to begin with or, if they are, your ability is such that you can confidently handle them.

Avoid stress overloads.

Take Action
Coping satisfactorily with stress usually involves taking action to:
• **remove the cause; or**
• **remove yourself.**

For instance, you can minimise the cause of noise stress by wearing a good headset. You can minimise the cause of domestic unhappiness by discussing matters openly with your partner. These actions will remove or reduce the cause of the stress.

On the other hand, you can remove the stress caused from learning to fly aerobatics, by giving up aerobatics and taking up something less demanding – in other words by removing yourself from the scene.

You can remove the stress of flying in severe turbulence near a thunderstorm by turning back or landing – you will not remove the turbulence, but you will take yourself away from its stressful effect. You can remove (or reduce) the stress caused by an unhappy relationship by moving out, physically and psychologically.

Remove the cause of unwanted stress.

Acute stress is usually easily relieved. For instance, if you are under pressure of time to solve an undercarriage problem during an approach to land, make a missed approach and join a holding pattern. You can now take longer to resolve the problem, and the pressure of time is relieved.

Chronic long-term stress is another matter, and resolving it may mean a change in lifestyle or activity. Consult your spouse, your doctor, your adviser, your minister or priest, a friend, a counsellor, or some other appropriate person. Prolonged exposure to stress will accelerate the ageing process, unbalance the body chemistry, and lead to mental and physical illness – certainly no way to have a happy life.

Unacceptable Means of Coping with Stress

There are some means of trying to cope with stress that are not really acceptable if you want to be a pilot, such as:
- **closing your eyes** to the problem and pretending it does not exist; or
- **taking medication, drugs or alcohol** to relieve the symptoms of the stress, but not its cause.

The body and mind have certain **defence mechanisms** that sometimes operate subconsciously to remove painful matters from our consciousness. Defence mechanisms remove the symptoms but not the cause, and this can be dangerous for a pilot. Common defence mechanisms include:
- **lack of awareness** – the brain subconsciously denies or represses the existence of the stressor;
- **rationalisation** – a subconscious attempt to justify actions that would otherwise be unacceptable, often indicated by a person substituting excuses for certain behaviour rather than logical reasons;
- **somatisation** – physical symptoms caused by psychological stress (this tends to be a chronic condition);
- **daydreaming** – staring into space as a means of mentally escaping by creating a fantasy of being in more pleasant surroundings or circumstances;
- **resignation** – mentally lost or bewildered, and ready to accept whatever comes, including defeat; and
- **anger** – which may range from mild expressions of frustration, such as the use of bad language, to more violent expressions of physical behaviour, such as rough use of the flight controls.

None of these attempts to cope with stress will actually eliminate the problem. Instead, some realistic method of managing the pressure load should be adopted.

Avoid Self-imposed Stress

To some extent, the pilot has some control over the stress level, and can often reduce the pressures. Some ways in which this can be done are:
- **Think ahead** – particularly when approaching an airfield or different aispace.
- **Make early decisions** – turn back or divert before flying into bad conditions, or land well before last light if necessary.
- **Do not accept** an Air Traffic Control VFR clearance leading into clouds – keep clear of cloud and request a new clearance.
- **Do not be distracted** from checklists: request your passengers, flight instructor, or examiner not to interrupt.
- **Do not interrupt** or change your usual routines unnecessarily.

- **Request ATC to "stand by"** if you are busy coping with an emergency or having trouble handling the aeroplane – flightpath and airspeed always come first.
- **Be prepared for delays** – weather may force a delay, as can refuelling and aircraft unserviceabilities; always allow a time buffer, even for the drive to the airport.
- **Do not press on regardless.**

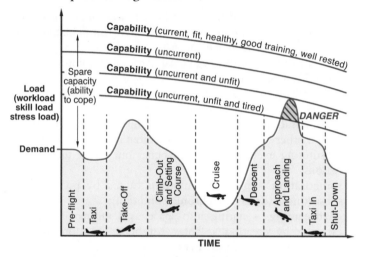

■ ✎ Figure 5-2 **Pilot capability versus workload**

The workload for a pilot during a normal flight is represented by the lower line in the Figure 5-2. High workload levels occur during take-off, and during the descent and landing. They may also occur with an emergency, or poor weather, at any stage of the flight. The ability of a pilot to cope with this workload is represented by the upper line, which can vary in position. Good training, being current, being fit and well rested, will raise the capability line, and increase the safety margin between it and the workload line.

Being fatigued, nervous, under-confident, not current, and feeling unwell, will lower the capability line, diminishing the safety margin, and perhaps removing it altogether.

Under normal conditions, you should be able to operate using only about 50% of your capability, with the other 50% in reserve to cope with unforeseen events and emergencies. During a long and tiring flight, you can expect your capability line to lower gradually.

Keep your capability level above the demand level.

Fatigue

Fatigue is a very deep tiredness that usually comes from:
- a lack of restful sleep;
- a lack of physical or mental fitness;
- excessive physical or mental stress and anxiety; or
- a desynchronisation of your body cycles (jet lag).

All of the items discussed earlier that cause stress, such as noise and vibration, high temperatures or a lack of oxygen, domestic or work-related problems, can lead to fatigue if they are not checked and resolved.

Rest properly.

The most essential immediate cure for *acute* fatigue is *sleep* – and this means restful sleep, not disturbed by the effects of alcohol or caffeine (tea or coffee).

Chronic long-term fatigue may take longer to eliminate, and may require professional advice. A pilot suffering from chronic fatigue, be it from physical or psychological reasons, should consider whether it is responsible to continue flying.

The Symptoms of Fatigue

We should always be looking for signs of fatigue in ourselves, in our cockpit colleagues, or in anyone associated with our flight. Aircraft maintenance engineers, for instance, often have to do highly skilled work in the middle of the night during very low points in their body cycles.

Symptoms of fatigue include:
- **lack of awareness** – radio calls or checklists that go unanswered;
- **diminished motor skills** – sloppy flying, writing that trails off into nothing as weather reports or clearances are written down;
- **obvious tiredness** – drooping head, staring or half-closed eyes;
- **diminished vision** – difficulty in focusing;
- **slow reactions**;
- **short-term memory problems** – unable to remember a clearance long enough to repeat it or to write it down accurately;
- **channelled concentration** – fixation on a single possibly unimportant issue, to the neglect of others and to the neglect of maintaining an overview of the flight;
- **easily distracted** by trivial matters or, the other extreme, impossible to distract – either extreme could indicate fatigue;
- **poor instrument flying** – difficulty in focusing on the instruments, fixation on one instrument to the neglect of others, drifting in and out of sleep, diminished motor skills with poor hand–eye coordination;

- **increased mistakes** – poor judgement and poor decisions, or no decisions at all, even simple ones like "Will I turn left or right to avoid this thunderstorm?"; and
- **abnormal moods** – erratic changes in mood, depressed, periodically elated and energetic, diminished standards.

Sleep

This discussion on sleep goes into areas which are of more concern to professional pilots, but it is included here for general information to pilots involved in more-demanding private operations.

Note: *Private pilots may not be flying across time zones, but they are likely to be involving a full-time job as well as engaging in flying and therefore fatigue is very relevant.*

A lack of properly restful sleep can lead to fatigue, so it is very important that you as a pilot obtain adequate sleep prior to a flight. Being fatigued is different from being sleepy or drowsy – it is being deeply tired to the point of being unable to attend satisfactorily to your flight duties for sustained periods. Fatigue is stressful and damaging for a person.

A flight in itself can be fatiguing, with the pilot being exposed to mental and physical stressors such as noise, vibration, hypoxia, temperature extremes, dryness, physical restraint, navigation problems, bad weather, technical problems, difficulties with passengers, etc. The additional influence of poor sleep and disturbed body rhythms imposed upon the natural tiredness of the pilot can have a very serious effect on the health.

The Purpose of Sleep
The purpose of sleep is to revitalise your body and brain in preparation for the activities of the following day. A typical person requires 8 hours of restful sleep in preparation for 16 hours of activity – in very approximate terms, one hour of sleep gives you an energy credit good for two hours of activity.

Sleep is revitalising, and is necessary.

■ ✎ *Figure 5-3* **8 hours rest for 16 hours of activity**

Strategies for Getting Good Sleep

There are some measures that you can take to assist you in sleeping well.

- **Sleep in a comfortable bed in a cool dark and quiet room.** Darkness and quietness encourage sleep, whereas bright light and noise have the opposite effect. Maintain a pleasant temperature, with fresh air available if possible.

- **Try to maintain a regular sleep schedule.** Going to bed at the same time each night, falling asleep, then waking up eight hours later feeling rejuvenated, will become a habit.

- **Keep fit, eat well, and go to bed tired, but not over-tired.** A body that is healthy as a result of exercise and a good diet will not only perform better during the hours of wakefulness, it will also rest better during sleep. Being fit and healthy is natural and desirable. Exercising earlier during the day so that you go to bed 'tired' will encourage sleep, provided that you have not had too many naps. A cup of warm milk or some form of carbohydrate before going to bed will also encourage sleep (but avoid caffeine, alcohol, animal fats and high protein foods). Exercising or eating a big meal just before going to bed should be avoided.

- **Try to turn off mentally.** If you can, avoid excessive mental activity or thinking about emotionally stressful matters before turning in for what you want to be a good sleep. Relaxing with a good book or soft music can sometimes take your mind off the worries of the day.

Sleep Disorders

Insomnia is an inability to sleep, or to obtain restful sleep. There are different types of insomnia. The most common one is 'nervous' insomnia. Most people experience this from time to time, especially when they are anticipating something potentially stressful that is about to happen in the near future, such as an examination or a flight test. Nervous insomnia might disrupt sleep for one or two nights, often to a lesser extent than the person thinks. It is not a serious problem, with a quick recovery from any resulting tiredness or fatigue.

Acute or short-term insomnia resulting from stress or illness, or disturbed body rhythms (jet lag), is also usually not serious, with a quick recovery within days when the cause is removed.

Chronic insomnia is another matter, however, when the person is unable to obtain restful sleep for a period of weeks or months as a result of long-term unresolved stress or illness. This continued sleep deprivation may require medical attention.

Other sleep disorders besides chronic insomnia that may require medical attention include the reverse problem, that of an inability to stay awake even when well rested, as well as very heavy snoring, and breathing interruptions during sleep.

Sleeping Drugs, or Hypnotics

Drugs used to aid sleeping are called hypnotics. They may assist sleep, but some of them also have fairly serious side effects that could affect the skill and performance level of a pilot. They should not be used by a pilot without advice and supervision from an expert aviation doctor.

Avoid sleeping pills.

Pilots should be careful when using medication in case of side effects which may drastically affect flying skills and performance. Subtle effects might also be very dangerous, since it is less likely that they will be noticed. Be cautious with the use of painkillers, decongestants to combat the effects of a cold, antihistamines to treat hay fever, antibiotics to combat infection, stomach tablets, or pills to combat gastro-intestinal infections.

Melatonin

The hormone *melatonin* has received much publicity recently as a 'quick-fix' to jet lag and other forms of sleep disturbance. In the UK melatonin is available only on prescription, but is freely available in the USA and some other countries.

Melatonin is produced by the pineal gland in the brain, mainly in hours of darkness. Its function is not fully understood, but it is related to biological rhythms such as sleep and activity patterns, and ovulation. Secretion of melatonin at night-time lowers body temperature, which helps to bring on sleep. Taking melatonin orally has a similar effect. Clinical trials have not been conducted on melatonin, but laboratory studies have shown that it may be helpful in improving daytime sleep. However, the incidence and extent of side effects are unknown at this stage. Furthermore, use of the substance for a period, followed by withdrawal, can worsen the effects of jet lag.

The CAA recommends that pilots should not fly for at least 12 hours after taking melatonin and should not take it while on duty.

The Stages of Sleep

Your sleep goes through various stages.

The nature of sleep is not the same throughout the whole sleep period. As we all know from experience, being woken at an early stage when we are just drifting off to sleep is quite a different matter from being woken from a very deep sleep, when it may take some minutes to return to full consciousness. Also, just prior to waking up naturally, we often feel in a semi-conscious state, with thoughts running around in our head, and eyes darting around behind closed eyelids – quite different from when we are in a deep stage of sleep, with the body relaxed and mental activity slowed right down.

The study of sleep is far from complete (we seem to know more of what is going on in outer space than what is going on in our heads); however, we can safely say that there are four different stages in terms of depth of sleep or unconsciousness.

After you drift from wakefulness into sleep, you go down through the four stages into ever-deeper sleep, where you stay for a while, and then rise through the stages, sometimes missing one or two, before sinking back into deep sleep. This occurs in a series of cycles that take about 90 minutes each. In a normal night, you may go through four or five cycles, each one perhaps a little different from the previous one, with some stages missing or lasting for shorter or longer periods. As can be seen in Figure 5-4, the very deep Stage 4 sleep is commonly more predominant in the early cycles than in the later cycles.

'Rapid eye movement' sleep is vital.

Often, after you rise back to an earlier stage of sleep and before you sink back down into a deeper stage (or continue rising into wakefulness), you experience a totally different type of sleep, known as *REM (rapid eye movement)* sleep. This is so different that sometimes the first four stages are known as *non-REM* sleep in contrast to it.

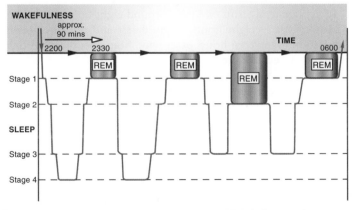

■ ✎ Figure 5-4 **Typical cycles of non-REM and REM sleep in the course of a sleep period**

Stages 1–4 non-REM sleep has fairly low-frequency electrical waves in the brain and so is sometimes referred to as *slow-wave* sleep, whereas the electrical waves in the brain during REM sleep are high frequency and short wave. REM sleep is sometimes called *paradoxical* sleep because, even though the muscles are very relaxed and the person is still asleep, brain activity is similar to a person who is awake.

The Stages 1–4 non-REM sleep and the additional REM sleep are different types of sleep and perform different functions. The non-REM Stages 1–4 sleep revitalise the body, and so is needed in abundance after a lot of strenuous physical activity, whereas the REM sleep restores the brain and is needed after strenuous mental activity. In the course of a long sleep period, you alternate between the two types of sleep, your body and brain organising it so that you obtain sufficient of the required type of sleep each night, according to your needs.

The first onset of REM sleep usually occurs about 90 minutes after commencing sleep, and recurs at about this interval throughout the sleep period as you rise out of deep sleep and sink back into it. Your brain is being rejuvenated during REM sleep, and **it is important that REM sleep is not disturbed.** This can be caused by alcohol, drugs, stress, or being forcefully wakened.

Sleep Patterns

Individual sleep patterns vary – different people require different amounts of sleep and prefer to go to bed and rise at different times. The need for sleep also varies with age, an older person may need less sleep, but on a more regular basis; this can cause problems for older pilots involved in long-haul international operations crossing many time zones. Daytime operations close to home might be easier from the sleeping point of view.

In very general terms, we need around eight hours of sleep in a 24-hour day – eight hours of good rest and revitalisation in preparation for sixteen hours of activity. Some people need only six hours; others need ten.

Some people prefer to retire to bed at 9 p.m. and rise with the sparrows, while 'night owls' prefer to retire at midnight or later and rise late the next morning. For the purposes of our study of sleep patterns, we will consider a person who goes to bed at 2400 hours and, after eight hours of sleep, rises at 0800 hours. You can move these hours forward or back, or reduce or increase them, to suit your own particular case.

The average sleep requirement is 8 hours per day.

Unfortunately, there seems to be a maximum limit on the number of sleep-hours credit you can build up. Once you get to eight sleep-hours credit, that is it! No matter how hard you try to sleep longer and gain more sleep credits, it will not be successful.

In broad terms, we can say that **one high quality sleep-hour is good for two hours of activity.**

Eight sleep-hours will prepare you for the sixteen hours activity of a 24-hour day. After this time of wakefulness, your sleep credits will have been used. Your credits are now zero, your energy level will be low, and you will begin to feel tired and ready for another sleep. If you do not go to sleep, you will go into a sleep *deficit*, which will probably cause a significant decrease in your alertness and performance capability.

An ideal, uninterrupted sleeping pattern for a person with regular habits is illustrated in Figure 5-5.

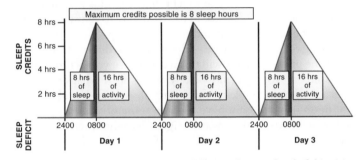

■ ✎ Figure 5-5 **One sleep-hour is good for two hours of wakeful activity**

Disturbed Sleep Patterns

It is not always possible to achieve the desired 8–16–8–16 sleep pattern due to the demands of work, family, illness or social life, in which case compromises have to be made.

If you reduce the sleep-hours credit, then you also reduce the hours of useful wakeful activity available to you before you are due for another sleep, or before you start to slip into a sleep deficit. If you are deprived of sleep you will not perform as well as when you still have some sleep-hours in credit.

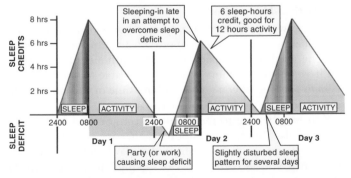

■ ✎ Figure 5-6 **Going into a sleep deficit (beyond 16 hours of activity)**

A very common sleep deficit occurs when you 'party on' late into the night, well beyond your usual bedtime. This can also happen to you if you work through the night and use up all your sleep credits. If you have the luxury of being able to sleep in until late the next morning, then you can recuperate and move out of the sleep deficit fairly quickly, provided that your sleep is restful and not disturbed by alcohol and the like.

An **alcohol-induced sleep** gives the impression that it is a deep sleep – but it is not! Your REM sleep will not be normal, your mental rejuvenation will not be as good as usual, you will probably wake earlier than you would otherwise and, most importantly, when you wake you may not feel refreshed. This is an important point to note for pilots who, in the past, may have used alcohol to relax after a stressful flight and to induce sleep.

Disturbed sleep is not as restful.

Trying to build up a store of sleep-hour credits by sleeping long hours the previous night will not work. Once you get to the eight hours credit, you will most likely wake up. Perhaps you could increase your energy level for a party, however, by taking a late afternoon nap after you have used up some of your sleep credits, and raise them back towards eight sleep-hour credits, which should then get you comfortably well into the night.

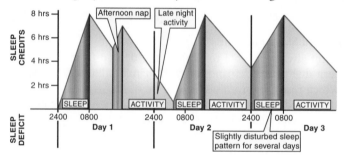

■ ✎ Figure 5-7 **Preparing for a late flight, or a party**

Shorter-than-Normal Sleep

If you are woken following only four hours of sleep instead of your usual eight, then (in very approximate terms, and on the basis that one sleep-hour prepares you for two hours of wakefulness) you have only eight hours of activity available to you before you begin to get tired. If you go beyond this time of wakefulness, then your performance is likely to deteriorate.

You may be able to recuperate to some extent by taking an afternoon nap, but this may not be as effective and restful as sleep at a normal time, and your sleep credits may build at a slower rate. With a nap, you also run the risk of sinking into a deep sleep from which it may be difficult to awaken before the sleep cycle runs its full course, the result being that you do not feel rested at all.

Naps can help overcome a sleep deficit.

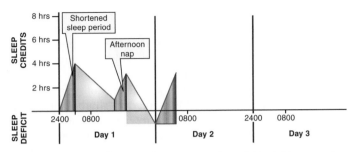

■ ✎ *Figure 5-8* **Normal sleep pattern shortened, followed by a nap later in the day**

Irregular Sleep Routine

For a person with a regular lifestyle, the *need* for sleep and the *ability* to sleep generally coincide, and going to bed when tired and falling asleep occurs naturally. This is usual for most of us working normal day shifts, and is also usual for the perennial night-shift worker whose body rhythms have adjusted to his lifestyle. His sleep pattern of 8–16–8–16 may be the same pattern as for a normal day worker, but it may occur at different times of the day.

Irregular shift work is fatiguing.

For the *irregular* night-shift worker, however, or the pilot who has to crawl out of bed at an unusual time to go flying, it can be quite a different matter. The body rhythms are synchronised for the normal eight hours of sleeping between 2400 and 0800 local time, followed by the sixteen hours of wakefulness between 0800 and 2400, and suddenly this pattern is broken.

Going to work in the late afternoon after a normal night's sleep will not feel too bad but, sometime after midnight, fatigue will make its presence felt. This is a similar situation to 'partying on'. A late afternoon nap before work, or a nap in the early morning during a break from work, may prove helpful.

Going to work in the early morning, however, is a different problem. The body is crying out to continue sleeping, but the pilot has to force himself against all of his body rhythms into wakefulness, and head off to what might be quite demanding activity. Trying to get eight hours of sleep at an unusual time prior to commencing work may not be possible.

The *need* for sleep and the *readiness* of the body for sleep depend not only on tiredness due to the time awake, but also on the time of day according to your body rhythms. The intermittent shift-worker may have trouble going to sleep, staying asleep, and then waking and feeling well rested. A few short naps during his period of 'wakefulness' might be necessary to overcome the sleep deficit.

Body Rhythms

The regular 8–16 sleep/wakefulness rhythm is only one of our body rhythms. Others include the rhythm of internal body temperature, and the digestive rhythm with its regular hunger pangs and elimination of waste products.

These body rhythms usually have a frequency of approximately 24 hours, and so are often called the **circadian rhythms,** from the latin *circa* (about) and *dies* (day). There are many of these circadian rhythms, and they seem to be connected to one another, in that a change in one leads to a change in others, not necessarily at the same rate, nor with the same amount of ease. In fact, it can be very difficult to change some body rhythms and have all body rhythms synchronised normally. Long distance east–west travellers know this from struggling to get their bodies into a new time zone and not fall asleep when everyone else is operating at peak efficiency.

The body has many rhythms.

The sleep/wakefulness rhythm is perhaps one of the rhythms that is easiest to change. There are other rhythms, such as internal body temperature, which are very tightly bound into a regular rhythm and which are much more difficult and take much longer to change. Our performance capability and our enthusiasm to perform is closely tied to our body rhythms – especially that of internal body temperature, which rises slightly by day and falls at night.

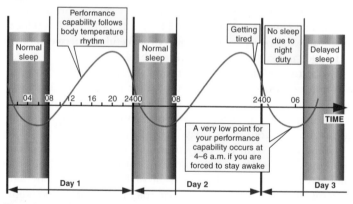

■ ✎ *Figure 5-9* **The body rhythm cycle**

The Sleep/Wakefulness Rhythm

The sleep/wakefulness rhythm seems to have a natural time span somewhat greater than 24 hours, more in the range of 25–26 hours, but it is regularly pulled back into a 24-hour time span by a succession of time-of-day reminders, known by the German word **zeitgebers.** *Zeit,* pronounced "sight", or more correctly "tsight" (if you can get your tongue around it) means **time,** and *geber,* pronounced "gayber", means **giver** – so that a zeitgeber is a *time-giver* – a reminder of the time of day.

Zeitgebers reduce the sleep/wakefulness rhythm to 24 hours.

Typical zeitgebers *(tsight-gaybers)* are the rising and setting of the sun, the everyday ringing of the alarm clock, the 8 a.m. breakfast pangs, the need to use the toilet before rushing off to catch the 8:23 train, lunch time, the ever-present wristwatch and clocks, the afternoon tea break, knock-off time, the 6 p.m. evening meal, the 9 o'clock news, and so on. Each person will have their own series of zeitgebers throughout the day pulling their sleep/wakefulness cycle into line, with the sun as a very powerful natural zeitgeber. The rising of the sun is a strong force moving us into wakefulness; darkness is a reminder that sleeping time is coming.

The *natural* length of the sleep/wakefulness cycle can be observed by removing all of the zeitgebers – for instance, by placing a person in a darkened room and removing all time clues. The result is a sleeping pattern that becomes later each day, as shown in Figure 5-10.

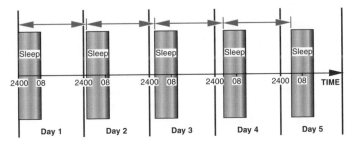

■ ✎ *Figure 5-10* **A typical sleep pattern on successive days without zeitgeber clues to time**

With zeitgebers, however, the sleeping pattern will be continually pulled back into the 24-hour cycle.

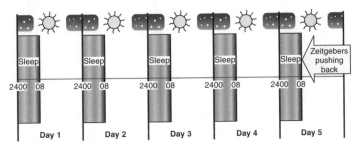

■ ✎ *Figure 5-11* **The normal sleep pattern on successive days with zeitgebers**

People who live in high latitudes, such as Scandinavia, Northern Canada and Siberia, have to cope with the loss of the sun as a zeitgeber. In summer they have continual light, and in winter they have continual darkness (or conditions approaching this). Stress levels, sleeping patterns, and fatigue may change with the seasons in some people living in these latitudes.

Body Temperature

Internal body temperature averages at about 36.5°C (98°F), with a regular circadian cycle of fluctuations 0.3°C above and below this. Its natural cycle is about 25 hours, but again zeitgebers pull it back into a 24-hour cycle, as shown.

The circadian rhythm of internal body temperature is a very strong rhythm that cannot be altered easily, as can other rhythms like the sleep/wakefulness cycle. For this reason, body temperature is often used as the standard rhythm against which to compare others.

The natural body temperature rhythm is hard to change.

A high body temperature is linked to alertness and good performance capability; a low body temperature is linked to low mental performance and drowsiness.

Alertness is related to natural body temperature.

The sleep/wakefulness cycle usually runs in tandem with the body temperature cycle. Your body is usually ready for sleep at a time of falling or low body temperature, and ready to be awake at a time of rising or high body temperature.

Sleep usually occurs at times of low or falling body temperature.

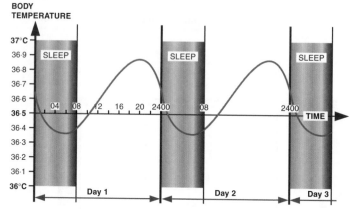

■ ✎. Figure 5-12 **The circadian rhythm of internal body temperature**

The Performance Cycle

Peak performance capability and alertness occurs at the time of a rising or high body temperature, which is when you are usually wide awake; low alertness and performance capability occurs at times of low body temperature, which is when you are usually asleep.

Different types of performance (such as *psychomotor* performance, hand–eye coordination, mental agility, reasoning ability, and reaction time) vary somewhat differently throughout the day; however, we can generalise and say that alertness and performance capability vary with body temperature.

> *If you are awake at a time of low body temperature, your performance could be lower.*

NOTE Even if your sleep/wakefulness pattern is disturbed, the temperature pattern will remain the same. If you are forced to be awake at 4–6 a.m., your alertness and ability to perform well will be impaired somewhat because of the low point in your body temperature cycle that will occur as normal. The lowest body temperature occurs about 4–6 a.m., when you are usually in a very deep sleep and, if you have to work at this time, you may have great difficulty in staying awake.

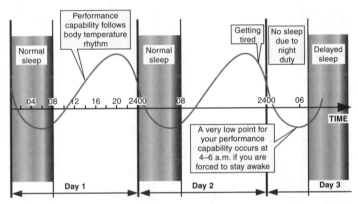

■ ✎ *Figure 5-13* **A generalised performance rhythm follows the internal body temperature**

It is possible to modify the performance cycle by lifting it, rather than by shifting it in terms of timing. Your performance graph will be raised if you are feeling well, if you are well rested, if you are highly motivated, and if you are well practised in the skills that you wish to use. Even the low performance points are raised, indicating that, if you are forced to stay awake during the normal sleeping hours, your performance will be better if you are fit and well.

Extroverts and night owls usually have their performance cycle moved slightly to the right, compared with introverts, to match their other body cycles. Similarly, perennial shift workers have their performance cycle moved to match their body cycles, which run to a different body clock compared with daytime workers, but their peak performance may not reach that of a daytime worker because of the inevitable disturbance to the sleeping periods of a night-shift worker caused by normal family life, and sunlight and darkness.

The ability to maintain a high level of performance decreases significantly if you are fatigued or deprived of sleep. This applies in particular to physically passive but mentally active tasks, which is often what a long-haul pilot is involved in when the aeroplane is in the cruise – systems monitoring, maintaining a navigation overview with correct radio communication – while the autopilot handles the physical task of maintaining height and track, and the autothrottle maintains speed.

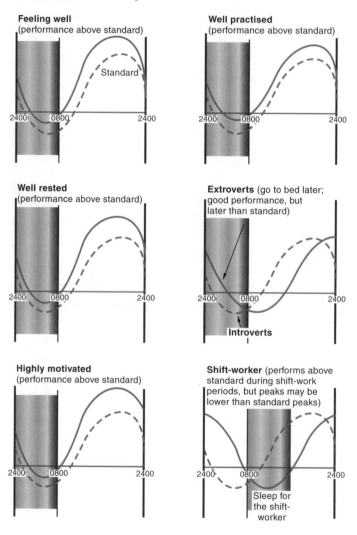

■ ✎ *Figure 5-14* **Modified performance rhythms**

Jet Lag – The Desynchronisation of Body Rhythms

Moving to a new time zone disturbs the body rhythms.

The long-haul pilot and the passengers are subject to the normal fatigue of a flight caused by a dry, oxygen-deficient atmosphere, vibration, noise, lack of exercise, and the stresses associated with any flight, plus, on east–west flights especially, the very significant problem of crossing time zones and finding yourself in a place where the local time differs from home time. The rising and the setting of the sun, and the habits of the local population are on local time, and out of synchronisation with your body clock, which is still on home time. You feel like going to sleep just as darkness turns to light with the rising of the sun, and just as everyone else is waking up ready to start the new day. The early morning sounds of garbage collection, milk delivery, trains running, church bells ringing, do not match the way your body feels.

The problem is: do you try to bring your body into the new time zone or not? This usually depends on how long the stay will be. For a pilot who will fly back home the next day, there is no point. For a long stay, such as a holiday, then the attempt is probably worthwhile making.

There are many body rhythms, the body temperature cycle being only one, although perhaps the most important one. Some rhythms can be brought into local time at the rate of about one hour a day, which means that, if the time zone change is four hours, then after four days this body cycle will be aligned with local time.

Each rhythm adjusts at a different rate.

Different body rhythms, however, change at different rates. Also, any disturbance of one body rhythm may lead to disturbances in other body rhythms. Some body rhythms change at one and a half hours per day, others at only one half-hour a day and therefore take much longer to move into local time – eight days in fact if the time zone change is four hours. This means that as your body attempts to transfer into a new time zone, many of the body rhythms that are normally synchronised are now desynchronised with one another and may be a little abnormal within themselves. This is known as *circadian disrhythmia*.

The result could be headaches, poor sleep, disturbed eating patterns, constipation, giddiness, poor mental performance, and even slight depression. Hunger pangs and toilet habits still based on the old home time could also disturb your new sleeping pattern as you try to move your body clock into the new time zone, making you generally tired all day long, and delaying further your move into the new time zone. The time between about 4–6 a.m. on your body clock, irrespective of what the local time is, will also be a period of low alertness and poor performance capability, which could be significant if you are in the middle of an important meeting or taking part in an activity that requires alertness. Accidentally falling asleep is not uncommon.

It may take three weeks or even longer before all the body rhythms are back 'in synch' again, and before you are operating at peak efficiency in the new time zone. Exposing yourself to sunlight, and allowing the powerful zeitgeber which is the sun to influence your body and mind, may speed the process a little.

Adjustment of the Body Clock

The adjustment process of the body clock is easier if you travel west. The time needed for the body clock to adjust if you are crossing time zones by travelling west may be less than if you are travelling east. This is because travelling westwards you are travelling with the sun, and the hours of daylight that you experience will be longer than normal. The day will appear to be longer than 24 hours.

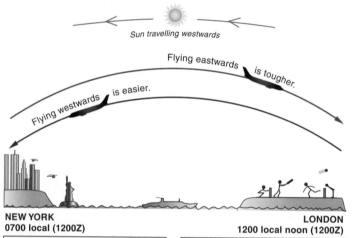

NEW YORK 0700 local (1200Z)	LONDON 1200 local noon (1200Z)
New York is 5 hours behind London, so noon occurs 5 hours later; this means that a person arriving from London experiences a 29-hour day. The body clock is 25 hours, so: **only 4 hours jet lag,** but the 25-hour body clock will tend to close the gap naturally in 4 days, and even less with the aid of 'zeitgebers'.	London is 5 hours ahead of New York, so noon occurs 5 hours earlier; thus, a person arriving from New York experiences a 19-hour day. The body clock is 25 hours, so: **6 hours jet lag,** i.e. 2 hours worse off than the reverse flight. 'Zeitgebers' alone work to remove this by reducing the body clock to less than 24 hours (hard work!).

■ ✎ *Figure 5-15* **Jet lag after travelling westwards is less than eastwards**

Because many natural body rhythms have a period of 25 hours if they are not pulled back by zeitgebers, they have a natural tendency to move towards the new time zone at the rate of about one hour a day.

Flying east is tougher than flying west.

Flying north-south is easy.

Conversely, when travelling eastwards, the days are shortened, and the body rhythms have to be pulled back to less than 24 hours, against their natural tendency to lengthen.

Although travelling north or south does not mean crossing time zones, there can still be jet lag problems, because of the usual fatigue from a long flight, and also from the somewhat displaced zeitgebers.

In winter, for instance, a Scandinavian or a Scot might be used to the sun rising at 10 a.m. If the northerner travels south to somewhere in Africa, the local time might be the same, but the sun now rises at 5 a.m. This change of time of an important zeitgeber may unsettle some of the body rhythms.

Now complete: **Practice Questions - Stress Management, Fatigue & Sleep**

1. In relation to stressors:

(a) If exposed to stressors, you should not fly.

(b) Stressors have a detrimental effect on pilot's performance.

(c) Stress management is a vital skill for pilots.

(d) Acute stress is long lasting and fatiguing.

2. When exposed to stress:

(a) A person deals with this better when adrenaline is in the system.

(b) When very high levels of stress are encountered, sleep has no effect on coping.

(c) General health, happy personal life and preparation for the task assist in coping.

(d) Tiredness or fatigue have no effect on coping.

3. Optimum arousal:

(a) Is found when not exposed to fear or sleep deprived.

(b) Is when exposed to low temperature.

(c) Is when adopting a relaxed attitude to the task.

(d) Is worse when noise pitch is low.

4. Stress caused by noise:

(a) Can be reduced by lowering engine RPM.

(b) Is increased when ambient noise is above 75-80db.

(c) Can be reduced by using a noise reducing headset.

(d) Is worse when noise pitch is low.

5. Acceptable means of coping with stress:

(a) Ignoring the source of stress.

(b) Helping to cope by using "Approved" drugs or alcohol.

(c) Recognising a potential overload.

(d) Putting off dealing with a source of stress until you are ready.

Answers: 1c, 2c, 3a, 4c, 5c.

Information Processing

If you understand how we humans process information, then the learning of a new skill, such as flying, becomes much easier.

The initial feeling of being overloaded and bombarded by sensations from all sides on early flights is quite typical. As the training progresses, however, actions that at first required your full attention, such as manipulating the aircraft, become *motor programmes,* which are also known as *skills.* Your brain is then freed to think of other things, such as maintaining an overview of the flight, handling the radio, and perhaps even conversing with your flight instructor or passenger.

Some information processing is involved with responding immediately to a stimulus – for instance, applying the brakes of a car when the traffic lights ahead turn red. Other information processing is concerned with longer-term items, such as *learning* and *remembering,* where the information processed is stored in the memory for later retrieval and use.

The System of Nerves

The brain is the central decision-maker.

The processing of information occurs within the nervous system, consisting of the brain and the spinal chord; these together make up the *central nervous system.* A series of smaller nerves radiating out through the body make up what is known as the *peripheral nervous system.* The highest-level decisions, i.e. conscious decisions that require consideration, are made in the brain, which is where our so-called 'intelligence' resides.

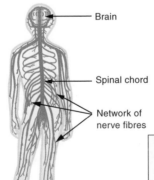

— Brain

— Spinal chord

Network of nerve fibres

The brain and spinal chord comprise the *central nervous system.*

The *peripheral nervous system* consists mainly of pairs of nerve fibres leading to and from the central nervous system.

■ ✎ *Figure 6-1* **The Nervous System**

The individual nerves can be thought of as telephone lines carrying messages to and from the central nervous system, especially the brain. It is more than just a central telephone exchange – more like a massively powerful computer that not only redirects messages, but makes major (and minor) decisions.

The main limitation of our brain as a **central decision-maker** is that it functions only as a *single-channel* computer, which means that we can consider only one thing at a time. Decisions made in the brain are therefore not made simultaneously, but are made consecutively in a series, one after the other.

The brain has only a single channel.

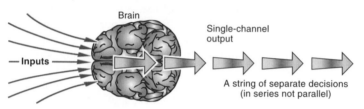

A Basic Model of Information Processing

How we process information is best explained by the use of a *model* – a hypothetical plan of what we think happens. Some models are simple, others are more complicated. We will consider a fairly basic model that is in accordance with conventional understanding.

The information-handling process involves:
• a stimulus;
• analysis (i.e. thinking or cognition) and decision;
• action; and
• feedback.

Stimulus

All models begin with a stimulus, the information that is detected by our senses in the form of images, sounds, feel, smells, and taste. This sensory information is sent as electrical signals along the appropriate sensory nerves in the peripheral nervous system to the central nervous system for attention. There is so much sensory information presented to us that only a fraction of it is absorbed, or *perceived*.

The brain perceives some stimuli.

Analysis

The perceived sensory information is analysed and considered, together with previously known information stored in our memory, and a decision made. This is the fundamental process of **conscious decision-making**, also known as *thinking* or *cognition*, which occurs between input and action.

The brain analyses the stimuli.

Action

After a decision is made, *action* is taken by the brain sending out electrical signals along small motor nerves to the appropriate muscles, which then move as commanded. *Feedback* on the effectiveness of the decision and the action(s) taken is provided by our perception (senses); follow-up action can then be taken if necessary.

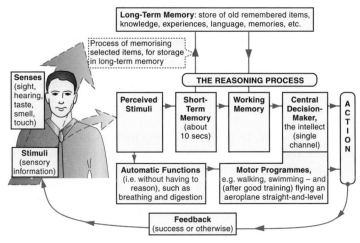

■ ✎ Figure 6-3 **A basic model of our information processing**

Different Levels of Mental Activity

If our brain can only consciously think of one thing at a time, how can we do several things concurrently, such as hold a conversation at the same time as we are walking?

The answer is because there are different levels of mental activity; conscious thinking (or *cognition*) is only the most advanced.

Thinking

Conscious decision-making occurs in a part of our brain known as the *central decision-maker*. This area can concern itself with only one problem at a time. The single-channel central decision-making channel means that only one decision at a time can be taken, although more decisions can follow quite quickly in sequence.

Motor Programmes

It is obvious that there is more than one activity going on within our bodies most of the time. For instance, when playing tennis and consciously thinking about tactics, we are still able to run about. This is because there are other levels of action that occur which may not be controlled by conscious decision-making, but by motor programmes or skills.

Motor programmes control skills that are so well learned that no conscious effort is required to control the actions (or very little conscious effort, and then only on an occasional basis). For instance, walking has been so well learned that it requires little conscious attention; for children or adults suffering brain damage, however, trying to walk occupies them totally.

Signing your name normally does not distract you from other tasks, such as holding a conversation, because you have trained your eye and hand so well that a motor programme controls the task – but try signing your name with your non-writing hand. Now your signature is no longer run by a motor programme but has to be consciously, and probably not too successfully, created. Continuing a conversation simultaneously is almost impossible because your single-channel decision-maker is already occupied.

Motor programmes (skills) are semi-automatic.

Reflexes

At a more primitive level of nervous activity, some actions, known as **motor reflexes,** occur with little or no involvement of the brain. In this case, the sensory nerve is linked closely to the motor nerve so that action occurs before the signal is consciously processed in the central nervous system. For instance, pricking your finger with a pin, or touching red-hot metal, will cause it to withdraw spontaneously without any mental activity in your brain, and before any conscious thought of pain occurs.

You have natural reflexes.

Conditioned Reflexes

A *conditioned* reflex is not a natural reflex, but a *trained* reflex. A conditioned reflex responds, not to the sensory stimulus that normally causes it, but to a separate stimulus which has been learned to be associated with it. A good example is 'Pavlov's dogs'. Pavlov, a Russian physiologist, trained his dogs to associate the sound of a bell with feeding time, and eventually the association was so strong that their mouths would water at the sound of a bell irrespective of whether food was present or not.

There are trained reflexes.

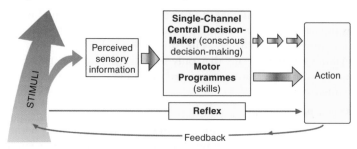

■ ✎ Figure 6-4 **The three main causes of action: conscious decision-making, motor programmes, and reflexes**

Autonomic Activities

Normal bodily functions such as breathing, the heartbeat, the digestive process, maintenance of body temperature, etc., continue under the control of the *autonomic nervous system*, which does not require any thinking on our part. Biological control systems and reflexes do not require learning and/or conscious thought. Many unfortunate children born with a poorly functioning brain still have normal bodily functions.

Thinking and Flying

Learning the basic flying skills initially requires a lot of conscious thought and decision-making (as did walking when you were a child).

Practising the basic skills time and time again allows you to learn the responses needed to certain stimuli so well that, eventually, manipulating the aeroplane can be run by motor programmes. An experienced pilot, for instance, will almost automatically apply back pressure on the control column when sinking below the flightpath, and add power if speed is decreasing. A trainee pilot must think it through before acting, which of course takes a lot more effort.

This illustrates how adaptable human beings are, 'routine-isation' is a very effective strategy as it frees up mental resources, but also illustrates their fallibility, through shortcomings and errors.

Flying gets easier as you learn the skills.

Well-learned skills being run by motor programmes leave the central decision-making part of your brain available for other activities, such as navigation, updating fuel calculations, making and receiving radio calls, handling emergencies, making judgements and, in general, just managing the whole flight from start to finish – a task which requires a lot of conscious thought. Using an autopilot can also off-load a pilot from mechanical tasks.

Stimulation, Sensing and Perception

An enormous amount of stimulation from the external world is presented to us in the form of visual images, sounds, smell, taste, and feel. These can be sensed by our so-called *sense organs* – the eyes, ears, nose, taste buds, and feel receptors in the skin and muscles. We can also use receptors within the balance mechanism of our inner ear to sense accelerations and balance, and to determine which way is 'up'.

Not all physical quantities are sensed, however. For instance, whilst our inner ear can detect accelerations, which are *changes* in velocity, it cannot detect velocity itself. Being stationary or travelling at a steady speed of 80 kph feels the same, and with your eyes shut you might be unable to tell the difference, but you would certainly know if you were accelerating from 0 to 80 kph, or vice versa, and decelerating from 80 to 0 kph.

Each of the sense organs is a collection of specialised cells, known as *receptors*. The receptors are capable of detecting particular changes in the environment (either outside the body or within), and triggering electrical impulses in the sensory nerves. The *sensitivity* of the receptors in each sense organ, which is their ability to respond to a stimulus, is different – for instance, those on the retina of the eye are sensitive to changes in light, whereas the receptor cells in the taste buds on the tongue respond to chemical changes, and the receptor cells in the skin are sensitive to heat, pain and touch.

There is a *sensory threshold*, below which the stimuli will not be detected by the particular receptors. For instance, very soft sounds, or sounds outside the frequency range of our ears, may go undetected. Similarly, electromagnetic radiation that does not lie within the visible light spectrum, or that is very faint, will go undetected by the light receptors in our eyes. The sensory threshold is a measure of the sensitivity of our sense organs, and is often tested in pilot medicals, especially for sound and visual images.

If the stimulation is continuous or repetitive, then the receptor cells run the risk of *adaptation*, which is showing a gradually diminishing response to that particular stimulus. For instance, the adaptation of touch receptors in the skin causes the presence of clothes to be no longer felt just a few minutes after putting them on. Similarly, after long exposure to a steady sound, such as an aeroplane engine or wind noise, the pilot may become completely unaware of it.

Sensory information, such as that from the optic nerve from the eyes and the auditory nerve from the ears, carry the sensed information towards the central nervous system (the brain and the spinal cord), where the messages are integrated, i.e. perceived. The sensory information is stored only briefly in a *sensory memory* before it is displaced by new information, unless we decide to absorb it and process it.

Each sense has its own memory, with the time of storage varying between the senses. For instance, a visual image lasts only about one second before it fades – illustrated by waggling a pencil in front of your eyes and noting that the blurred image of where it has just been quickly fades. Movies make use of this memory, enabling you to see a series of individual 'still' pictures as a moving image.

Sounds last considerably longer than visual images – about five seconds – before they begin to fade. This is time enough for us to recognise half way through a sentence that it is being directed at us and recall its beginning, or for us to be able to count back the number of times a clock has struck.

Sensed information is stored only briefly in the sensory memory.

You can develop mental models from sensed information.

Perception involves the senses receiving some information about the environment, and analysing it to make it meaningful. For instance, a group of sounds may become a sentence with meaning, and a sequence of visual images may become an aeroplane moving across the sky. Your senses are continually collecting new information to enable you continually to update your mental model of what the situation is. 'Top down' vs 'Bottom up' processing.

The flow of this information is described by Psychologists as either 'top down' or 'bottom up processing', - sensory input is 'down' and higher cognitive processes are 'up'.

A 'bottom up' process involves sensing and building up a mental picture using raw, detailed sensory data only, with NO influence from previous knowledge and experience. This obviously depends on the quality of the raw data – the stimulus must be presented clearly and for a long time. Given the speeds at which aircraft fly, raw data quality is often poor and so the pilot's brain must fill in the gaps, leading to 'top down' processing, where the sensory perception is *guided* in trying to confirm that the pilot 'saw what he *thought* he saw'. Like eyewitness testimony, it is prone to errors and is often extremely unreliable -pilots must exercise caution. Conversely, too much 'bottom up' processing 'you can't see the wood for the trees'.

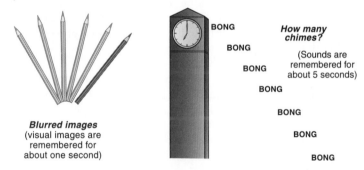

Blurred images
(visual images are remembered for about one second)

BONG
BONG
BONG
BONG
BONG
BONG
BONG

How many chimes?

(Sounds are remembered for about 5 seconds)

■ ✎ *Figure 6-5* **Sensed information lasts briefly in each sensory memory**

Experience and Expectation

The amount of sensed stimulation that is actually perceived and integrated depends to some extent upon our experience and expectation.

If we recognise the stimulus through previous experience, then we can more readily absorb it and integrate it into a model of the world around us. For instance, through experience we know that red-hot metal can cause pain, and when we feel pain and then see that our finger has just touched a piece of glowing metal, then we have no difficulty in forming a mental model of the situation – hot metal has burnt your finger.

Another example of useful experience is to do with radio messages from Air Traffic Control. Pilots can understand these messages through experience, but no one else can – all they hear is a jumble of sounds and a lot of static.

Experience helps perception.

Some radio messages are even difficult to understand for pilots, but an *expectation* of what the message will contain often helps. But we must guard against hearing what we want to hear or expect to hear, rather than what is *actually* said! In the lined-up position on the runway at a controlled airport, for instance, we expect to hear, "cleared take-off", and this is also what we want to hear. We are mentally geared up for the take-off. The actual instruction, however, might be 'taxi clear of the runway'. It can be dangerous if we only hear what we want to hear, and see what we want to see – this is known as having a *mind-set*.

Do not have mind-sets.

Sensory Confusion

When we hold our hand under a water tap marked 'C' and turn it on, we expect to feel a cold sensation, since we associate the letter 'C' with the word 'cold'. Many travellers to Italy are thrown into confusion, however, when they feel hot water rather than cold coming out of the tap marked 'C'. 'C' in this case represents *caldo*, the Italian word for *hot*, while 'F' for *freddo* would be labelled on the cold tap. This mixing of signals can cause sensory confusion in our brains. These are examples of top-down processing - perception distorted by 'higher mental processes'.

Another example of sensory confusion occurs when our eyes present an image to the brain that does not match up with the signals from our balance mechanism – for instance, after recovering from a prolonged spin, the wings of the aeroplane appear to be level with the horizon (eyes), but we feel as if we are still turning (balance mechanism). In this situation, we need to show sufficient discipline, as a result of good training, to take note of the signals from our eyes and discard those from the balance mechanism.

Anticipation

Anticipating an event or message is good, provided that we do not have a *mind-set* that locks out other possibilities and causes us to interpret a stimulus to be what we expect it to be, or want it to be, even though that might not be the case. Pilots are prone to this, especially when under high levels of stress.

During an early cross-country flight, trying to convince yourself that the ground features below match the mental model of your position (i.e. where you think you are), when in fact they do not, is a common feeling, and one which must be resisted. Similarly, hearing ATC clearances that we want to hear ("clear to land") rather than what is actually said ("go around") can lead to disaster.

Continually reassess sensed information.

Expectation and anticipation can help us, but it can also lead us into trouble if we are not disciplined enough continually to reassess the information that our senses present to us.

Attention and Motivation

Attention refers to the (limited) control that you have over what sensed stimuli you choose to process, which will usually be the stimuli that you consider to be relevant to the task in hand.

You can consciously focus your attention on a particular item – for instance, if you are specifically looking out at night for lightning flashes or for other aircraft, or your attention can be drawn to a particular item by external events – for instance, when you overhear your name being mentioned your attention will almost automatically be diverted from your current activity to what is being said about you in this distant conversation.

When stressed, you can overlook important information.

Selective attention refers to the sampling of stimuli and the selection of some of them for further processing, the remainder being allowed to fade away. The selected stimuli are usually associated with the subject currently under consideration, which might be controlling the flightpath and airspeed of the aeroplane. Most of the time, however, if stress levels are not too high, there is sufficient additional capacity to notice stimuli not associated with the current task, such as emergency signals (bells, horns, etc.), your name, or your aircraft callsign.

Selecting what we think are the important stimuli for us to attend to consciously is known as *precoding*, and it usually depends upon what we think is important, how strong the stimulus is, and also upon our mental state (e.g. stress level).

Divided Attention

Learn to divide your attention.

Whilst we often concentrate on one task at a time, it is not possible to devote all of our time to the prime task to the total exclusion of all others. There are often secondary tasks that have to be considered, such as raising the flaps following take-off when your attention has to be diverted briefly from the main task of monitoring and controlling the flightpath, or when making a radio call in the middle of handling an emergency. Switching our attention from one set of stimuli to another is known as *divided attention* or *time-sharing*.

Stress Can Diminish Perception

Usually we can switch our attention between tasks quite quickly, but stress and over-concentration on one task can inhibit this. Calls from ATC often go unnoticed when pilots are dealing with an emergency and their attention is fixated on this one task.

On some occasions, attention has not been divided enough to monitor the flightpath concurrently with handling an emergency and, even though the emergency was resolved, the aeroplane crashed. Pilots under stress have also failed to hear warning signals, and have landed wheels-up or flown unexpectedly into the ground when warnings were there, but not perceived. Learning to divide your attention and share your time between tasks is an important skill, particularly for a pilot.

Motivation

Too much of a workload may diminish our ability to perceive, but so also may too little stimulus – for instance, when a person is drowsy. Our perception of stimuli, and indeed our overall performance, is generally best with some degree of stress.

In order always to be ready to respond to important stimuli, pilots must be *motivated* to remain sufficiently aroused – for instance, a pilot should avoid becoming drowsy in the cruise even though the autopilot is plugged in. At the other end of the scale, a pilot should avoid becoming unable to cope with the incoming signals as a result of being overloaded.

Be adequately aroused for the task at hand.

Being under-aroused and half asleep, or being over-aroused and stressed-out or in a panic, can cause you to miss important stimuli, especially stimuli not associated with the prime task, and hence lead to poor performance.

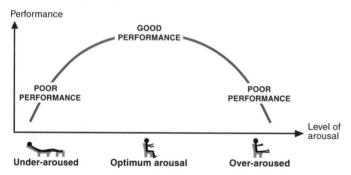

■ ✎ *Figure 6-6* **An optimum level of arousal leads to best performance**

Abnormalities in Perception

Perception is the process of receiving information through the senses, analysing it, and making it meaningful. This process is, on occasions, subject to certain abnormalities, which include:

* **hallucinations** – false perception of something that is not really there, i.e. *imagined* and not real, with no actual stimulus, only an imagined one;
* **illusions** – false perception due to *misinterpretation* of the stimuli, e.g. psychological illusions due to misinterpretation of

signals from other people, optical illusions due to deceptive qualities in the stimuli received, such as sloping ground when we expect flat ground; and

- **agnosia** – a brain disorder that interferes with the correct interpretation of sensation, and which would disqualify a person from holding a pilot's licence.

Problems in perception also arise when we receive conflicting information from different senses, such as between our eyes and our balance mechanisms during a prolonged turn.

After settling down into a prolonged turn, the balance mechanisms of the ear no longer signal entry to a turn, and it feels (in balance terms) like flying straight; visual information from our eyes, however, such as the relative position of the horizon (real or artificial), indicate a turn. In this case, good instrument training should encourage you to trust your eyes and believe what you see on the real horizon or on the artificial horizon, rather than rely on your sense of balance and 'seat-of-the-pants'.

Memory

Memory is the ability to store information and retrieve it when needed.

Memory is an amazing thing. Events from years ago can be brought immediately to mind, words not used for a long time fit readily into sentences, which are correctly structured according to rules of grammar learnt in schooldays, smells not experienced for decades can be recognised immediately, and so on. Memories of events, and a store of language, appear to be filed away in our brain for use at any time.

The memory has various components.

How the memory functions precisely is not fully known, but it seems that memory consists of electrical signals passing between millions of brain cells, with different sorts of memories, based on the period for which the information is retained, available for use. These different sorts of memory can be thought of as:

- the **sensory memory** – where sensed items remain briefly (1 second for visual images, 5 seconds for sounds) – also known as the ultra-short memory, and already discussed under 'stimulation', sensing and perception;
- the **short-term memory;**
- the **working memory; and**
- the **long-term memory.**

In some models, the short-term memory and the working memory are considered to be one.

The Sensory Memory

The sensory memory retains images, sounds, and other sensed stimuli, for just a second or two – long enough for us to select which ones to attend to – before they are lost.

The Short-Term Memory

The short-term memory in the brain is capable of holding only a few items for a brief period, typically seven items for 15 seconds, before they are forgotten. For instance, when you hear a telephone number spoken, or read the number in a telephone book, and then immediately dial it without error, you are using your short-term memory. If you delay the dialling for say 30 seconds, and do not rehearse (i.e. repeat) the number to hold it in your short-term memory, you will most likely dial a wrong number.

You can remember about 7 new items for 15 seconds.

Similarly, a message from ATC to *change frequency to one three two decimal one five zero (132·150 MHz)* will remain in your short-term memory long enough for you to select the frequency. Any delay, however, or any excess of additional information, and you will probably select the wrong frequency. Well-trained air traffic controllers pass only a few pieces of information at the one time, especially when they are aware that a pilot is inexperienced or may be under stress.

An ATC *route clearance* may contain four or five or even more items, and so is best written down as it is received. Your short-term memory may not be able to cope, both in terms of number of items and also in time of retention.

ATC clearances must be read back by the pilot to ensure correct understanding. You can try this out by reading the next sentence once, and then repeating it aloud as a read-back. *"Golf Alpha Charlie Delta X-ray, cleared to destination Glasgow, via Ponteland, Wallsend, then flight planned route, initially climb to flight level eight zero, squawk 4206, call 129.500 after departure."* Not so easy is it – hence the need to write clearances down as they are being given.

The seven items for 15 seconds is very variable between people (some might only be able to remember three items for 10 seconds), or for the same person under different levels of stress or tiredness.

It is possible to increase the capacity of the short-term memory, not by trying to remember more items, but by combining several items into one, a process known as *chunking* information, i.e. making chunks of information instead of individual items.

For instance, when you are given a new telephone number, such as 315 3023, it is better to remember it, not as seven pieces of information 3-1-5-3-0-2-3 but as two chunks 315 3023, or three chunks 315 30 23. This still leaves some capacity in your short-term memory, if needed immediately, say, for a name, before the number of items reaches 7 or thereabouts.

Chunking information aids short-term memory.

Memory 'joggers' also help.

Also, mnemonics can be used to chunk information, such as in checklists. It is a lot easier to remember the mnemonic *PUF* on short final than it is to remember each of the items individually, which are 'Propeller Pitch', 'Undercarriage', and 'Flaps'.

The Working Memory

The working memory contains the information that we are currently using, and which may be drawn from the short-term memory or the long-term memory, with electrical signals passing back and forth between the memory and the central decision-making part of the brain. The working memory does, however, have limited capacity.

In the working memory, we work on the information to which we have chosen to attend. We either:

- **rehearse it,** i.e. repeat it a number of times in an attempt to remember it, as in rote learning; or
- **encode it,** by trying to understand it, or relating it to something we already know.

The working memory works on information, trying to remember it by repetition or by understanding it.

Encoding (understanding) is usually a better way of remembering something over a long period than rehearsal (rote learning).

As mentioned earlier, some models treat the short-term memory and the working memory as one.

The Long-Term Memory

The long-term memory is where information is filed away for later use after being rehearsed or encoded in the working memory. The information may have to be retrieved several minutes later, or as long as several decades later.

Information seems to be stored in two areas, one involving *meaning*, such as the use of language, and the other involving *events*. The information can be reconstructed and brought together in the working memory when needed. Unfortunately, the reconstruction is not always totally accurate, as we all know when comparing our memory of an event with someone else's, or even with our own diary.

The long-term memory stores remembered information.

Items that are encoded (entered) into the long-term memory are thought to stay there for ever, although there may be problems and delays in retrieving the information, especially if it has not been recalled or used for some time. Periodically recalling important information from the long-term memory, i.e. practice, enables it to be recalled more readily when you really need it. For this reason, it is good technique occasionally to practise recalling items that should be known, such as limitations and vital emergency checks.

The information stored in the long-term memory is of value when the brain is trying to evaluate new information that has just been sensed. Usually, the brain will try to associate new data with data already stored in the long-term memory.

Totally new information, bearing no relation to anything previously sensed and stored, will probably take longer to process mentally than familiar information, because the brain cannot associate it with anything. An example of this could be when attempting your first visual approach, with no experience of how the runway should appear, or how the aircraft should feel. You have to think everything through from first principles. With experience, however, you will be able to compare the current situation with previous earlier situations.

The **meaning memory** part of the long-term memory is also known as the *semantic* memory. It is where information is stored in terms of words. Knowledge stored in this part of the long-term memory includes the meaning and use of language, remembered items such as home telephone number and address, vital checklists, and so on.

New material being learned and entered into the meaning part of the long-term memory should be given our full attention. We should try to understand it thoroughly, organising the various pieces of information logically into word messages so that our brain can encode it accurately and then store it. Association with items already in store helps with the encoding process.

Learning in position – for instance, learning checklists in an actual cockpit or simulated cockpit – often helps with encoding, and with the retrieval later on, since the information was learned in a familiar environment. Good encoding into the meaning memory makes later retrieval of the information easier and more meaningful. If the meaning of the information is understood, it can often be retrieved bit by bit through logic.

Meanings are remembered.

The **event memory** part of the long-term memory is also known as the *episodic* memory. Interesting events and episodes are stored here. Unfortunately, they are occasionally stored not all that accurately, sometimes being coloured by our attitudes and expectations, i.e. what we think must have happened, what would have been logical to have happened, or what we would like to have happened.

Accident investigators are often faced with expert witnesses of aircraft accidents, such as pilots, not remembering the event totally accurately. Their knowledge of aviation and their attitude and expectations as to what must have happened, or at least of what possibly happened, interferes with their memory of what actually happened. Non-expert witnesses, with no prejudices or expectations, can often recall the details more accurately, and without interpretation.

Events are remembered, but not always accurately.

Visual images can also be stored in the *spatial* part of the memory.

Sometimes information cannot be retrieved because of poor encoding, and sometimes as a result of brain damage. *Amnesia* is the total or partial loss of memory following physical injury such as concussion, disease, drugs, or psychological trauma. It usually affects the event (episodic) memory, with the meaning (semantic) memory relatively untouched. A person suffering amnesia or brain damage may be able to speak sensibly with a good use of language, but be unable to remember events.

The Central Decision-Maker

Conscious decisions are made in the so-called *central decision-making* part of our brain. This is where thinking, reasoning and decision-making occur, with electrical signals then being sent out along the motor nerves to activate the appropriate muscles.

Signals come into the central decision-maker from many sources, the sensory memory, the short-term memory, the working memory, and the long-term memory, with messages often being passed back and forth until a decision is made.

Single-Channel Decision-Making

Decisions are made one at a time.

It seems that the central decision-maker is capable of only making one decision at a time, i.e. it is a **single-channel decision-maker.** This means that conscious decisions on separate matters are made consecutively (one after the other), and not simultaneously.

Sequential decisions can be made quite quickly if we switch our attention between tasks, i.e. by **time-sharing,** so that the more complicated tasks move forward in stages. For instance, when attempting to fly straight-and-level at a steady airspeed, we need to monitor three things (at least) – altitude, heading, and airspeed.

- If we concentrate on **heading alone,** then we will probably drift off altitude and the airspeed may gradually change.
- If we concentrate on **airspeed alone,** then altitude and heading may vary.

In the early stages, when we are still learning to fly accurately and are having to make *conscious* decisions about handling the aircraft, we need to share the time of our central decision-maker between various tasks:

- **check altitude** and adjust with a change in pitch attitude if needed;
- **check airspeed** and adjust with a change in power if needed;
- **check heading** and adjust with a change in bank attitude if needed;
- **then return** to check attitude again and repeat the process.

Over-concentration on one specific task to the neglect of others can prevent completion of the overall task.

Time-sharing will at first be poor, the result probably being rather late and jerky corrections, or over-corrections. With practice, however, time-sharing between different items will occur more quickly and the resulting corrections be smaller and less noticeable. An experienced pilot will fly much more smoothly and accurately than a beginner, because of spotting deviations sooner and thus making smaller corrections immediately.

Divide your attention.

The **response time** between perceiving a stimulus and responding to it depends to a large extent upon how much mental processing is required. If the central decision-maker is involved, then the response time will be longer than if the response comes through a reflex or a motor programme not involving the central decision-maker.

Motor Programmes or Skills

A motor programme can run an activity without conscious reasoning. This means that the activity proceeds without the continuing involvement of the central decision-maker, which is therefore freed for other decision-making tasks.

Motor programmes are often the result of well-learned skills, such as walking, speaking, writing, riding a bicycle, driving a car, and (eventually) flying an aeroplane. A child learning to walk, or to ride a bicycle, has the mind fully occupied. Nothing can intrude. Having learned to balance the bicycle, however, the child can navigate a bit better, hold a conversation while riding, or perhaps even juggle balls at the same time.

Flying as a Motor Programme

While a beginning student is concentrating on learning to fly the aeroplane accurately, the central decision-maker will be almost fully occupied. There will be very little capacity remaining for other tasks such as navigation and radio calls.

Once the student has learned the handling skills well, however, and practised them until they are almost second nature, flying the aeroplane will occur with little conscious thought. In this case, the activity is said to be run by a motor programme in the brain, leaving the central decision-maker available for higher-level decisions that require reasoning, such as generally managing the entire flight.

Motor programmes are often *initiated* by the central decision-maker. You might make a decision to get up and walk towards the door, but once this decision has been taken, the central decision-maker can drop out of the picture temporarily and let the motor programme run the activity. As well as *initiating* the activity, the central decision-maker should also return to *monitor* the motor programme from time to time, first to check that the proper motor programme is in use, and secondly to check progress and decide when to stop.

It is possible that, even though a decision to commence a certain motor programme has been taken, the wrong programme swings into action. This could be walking in the wrong direction, or it could be raising the flaps instead of the undercarriage – something which is especially likely when flying a different aeroplane type in which the position of the two controls has been interchanged. Motor programmes need to be periodically monitored.

Monitor your motor programmes.

Using the wrong motor programme can also be dangerous with respect to movements of the throttle, mixture control, pitch control, and carburettor heat in an aeroplane. More than one aircraft has landed short of the runway because the mixture control was pulled fully out instead of the carburettor heat, stopping the engine instead of protecting it from ice. Hence the need for the central decision-maker to monitor the motor programme in important cases, even *before* the first action is taken. For instance, when about to raise the undercarriage after take-off, visually check which lever your hand is on before you move it.

Errors because of old habits, such as moving the wrong lever, are more likely to occur when a pilot is tired and under-aroused, or when over-aroused and in a state of near panic. You will remember that there is an intermediate level of arousal where optimum performance occurs. This is another reason why you should never fly when fatigued, and never get into a situation beyond your capacity. Fatigue will lead to *under-arousal* and reduced capabilities; a situation beyond your capacity might lead to *over-arousal* and reduced capabilities.

Practise your skills.

Motor programmes are the result of learned skills. If these skills are not used regularly, however, they may be lost, and an activity that was once run by a motor programme may now have to be controlled by conscious decision-making. This will occupy the central decision-maker and, as a result, you can expect a deterioration in the performance of other tasks. Professional pilots returning from holidays notice this, as do musicians and others who have to perform skilled tasks. Keep your skills well honed!

We can certainly *do* more than one thing at a time, thanks to motor programmes, but we can only *think* about one thing at a time.

Action and Feedback

Action will be initiated by a conscious decision from the brain (a thinking-based response) or by a motor programme that is running (a skill-based response). A series of electrical signals will be sent along motor nerves to the appropriate muscles for the action to commence. It could be speech, body movement, or a decision not to move. The results of the action can then be observed by our senses, with important feedback hopefully being perceived, i.e. noticed, analysed, and interpreted. If the feedback indicates that action is not having the desired result, then we can take further action.

For instance, during the take-off or landing roll, we attempt to maintain the runway centreline by moving the rudder pedals. A student may have to think consciously about this; an experienced pilot may allow a motor programme to run the operation. In both cases, the result as to how well we are holding the centreline needs to be monitored every few seconds, and adjustments made if necessary. In any manoeuvre, there is a continuing process of **action–feedback–action–feedback–action**, etc.

Monitor the results of your actions.

Response Time

The time it takes for any initial stimulus to be perceived, considered, and acted upon can take between a fraction of a second and several seconds, depending upon the complexity of the decision, or decisions, to be made. Responding to a stimulus often requires a series of sequential decisions to be made; this of course needs time because of the single-channel nature of the brain's central decision-maker.

On approach to land, for instance, the undercarriage has been selected down and a horn unexpectedly sounds. Some of the decisions that now need to be made are:

• **Silence the horn** to remove the distraction now that the warning has been noted, how do we do that?
• **What does the horn mean?** Is it undercarriage not down, or something else? It means that the undercarriage has been selected down, but is not actually down.
• **How else can we check** if it is down or not? Check for three green lights, or lack thereof.
• **Is there time** to rectify the problem and continue with the approach?
• **Should we initiate** a missed approach immediately?
• **Should we advise ATC?**, etc., etc.

Throughout all of this decision-making following a very simple unexpected event, we must periodically switch our attention to monitoring the flightpath, and the speed and configuration of the aeroplane.

In a situation like that above, we can remove the time pressure (by making a missed approach, joining a holding pattern, or taking some other delaying action), and so make more time available to solve the problem.

Allow time to respond.

In other situations, we may not have that luxury – for instance, in a take-off that is rejected at a high speed on a limiting runway. This will require a split-second decision and immediate actions.

If the pilot of a large aircraft suspects a problem during the take-off run, especially as the decision speed, V_1, is approached, there is only a second or two to decide what to do, "Stop or go?" Stopping may not be possible if a tyre has blown and reduced the wheel-braking capability. Flying away may not be possible if the problem is with the flight controls, or if the problem is multiple engine failure because of bird strikes. The enormous pressure of limited time between input and a necessary decision can sometimes lead to a faulty decision and response.

Rehearse critical manoeuvres.

A pilot can minimise the risk of making a poor decision, and increase the possibility of a good decision, by maintaining a high level of knowledge, and by practising the manoeuvre frequently. Simulators can play a big role here, particularly when practising critical manoeuvres, such as aborted take-offs from a high speed on a short runway, or engine failure after take-off.

Mental Workload

Best performance is achieved with high levels of skill, knowledge, and experience, and with an optimum degree of arousal. Skill, knowledge and experience depends upon the pilot; the degree of arousal depends not only upon the pilot but also upon others, such as the designer of the cockpit, the air traffic controllers, as well as upon the environment, weather, and so on.

Low levels of skill, knowledge and experience, plus a poorly designed cockpit, bad weather, and poor controlling, may lead to a high mental workload and a poor performance.

If the mental workload becomes too high, then decision-making will deteriorate in quality, or maybe not even occur. This could be the result of concentrating only on one task, sometimes called *tunnel vision.* Conversely, too little workload can lead to under-arousal, with some important stimuli not being noticed, and performance consequently being poorer. A healthy level of workload keeps us aroused.

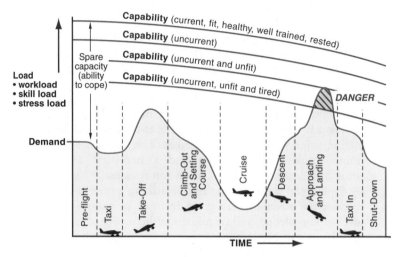

■ ✎ Figure 6-7 **Typical workload requirements and capacity**

All pilot tasks designed into the operation need to be tested so that at no time do they demand more of the pilot than what the pilot can give. There should always be some spare capacity left to ensure no overload occurs, and to allow for handling unexpected abnormal and emergency situations.

At the design stage, the pilot to be considered should not be the average pilot, because then half of all pilots would be below this standard, but the weakest pilot who maintains only the minimum required standard. Make sure that this is not you! Many pilots feel that, under normal conditions, they should be able to operate at only 40–50% of capacity, except during take-offs and landings, when that might rise to 70%. This leaves some mental capacity to handle abnormal situations.

You can raise your capability line on the graph in Figure 6-7 by studying and practising, and by being fit, relaxed and well rested.

Increase your capacity.

Mental Overload

Different parts of the brain can be overloaded, in which case mental efficiency will break down. Flying by using well-honed motor programmes will leave space in the brain for strategic thinking, overall management, and airmanship considerations. The student pilot, however, may not yet have reached this stage of skill.

The **sensory memory** can be overloaded if there is too much stimulus, with too many important incoming signals to be perceived. A pilot coping with an abnormal or emergency situation, such as a ringing fire bell, might miss an ATC radio call advising details of conflicting traffic.

The **short-term memory** can be overloaded by excessive information or by time delays. It cannot cope with more than about 7 items, and these will only be retained for 15 to 30 seconds unless rehearsed (repeated). New information coming in will replace these items.

The single channel of the **central decision-making** part of the brain can be overloaded if:

- **conflicting information** that cannot be resolved is received;
- **too many decisions** are required in too short a time; or
- **if the person is overstressed.**

Conflicting Information

Conscious decision-making is easier if all the information coming to the brain is in conformity and matches up. For instance, the clap of thunder that is heard is more easily assimilated if it matches up with a flash of lightning that occurred a few seconds before.

Unfortunately, the brain often receives *conflicting* information during flight, especially information that comes from the eyes and that which comes from the balance mechanism of the ears and bodily feel. Your balance mechanism and bodily feel might tell you that you are turning, but your eyes will tell you that the wings are level.

Try to resolve conflicting information.

Good instrument training will ensure that you trust your eyes and what the instruments tell you over and above the other information. If, however, the situation is not so simple, say flying in cloud with a toppled attitude indicator or other failed instruments, resolving the conflict may be more difficult, and may lead to some stress.

Excessive Workload

As we have seen in the previous chapter, a high level of demand can adversely affect a person and thereby limit the number of stimuli that are perceived, as well as limit the degree of attention available to consider the stimulus which is perceived and acted upon. For instance, concentrating on a single task, such as handling an engine malfunction, can lead to neglect of other essential tasks like monitoring the flightpath or responding to radio messages.

The mental overload could arise because of an inability to handle the task through lack of knowledge, or because of too much stimulus, with too many items to be perceived, considered and acted upon. Alternatively, the mental overload could be a result of lack of time, with too much time pressure to make the decisions required.

Try and avoid mental overload.

Ideally, we need to have sufficient knowledge and skill, and be calm enough and have enough time available, to be able to sit back almost as an observer in all situations and watch our own actions, with enough spare capacity to maintain an overview of the flight. Even in an emergency, we should try to be involved but detached.

We can conclude that information processing and our understanding of it is fundamental to decision-making, which will be the subject of the next chapter.

Now complete: **Practice Questions - Information Processing**

1. The brain and spinal cord:

(a) Comprise the central nervous system.

(b) Comprise the peripheral nervous system.

(c) Comprise the autonomic nervous system.

(d) Comprise both the central and peripheral nervous system.

2. A basic model of information processing:

(a) Stimulus; Action; Analysis; Feedback.

(b) Action; Feedback; Stimulus.

(c) Stimulus; Action; Feedback.

(d) Stimulus; Analysis; Action; Feedback.

3. Motor programmes (skills) are:

(a) Automatic.

(b) Semi-automatic.

(c) Autonomic.

(d) Semi-autonomic.

4. Sensory information:

(a) Is stored in long-term memory.

(b) Is stored in short-term memory.

(c) Is stored in working memory.

(d) Is stored in sensory memory.

5. Anticipation:

(a) Is a useful part of the brain's function.

(b) Makes the identifying of features on the ground easy.

(c) Can cause the misunderstanding of a clearance to land.

(d) Is something that we all do and so it does not matter.

Judgement and Decision-Making

Good judgement and the ability to make good and timely decisions are skills that a pilot needs to develop. They can be learned.

Faulty judgement and incorrect decisions or indecisiveness are major causes of aircraft accidents and incidents, rather than poor flying skills. For example, a serious accident is more likely to be caused by a faulty decision to continue visually into poor weather conditions over hazardous terrain rather than by an inability to land the aeroplane.

Learn to make well-judged decisions.

In some situations the actual decision is not all that important, rather the fact that a decision has been made. Turning either left or right to avoid an obstacle or to fly around a thunderstorm is probably acceptable; not turning, through indecision, is far worse. Similarly, deciding to hold position on a taxiway after having been cleared for an immediate take-off by the tower, because of another aircraft on short final, shows better judgement than going along with the clearance and taking off without being fully prepared.

Judgement is the mental process used to make a decision. It can be divided into two extremes:

- **Learned skills,** 'stick and rudder behaviour' such as landing an aeroplane, where judgement of flare height, rate of descent, and touchdown becomes almost automatic and requires little brain power once learned. This is known as *perceptual* judgement. In between the two extremes are – 'Rule-based' behaviours, e.g. If I do X then Y will happen. Simple mental rules are known as heuristics; basically they involve pattern recognition. Caution – make sure you recognise the situation *correctly* and apply the relevant heuristic.

- **Thinking judgement,** 'reasoning' or 'problem-solving behaviour', often where rule or skill-based behaviour are not available where multiple information has to be assimilated, compared and evaluated, situations have to be responded to, and a series of smaller decisions made en route to an ultimate decision (for instance, whether to continue or to divert, and if so where to). This is a much more complex process involving forming an opinion or conclusion from information presented to the mind. It is a process of risk-analysis and decision-making based on skill, knowledge and experience. It often requires a lot of brain power, and is known as *cognitive* or *thinking* judgement.

There is a range in between the two extremes of semi-automatic skills and thinking judgement. The aim of *training* is to move as many of the situations that initially require a lot of thinking (i.e. requiring *cognitive* or *thinking* judgement) more and more into the learned skill area (or *perceptual* judgement area), so that correct decisions can be made without placing extreme demands on your concentration and thought processes.

Experienced pilots can generally make sound decisions with less difficulty than new pilots, because of their extra exposure to good training and operational experience. It is a lot easier to make a good decision when you have seen the situation before, or have read about similar situations.

As a new pilot, you can look forward to decision-making becoming easier as you gain more experience. Learn from the experience of others by reading widely and listening to other pilots. It is often more comfortable to learn from the experience of others than to make the same mistakes yourself.

When using your judgement, especially if dealing with something that requires serious thinking, you will make use of:
- **your knowledge** (hence the need to keep current with the bookwork);
- **your dedication** to standard operating procedures (SOPs);
- **your understanding** and thinking ability;
- **your practical skills.**

Making a Decision

When making a decision, you need to:
- **recognise relevant information** and evaluate it, comparing it with past events (using your knowledge and experience);
- **separate facts from emotions** and see what the real situation is (rather than what you would like it to be), and identify the problem (if any);
- **diagnose;**
- **consider alternative solutions** taking into account the time available, the aircraft (e.g. fuel situation), the environment (weather, daylight/darkness), and your skill level;
- **balance the risks;** and then
- **make a timely decision.**
- **review** - see if the decision is working.

There are only really 4 basic decision scenarios

1. the pilot *recognises* the situation and applies a *known* solution (rule based).

2. the pilot faces an *unusual* situation but applies a *known* solution that appears suitable.

3. the pilot faces an **unusual** situation and applies a **NEW** solution (knowledge- based behaviour).

4. the pilot **recognises** the situation and applies a **NEW** solution. This is the least likely statistically as in-flight experimentation seems to conflict with good airmanship, but must not be ruled out as it may just be the solution that works especially if other (poor) options are eliminated.

In practice, the most common causes of decision errors are:
- **Workload and Stress** – overload causes deterioration of mental processes.
- **Situational factors**, the pilot has a poor representation of what is going on around him (situational awareness) and does not see the need to act.
- **Erroneous risk** – misperception of threat levels and ability to deal with them e.g. flying near clouds.
- **Goal confliction** – where safety conflicts with other 'flight objectives' e.g. peer pressure wanting to please others, can lead to 'press on-it-is', an en route diversion can lead to 'loss of face'.

Action

Having considered the situation, used your (good) judgement, you then put your thoughts into action. Good judgement and decision-making is valueless if not acted upon.

Think, decide, then act.

You need to develop confidence in your ability to judge and decide, and then to act. These skills will develop together with experience. Under-confidence is damaging to decision-making; over-confidence can be dangerous; well-placed confidence is essential! With good training and with good application you can develop well-placed confidence in your ability both to judge and decide, and to act.

When using heuristics based on experience, always be aware that a good decision outcome does NOT necessarily mean that a good decision process was used, so a post-flight debrief is **essential**, either self-review or with other more experienced pilots. Ideally a pilot should aim to balance well placed confidence with a 'healthy paranoia'.

Personality and Attitude

Personalities vary from extroverts to introverts.

The work of a pilot is very difficult for a non-pilot to understand, with its conflicting demands and characteristics, something that a student will have to deal with when making the transition from layman to pilot. A pilot's personality reflects this, with many diverse and seemingly conflicting traits being required as the flight progresses *(see Pilot Personality Traits Table)*.

Pilot Personality Traits Table:

UNSTABLE	
Moody	Touchy
Anxious	Restless Aggressive
Rigid	Excitable
Sober	Changeable
Pessimistic	Impulsive
Reserved	Optimistic
Quiet	Active
Introverted	**Extraverted**
Passive	Sociable
Careful	Outgoing
Reliable	Talkative
Calm	Easygoing
Controlled	Carefree
STABLE	

For example, whilst some parts of the flight are hectic such as the take off, requiring an outgoing and optimistic outlook, other parts require quiet and sober reflection. Especially in emergencies, pilots are trained NOT to rush! A slow and calm response may be misinterpreted by an observer as lackadaisical. So use the surgeon analogy, 30 seconds of calm reflection could save a life, whereas a quick and poorly thought out response could cost one. Many a healthy engine has been shut down instead of the correct one.

Sound knowledge, a high skill level and experience will help you use your judgement and make good decisions. We must recognise, however, that some deeply in-built characteristics, such as personality and attitudes, play a role in how we think and behave. Some people are cheerful, others are erratic and unstable. Some people are natural extroverts (outgoing, often noisy and confident, and sometimes noisy to cover a lack of confidence), others are introverts (inward looking, often quiet, and perhaps shy).

Both personality types, extraverts and introverts, plus those in between, can make good pilots. Absolute extremes of personality, or an inability to modify behaviour, however, may mean that a person is not suitable to be trained as a pilot.

As well as 'checking the aircraft out' and your physical self (I'M SAFE), sometimes it pays to self-check your own mental functioning:

Here are 5 main 'bad attitudes' which could endanger a pilot's flight, with practical advice on correcting them. Have you demonstrated any of these recently?

Macho/Self Centred – 'I'll show'em', 'look at me', the risk takers who want to impress. Remember risk takers are foolish!

Resignation – 'what's the use, I can't do anything about it' e.g. when a pilot breaks the rules just to 'fit in'. Remember, you're **NOT** helpless, be the captain of your own ship - you **CAN** make a difference.

Invulnerability – 'It won't happen to me, accidents only happen to others'. Linked to Machismo, it **COULD** happen to you too!

Impulsivity – 'I must do this now!' - people who 'must do something/anything immediately', blinded to the risks e.g. a flight when weather conditions would suggest otherwise - i.e. not thinking it through. Always think twice, flying is always potentially dangerous.

Anti-Authority – 'don't boss me around' - rules, regulations and procedures 'don't apply to me'.

Follow the rules, they are there for a reason.

Develop positive attitudes.

Some positive attitudes to develop include:
* **respect for the rules** and standard operating procedures (SOPs);
* **recognition of your own ability,** especially your ability to handle unusual situations;
* **an ability to manage the cockpit;**
* **an ability to manage people;**
* **calm but timely decision-making;**
* **an ability to control stress levels;**
* **an ability to control risk level;**
* **an adventurous, positive spirit,** but with new tasks approached with careful consideration, risk assessment, and preparation; and
* **well-placed confidence in yourself.**

Cockpit Resource Management

Manage your resources.

You, as pilot-in-command, are responsible for the whole flight, and must coordinate the activities associated with your flight. *Cockpit resource management* means using whatever resources are available – and this includes people, equipment and information – to maximise the safety, efficiency and comfort of your flight. Cockpit resource management is often referred to as CRM.

Cockpit resource management in a single-pilot cockpit involves:
* **a good pre-flight preparation;**
* **a tidy cockpit** with all equipment possibly required in flight placed in a secure and accessible position;

- **an orderly approach** to the whole operation, with standard operating procedures being followed in an unhurried but efficient manner;
- **situational awareness** at all times (position and weather);
- **time awareness;**
- **a setting of priorities,** with vital tasks being performed and monitored before less important tasks (for instance, regular monitoring of the flightpath, main instruments, and main systems such as fuel should occur even when other tasks have to be performed);
- **using all the information** and resources available to you when necessary;
- **stress management** (avoid becoming overloaded);
- **risk management** (making well-judged decisions such as whether to continue into doubtful weather or to divert);
- **well-placed confidence** in your own ability; and
- **maintaining a good overview** of the flight and managing its progress.

Cockpit resource management involves two-way communication with others, be they fellow crew members, air traffic controllers, flight service staff, a maintenance engineer, or your flight instructor.

Crew Coordination

Crew coordination is the term used to describe the organisation and distribution of tasks associated with a particular flight in a multi-crew cockpit environment.

In a two-pilot cockpit, the tasks should be systematically organised and distributed so that one pilot has the primary task of handling the aircraft, this person being known as the *pilot flying* or PF, supported and monitored by the *pilot not flying* or PNF. The systematic organisation tasks and distribution of duties between the PF and PNF will be found in the Operations Manual of the organisation operating the aeroplane, but the success of the flight will be determined mainly by the strength of leadership exerted by the pilot-in-command, and by adherence to standard operating procedures (SOPs).

Make good use of your crew.

Each person's duties should be clearly defined either by the standard operating procedures, or by the pilot-in-command, with the workload being fairly evenly divided. There must be systematic cooperation between the PF and PNF, with an open flow of information in both directions. The tasks being performed by one must be monitored by the other, in both normal and abnormal situations. Vital tasks, such as the performance of checklists, are usually performed together.

In a single-pilot cockpit, the abilities of a passenger, especially if the passenger happens to be a pilot also, can sometimes be used.

Handling the radio and the navigation charts could easily be delegated to such a person, provided that the pilot-in-command monitors everything and keeps firm control of the situation.

Make good use of other human resources.

Crew coordination should be used in ground operations as well. The captain can make good use of the many resources available, such as briefing officers, maintenance engineers, refuellers and ground staff. You can make best use of these resources by first of all knowing your own tasks thoroughly and knowing what you want. Having established in your own mind what you want, then request it from the appropriate person in a professional manner. This usually produces the desired result.

The *crew coordination concept* is sometimes referred to as *'ccc'*.

Leadership Qualities

The pilot in a multi-crew cockpit must have leadership skills if the operation is to function safely and efficiently. A good leader will be:

- self-confident;
- not egotistical – i.e. can recognise *own* mistakes and limitations;
- understanding of others;
- able to communicate;
- able to listen to the opinion of others and accept their input;
- able to separate facts from emotions;
- able to impart views and opinions clearly;
- able to persuade;
- able to give good briefings;
- able to manage a team, on both technical and emotional levels;
- able to show good judgement and make good decisions with which the rest of the team will agree (or at least accept);
- able to breed confidence in others and enable them to learn and develop;
- able to delegate tasks and responsibilities, but cross-check task performance and accept ultimate responsibility;
- able to set priorities;
- able to maintain a good overview of the flight and manage it to a successful conclusion;
- able to fly well according to standard operating procedures;
- able to show flair and an ability to deal with non-standard and unusual situations (this comes with experience); and
- able to handle him/herself socially.

Leadership Style

When leading a team to accomplish a task, there can be a variation in emphasis between:

- total task orientation, where completing the task at all costs occurs without regard to the human aspects of the team; and

- **total people orientation,** where keeping everybody happy takes precedence over completing the task safely and efficiently.

The ideal leader will encompass both aspects in completing the task safely and efficiently, but in a manner that involves the team and takes advantage of their input and skills. This person will be a captain who is respected and liked by the crew.

Manage both the task and the people.

The totally *task-oriented* captain will be seen as a good pilot (possibly), but as a poor captain. He or she may even be viewed as a bit of a tyrant.

The totally *person-oriented* captain may be seen as weak. Aeroplanes cannot be run by committees. Even though a contribution from team members is required, someone has to make the final decision, and within a suitable time frame. In emergency situations especially, this decision-making person is usually the captain (or should be). The totally person-oriented captain may be well liked – until the time for tough decision-making comes and he is found to be indecisive or weak, or makes serious mistakes.

The captain who is neither task-oriented nor person-oriented will be avoided by all. Such an unmotivated person has no place in a cockpit.

You can become a good captain. By gaining the required skills, which can all be learned, and displaying the leadership qualities listed earlier, you can train yourself to be a good leader – one who encourages confidence, looks like a leader, and is a leader. Being a good captain is also closely linked to being a good person in other aspects of your life.

Develop leadership skills.

Who is in Control?

As pilot-in-command, you must always be in command, even if you have delegated flying duties to a second pilot. Even in a single-pilot cockpit, the problem of who is in command can arise, especially if the pilot acts in a passive manner and allows others to make decisions for him. Domineering and demanding crew members or passengers can sometimes be a problem, and occasionally the pilot-in-command has to exert authority.

Unsatisfactory clearances from ATC (such as: "cleared immediate take-off" before you are fully ready, or a VFR clearance that would take you into cloud) must be rejected with confidence; this will be understood and accepted by ATC. The student pilot must learn what the role of *pilot-in-command* is, and how to act in this capacity.

The Pilot-in-Command

The role of the pilot-in-command is indeed to **be in command.** This means being in control of the whole situation as well as being responsible for the smooth and professional handling of the

Be in command.

aircraft. It is as much a task of management as of physically flying the aircraft.

You should **know your aircraft well,** and know how to operate it efficiently according to the laid-down standard operating procedures. You should **plan each flight thoroughly,** and **be well rested** prior to flight.

Arrive early for each flight if possible and plan at a professional pace, making use of the resources available. **Do not allow distractions** to interfere unduly with your planning. This may mean a polite "I am busy right now. I will talk with you shortly."

The pilot-in-command is in command.

Establish your command role on the ground prior to flight. Often your passengers will be people who have a 'senior' position to you in normal life, such as a parent, or the chief of your airline or flying school, but when it comes to achieving a sound and safe flight, you have to be in command. You can do this in a polite manner at the flight planning stage, or even earlier such as on the drive to airport, by acting in a professional manner and setting the pace so that the flight can depart on time.

After planning the flight, you will then probably need to **organise and supervise** the refuelling of the aeroplane, and then the loading of the baggage and **embarkation of the passengers.** An efficient preparation of the aeroplane for flight and clear communication with mechanics, ground staff and other crew will give everyone a feeling of confidence.

Do not allow your walk-around check to be unnecessarily interrupted, since an overlooked control lock, missing fuel cap, or chocks that have not been removed can have unpleasant, embarrassing, or even fatal consequences. Be aware of exactly where you are, what it is you are looking at, and how it should look.

Organise the loading efficiently, according to weight-and-balance requirements, with heavy articles tied down. Organise your equipment in the cockpit so that everything necessary is at hand. Make your passengers comfortable, and **carry out any required briefings** (seat-belts, route of flight, etc.). Doing this prior to start-up shows good airmanship.

Often you will have a passenger with an interest in flying, or who might even be a qualified pilot, and who questions you continuously about aeroplane characteristics, new equipment, navigation procedures, etc., which can distract you from vital tasks. It is good to satisfy a passenger of course, but there are times when you need to say "I really need to concentrate now", or "The workload will increase shortly, so we will finish this conversation later." Passengers, including other pilots, respect this strength of command which does not allow you to be carried along by others who are not in command.

Make your radio calls professionally and with an air of authority (which should be genuine and not just acting). Handle the aeroplane smoothly and also with authority, both on the ground and in the air.

If you wish to distribute some tasks to others, then do so in a sensible manner, and retain control of the situation by providing clear guidance and then monitoring the actions. Do not allow any confusion to be present in the cockpit. If a second pilot is assisting by operating the radios or some of the controls, such as the flap control or the undercarriage (or landing gear) lever, then be especially careful.

Informal assistance without overall control from the pilot-in-command can be dangerous. Do not allow uncalled-for assistance, even from a more experienced pilot, as it may interfere with your operation and how you want to run it. This is not to say that you should not listen to advice as part of a normal learning process, but as pilot-in-command you must **set the pace.** In a training context the situation is a little different, since you will normally have to defer to your flying instructor, but even then, you should think independently and express any difference of opinion.

Remember that your flying instructor is training you to be a pilot-in-command. In fact, even in a two-pilot cockpit with both pilots fully trained and operating as a team, they should be thinking independently and informing each other of any differences of opinion. When flying with a more-experienced pilot who, in your opinion, has chosen a course of action that might endanger the aircraft, *always* express your doubts! In a two-crew cockpit, always be certain who has physical control of the flightpath of the aeroplane by using the phrases "I have control" and "You have control" appropriately.

Remaining in Command

To stay in total command of the flight, you must ensure that you do not get into situations for which you are not prepared or trained for, or for which the aeroplane is not equipped (such as night flight, or instrument flight). You should know your own limitations and capability, and you should assess the expected workload on this basis.

You should be able to operate safely right up to the point where the workload meets your capability, but if the workload exceeds your capability at any time, because of increased workload or diminished capability, then you are a candidate for an incident or an accident. If you feel that the workload at any point in the flight could exceed your current capability, then do not perform the flight. Say "No."

Know your limits.

For instance, the workload associated with normal take-offs and landings at your home airport has always been well within your capability, but today you feel tired (diminished capability) and there is a gusty crosswind (increased workload). In this situation, you need to make a rational *go/no-go* decision. This could be the most important decision of the whole flight.

Keep in practice.

Sometimes the workload imposed by individual items are within your current capability, but a combination of factors (such as an unfamiliar airport, a radio communications failure, and difficult weather conditions including rain and a gusty crosswind) might add up to a total workload beyond your capability. Be prepared for this by keeping yourself current so as to maintain a high capability, which will enable you to keep something in reserve for emergencies.

The best advice for a new pilot is:
• **gain the knowledge** and learn the skills to be a good pilot;
• **have well-placed confidence** in yourself;
• **know your limitations** and the limitations of the aeroplane;
• **exert command** over your flight from the planning stage to the signing-off stage; and
• **approach each and every flight** with total professionalism.

Now complete: **Practice Questions - Judgement & Decision Making**

1. The decision making process:

(a) *Is all about speed of the course of action.*

(b) *Is always made in the same way.*

(c) *Cannot be learned.*

(d) *Is made up of learned skills, thinking judgement and reasoning.*

2. When pilot-in-command:

(a) *If duties are delegated, responsibility rests with the person to whom duties have been delegated.*

(b) *Clearance from ATC must be adhered to promptly.*

(c) *Must be appropriately assertive with demanding crew members.*

(d) *Must be physically in control of the aeroplane at all times.*

3. Cockpit resource management:

(a) *Is the skill of managing all the available crew resources to ensure the safest possible flight.*

(b) *Is not applicable to single crew aeroplanes.*

(c) *Is all about knowing you are in charge.*

(d) *Allowing the whole crew to make decisions.*

4. When making decisions:

(a) *Make them quickly during busy parts of the flight.*

(b) *Always be chatty and cheerful when making decisions.*

(c) *Use sound knowledge, high skill levels, experience and judgement.*

(d) *It is important to make decisions independently of others.*

Answers: 1d, 2c, 3a, 4c.

Airmanship and Threat and Error Management

Airmanship

The fundamental aim for any pilot is to ensure the **safety** of the flight. There are many factors that contribute to flight safety and it is important for the pilot to be aware of these. One of the factors that is important in maintaining flight safety is to practise 'Airmanship'.

This is defined as 'the consistent use of good judgement and well-developed knowledge, skills and attitudes to accomplish flight objectives'.

But exactly **how** do we demonstrate this, how can we measure pilot performance in Airmanship terms and what does it mean practically? It may be easier to say than to do and Airmanship has traditionally been thought of as merely 'formalised common sense'.

In the commercial flying world, the concept of airmanship has been developed by the incorporation of '**Crew Resource Management (CRM)**' and '**Threat and Error Management (TEM)**' into operations. Aspects of these concepts have a useful application in general aviation and under the new EASA regulations, all pilots are now required to have a basic understanding of CRM and TEM.

The aim of this chapter is to show that a pilot with high level of Situational Awareness (SA) can then make better, more informed decisions so that his Airmanship performance increases i.e. he delivers the safest flight that he can, with practical advice on how to do this. 'You can make a difference'.

It may be the other way around; good airmanship can lead to better SA, which in turn can impact flight safety.

Situational Awareness (SA)

The pilot's task involves continuously processing a vast amount of information. The primary aim of this is to develop 'Situational Awareness', from which we can make 'Judgments' and 'Decisions'.

Situational Awareness (SA) is defined as 'the **perception** of the elements in the environment within a volume of time and space, the **comprehension** of their meaning and the **predictions** of their status in the near future' - *(Endsley, 1988)*

Basically – know what is going on around you and be able to interpret this information, and predict what may or may not happen in the future, i.e. seeing the 'Bigger Picture'. The picture analogy is fundamental in flying. Your aim is to be able to know what seems right and what seems wrong.

A useful mnemonic is '**NUTA**' – **Notice, Understand and Think Ahead**, (corresponding to Perception, Comprehension and Projection from the Endsley definition).

This establishes the 3 levels of increasing quality of SA.

A practical example of this is:

1. **Perception** - you notice a thunderstorm in the direction of your intended destination;

2. **Comprehension** - you understand the implications (from your Meteorology studies) of thunderstorms and think about changing route or even cancelling the flight;

3. **Projection** - you think ahead about the implications of avoiding the Storm, e.g. more fuel required, or cancelling your slot at the Flying Club.

It can be further subdivided into further elements – **Plane, Path, People.**
* **Plane** – inside the aircraft, e.g. Instrument settings and inside referenced to outside, e.g. configuration and heading.
* **Path** – what's happening outside the aircraft e.g. on track? Collision avoidance.
* **People** – crew, passengers, ATC.

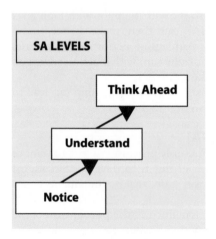 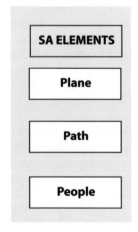

■ ✎ Figure 8-1 **Situational Awareness (SA)**

SA is not the *sum* of our knowledge, it is dynamic and can vary throughout the flight. Consider high workload areas of the flight, you may not have much spare capacity to 'think ahead' e.g. during landing *but* you could have 'thought ahead' about the landing when in low workload periods such as the cruise.

NOTE that too much thinking ahead can be to the detriment of what's happening **NOW** so perhaps we can now say:-

Aviate (NUTA)
Navigate (NUTA)
Communicate (NUTA)

A useful analogy is if we were to walk along a 'Travelator' (which are present at some airports!) BUT in the opposite direction - it is easier to walk along it when it is travelling slowly and there are fewer other passengers to navigate around (low workload) than when it is fast and busy!

It must be emphasised that a good attitude is an important factor in airmanship and should be applied to ALL aspects of the flight- from the moment planning begins until the Tech Log is signed. If a pilot cannot be bothered with paperwork then that is poor Airmanship.

Similarly with 'knowledge', by knowing how to interpret and apply the information that is processed, a pilot can apply the principle involved to *improving* Situational Awareness.

Importance of Situational Awareness (SA)

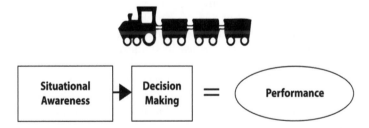

■ ✎ *Figure 8-2* **The Importance of SA**

- SA DRIVES the decision – making process.
- Most accidents are caused by low SA, rather than poor decisions.

Poor SA is often a result of, and in combination with, other factors e.g. busy at day job, needing to fly, not taking time to check the weather thoroughly, inadvertently getting into IMC, not turning back, low SA.

Decision Making

Research has shown that pilots are generally good decision makers once they have high levels of SA http://www.skybrary.aero/bookshelf/books/239.pdf

Many normal and unusual situations are covered by checklists – rule based decision making.

For a more complex problem, a more analytical process is required e.g. **TDODAR**

Time – how much time do we have available?

Diagnose - diagnose the problem

Options – options available, the risks and consequences

Decide - make a decision

Assign - assign tasks

Review – test the solution and try to prove it is WRONG. This protects against confirmation bias.

It should be emphasised that this does not apply to emergencies (i.e. checklist procedures)! Example, you would not apply this to engine failure.

The Link between SA, TEM and CRM

TEM is the process of detecting and responding to all of the various Threats and Errors which occur when conducting a task and to ensure that their ensuing outcome is inconsequential. A pilot with a high level of SA will therefore be able to detect and respond to such errors and threats much EARLIER than with low situational awareness, and to use a Medical term 'Prevention is better than cure'. CRM is the effective utilisation of available resources *(crew members, aeroplane systems and supporting facilities e.g. ground personnel)* to achieve a safe and efficient operation'. CRM and TEM are both frameworks for effective management of certain situations. Although they are consistent with some features of good airmanship, they are not all encompassing: airmanship as a whole goes further than CRM or TEM.

Threat and Error Management (TEM)

The automated flight deck did not necessarily bring a commensurate increase in flight safety. Data from the Continental Airlines Line Operations Safety Audit (LOSA) illuminated that this was probably due to the human factor. Threat and Error Management (TEM) was developed as a psychological framework to improve Human Performance in dynamic, operational environments. [1]It has the following components: 'Threats', 'Errors' and 'Undesired Aircraft States' (UAS) which must be 'Managed' using 'Countermeasures' with three layers of defence *(Avoid/Trap/Mitigate),* to avoid an 'Adverse Outcome' *(see diagram below).*

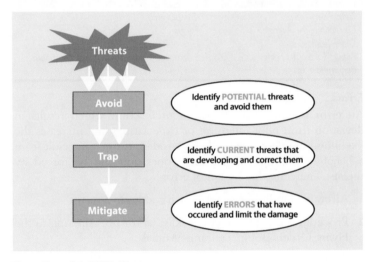

■ ✎ *Figure 8-3* **TEM Components**

Threats

A threat is defined as an external event or error that occurs outside the influence of the pilots that requires immediate attention and management if flight safety is to be maintained. There are two main types of threats:

(1) Environmental: weather, airport conditions, air traffic control and terrain.
(2) Organisational: flight deck and operational pressure.

Threats should be analysed relative to the pilot, airframe and route to be flown at any given time. Threats can be immediate and known (e.g. thunderstorm), latent (e.g. inadequate fuel) and

1.http://legacy.icao.int/anb/safetymanagement/CIRC_314-AN_178-INP-EN_EDENPROD_195309_v1.PDF

unknown (e.g. erroneous radar vectors by ATC). All types of threat require attention of the pilot if safety margins are to be maintained.

To use our earlier thunderstorm example, the storm itself would be an external threat, expected if the pilot is vigilant with his pre-flight planning; a latent threat could be certain cockpit layouts *(ergonomics)* e.g. flaps and gear lever too close together. Organisational could be that the flying club has poor facilities e.g. No computer to access met information, and encourages a 'just fly anyway' attitude.

Further Threat Examples:

External	Internal
Surrounding Terrain	Complacency
Condition of the Aircraft	Fatigue
Other Traffic	Lack of Recency
Airfield Take off/Landing performance Issues	Hazardous personality traits e.g. Machoism

Errors

An error is defined as an action or inaction which results in deviation from pilot intention or expectations and increases the likelihood of safety margins being eroded. Errors can result from a belief or assertion of the flight operation and be forced by threats. There are three types of error:

1 **Aircraft Handling** e.g. too much rudder in a turn.

2 **Procedural** e.g. incorrect checklist use or not adhering to the Flying Orders Book/Training Manual.

3 **Communications** e.g. using non standard RT.

Errors must be identified and managed before safety margins are compromised, or this will lead to an Undesired Aircraft State (UAS).

An Undesired Aircraft State (UAS) is defined as a position, condition (speed/handling) or attitude of an aircraft that can arise from errors and result in a significant reduction in safety margins that could result in anything from minor inconvenience or major loss of life/airframe. TEM proposes that pilots who identify and manage errors are able to prevent UAS and maintain flight safety.

Management

Management involves anticipation of threats before flight and developing a plan which may be implemented to countermeasure them during the flight operation. There are three phases to TEM:

1 Anticipation (Avoid) - identifying threats that could affect a particular flight operation, planning to prevent them and developing countermeasures to implement if they are encountered.

2 Recognition (Trap) - being vigilant to anticipated threats and resultant errors, monitoring them when they are encountered and require management.

3 Recovering (Mitigate) - implementation of countermeasures, review of their effectiveness and modifying flight plan to maintain flight safety.

There are three types of countermeasure:
(1) **Planning:** planning and contingency.
(2) **Execution:** monitor and cross-check, workload management, automation management.
(3) **Review:** challenge and modify course of action.

- A pilot who is merely reacting to events is at the lowest level of SA i.e. '*Notice*'.
- A pilot who is trapping errors as they occur is at the middle level of SA = '*Understanding*'.
- A pilot who is projecting ahead to avoid errors and hazards is at the highest ideal level = '*Think Ahead*'.

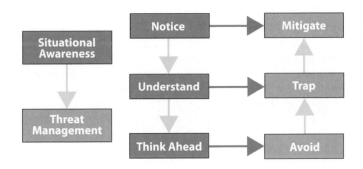

■ ✎ *Figure 8-4* **Table of Three Levels of SA**

Practical Applications

The principle of the TEM framework must be integral to every flight. It is a simple concept but provides flight crew with a framework that can help withstand the psychological pressure of a flight operation. Thunderstorms are environmental threats frequently faced by aviators and can help demonstrate the application of TEM. A light aircraft flying at the safe limits of its fuel endurance with a pilot qualified to fly in visual meteorological conditions might consider the following:

Anticipation (Avoid)

• Weather forecasts are interpreted to ascertain the frequency and intensity of thunderstorms en-route and at departure and destination airfields. Isolated (less than 25% of route) are anticipated.
• A set of planning countermeasures are developed to avoid thunderstorms: Divert en-route, Hold en-route until thunderstorm is clear and proceed to destination, Re-route around thunderstorm and proceed to destination.
• Latent threats are then identified as each thunderstorm countermeasure has implications for fuel consumption and can limit options to mitigate other threats, such as if the destination airfield is closed due to an incident.
• Identify how other factors such as airspace or terrain can limit implementation of countermeasures and contribute to increasing workload or operational pressure.
• Use this understanding to decide whether the threat can be managed safely.

Recognition (Trap)

• The pilot and instrumentation are used to observe the environment during the operation.
• Anticipation leads to increased vigilance and recognition of the thunderstorm threat, its intensity and comparison to what was expected pre-flight.
• In this case, it also helps trap the error of inaction and monitoring of fuel status and workload so as to dictate which planned countermeasure would be most suitable.

Recovery (Mitigate)

• The anticipation phase prepared the pilot for action on recognition of the threat. In this case the most suitable countermeasure is initiated.
• Review of countermeasure effectiveness in mitigating both the immediate threat of the thunderstorm and latent threat of insufficient reserve fuel on arrival at destination.

- Review of the fuel situation may challenge the re-route countermeasure being employed and a diversion en-route is then pursued to maintain safety margins.
- Post flight review of the threats, errors and countermeasure effectiveness can help the pilot learn from the experience and calibrate future decision making and planning associated with similar scenarios.

TEM is not just about errors made by the pilot but the bigger PICTURE of internal and external threats and errors that confront the pilot throughout the flight. By adopting high CRM standards and using SA's philosophy of thinking ahead, a pilot can avoid these threats and errors and practise good airmanship.

A pilot should aim to build the best 'AVOID' layer in the time available. Pilots should strive for this as it gives them the highest level of protection.

The pilot is the most important component for delivering a safe flight. The principles of TEM and CRM relate to the interaction between the pilot, the aircraft and other factors such as ATC. The whole purpose of these frameworks is that these factors do not exist in isolation but it is the interaction that can cause problems.

You can make a difference to flight safety.

Now complete: **Airmanship and Threat & Error Management**

1. Airmanship:

(a) Is the skill of flying the aeroplane.

(b) In conjunction with TEM is fundamental to the safety of the flight.

(c) Can only be learned after qualifying as a pilot and with experience.

(d) Does not include threat and error managment.

2. Situational Awareness:

(a) Is the skill of 'Lookout'.

(b) Listening on the radio when approaching an airfield.

(c) Is a 'Gross Error Check' during a heading change on DR Navigation.

(d) The perception and comprehension of the elements of your environment.

3. The link between SA, TEM and CRM:

(a) These are all independent of each other.

(b) Situational awareness is the most important skill in these three skills.

(c) With high SA, TEM becomes more effective, combine with CRM brings the best possible outcome.

(d) Are best used when there is an emergency.

4. TEM:

(a) Uses a sequence 'Avoid'; 'Trap'; 'Mitigate' to reduce threats.

(b) Is just common sense.

(c) Is a new term for Airmanship.

(d) Is relevant to two crew operations.

5. Management of Threats:

(a) Is carried out all the time the aeroplane is airborne.

(b) Happens as a result of an undesirable aircraft state.

(c) Has three phases 'Anticipation'; 'Recognition'; 'Recovering'.

(d) Is another way of describing CRM.

Answers: 1b, 2d, 3c, 4a, 5c.

The Flight Deck

Ergonomics and Flight Deck Design

A visit to the flight deck of any recently designed aeroplane will convince you that cockpit design is an improving art. Beautiful instrumentation, well-designed and well-positioned controls, good lighting, and comfortable seats, are a vast improvement over earlier cockpits – at least in most cases. As with all things, there is still room for improvement.

Cockpits are usually at the front of the aeroplane, with large windscreens to give the pilots a good view of the surrounding environment. In some aircraft, the pilots sit a little back from the nose – for instance, in the *Boeing 747* where the pilots up on the flight deck actually have passengers on the lower deck ahead of them. The *Tiger Moth* is flown solo from the rear cockpit for weight and balance reasons, creating vision problems during the flare for a three-point landing, and during taxiing.

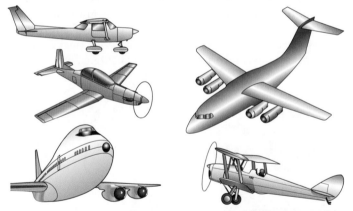

■ ✎ *Figure 9-1* **Most cockpits are at the front, but not all**

Early Cockpits

Some early cockpits were draughty, smelly places, often with poor forward vision and poor internal lighting. Instruments were spread around the panel in a haphazard and cluttered manner, placed wherever there happened to be space, often in different places in different aeroplanes of the same fleet, and often widely displaced from their associated control. Some displays were so small, or poorly lit, or poorly placed, as to be almost impossible for the pilot to read.

Many aircraft currently used in general aviation training have a design that is over thirty years old. These designs, despite some limitations, have served their purpose very well, and continue to do so. They were certainly a big step forward in their time, and brought safer aviation to ordinary people. Many of these aircraft have been modified to accommodate newer and better instrumentation, and operate efficiently in the modern aviation environment.

The Pilot and the Machine

The pilot and the aircraft form a very important combination that depends on a good pilot, good controls and good cockpit displays. The pilot–aircraft combination is a *closed-loop* system, in that the pilot makes a control movement, observes the effect as displayed on the instruments (or through the windscreen), decides if the response is what is desired, and then makes further control inputs to bring the *actual* even closer to the *desired*. It is a closed loop of: *pilot–control–display–pilot* repeated again and again.

The pilot and aircraft form a closed loop.

When controlling the aircraft, you, the pilot, decide where you want it to go and then manipulate the flight controls to achieve this desired flightpath. You then observe the effect of the control movement on the flightpath by reference to the instruments and/ or the outside environment. Next, you decide if any further action is needed – any *fine-tuning* – and then make further movements on the controls, check their effect, etc., etc.

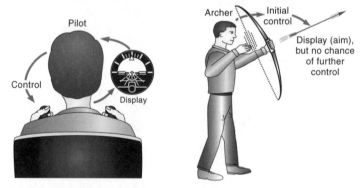

■ ✎ Figure 9-2 **A closed-loop system; an open-loop system**

Good pilots have the skills to make the closed-loop system work so quickly that flightpath and airspeed, for instance, are kept within tight limits. For beginning pilots, however, the closed-loop may take a little longer to operate, and so flightpath and airspeed are not controlled as tightly (but will be with practice and determination!).

Another example of a closed-loop system is a radio-controlled glider which the operator can control from the ground. A glider *without* radio controls, however, is out of the control of the operator once the glider is launched. There is no means of altering its flightpath, even though the glider is visible to the observer. In this case, the loop is not closed. Similarly, an archer has no further control over the path of an arrow once it has left the bow, even though it is apparent where the arrow is going.

There are many closed loops in the cockpit – for instance, when controlling cabin temperature, the pilot adjusts the control then checks the cabin temperature gauge; or when adjusting the cockpit lights at night, the pilot dims them and then sees charts are readable, then makes further adjustments if necessary. Action, feedback, and further action is a continual process in the cockpit.

In automatic flight, the pilot shares the tasks with the automatics to a certain extent, but there are further closed loops in this relationship, since the performance of the automatics must be monitored.

Designing the Work Space of the Flight Deck

In designing the cockpit or flight deck, account has to be taken of the limited space available, the size of the pilots, their need to reach and operate the controls, their need to see both the internal displays and the external environment, preferably while strapped into a comfortable seat.

Good ergonomics is important in aircraft design.

Improving the efficiency of people in their work place is called **ergonomics,** from the Greek words *ergon* meaning work and *nomos* meaning natural law. In aviation, the term ergonomics refers to cockpit design and the improvement of the pilot–machine interface, taking into account human factors such as expected human behaviour and performance which, as we all know, is a variable – not only between people, but also within the one individual at different times.

The cockpit or flight deck has to be designed to cater for us human beings, allowing for our foibles and weaknesses, and encouraging us to operate safely and efficiently. The first thing a well-designed cockpit has to provide a pilot with is a good view.

The Design Eye Position

Adjust your seat properly.

The pilot needs to be seated with the eyes in a position so that, with as little head movement as possible, there is:

- an unobstructed view of the **main instruments** in the cockpit; and
- a good view of the **outside environment,** not only the general area ahead for traffic avoidance reasons, but especially the area forward and down from the nose to assist in judging the final stages of the approach and landing.

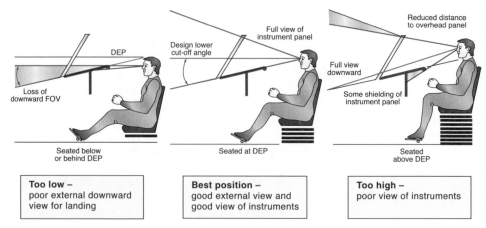

■ ✎ Figure 9-3 **Sitting too high, just right, and too low**

Pilots Come in All Shapes and Sizes

Having determined the design eye position for the pilots who are going to fly the aeroplane, the designer now needs to plan other aspects of the cockpit or flight deck, and this will depend to a large extent on the size of the pilots.

People vary a lot in size and shape, with some very short people in a given population and some extremely tall people, but with most of us somewhere in the middle. Race and gender are also significant, with the average Japanese female likely to be shorter than the average European male. The task of the flight deck designer would be complicated if it was necessary to cater for 100% of the population, and it is generally accepted that the small number in the 5% at either end of the size-and-shape range may be neglected. The designer therefore plans for those who lie in the range from 5% to 95% of the population.

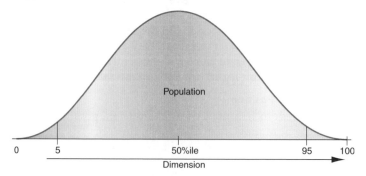

■ ✎ Figure 9-4 **The design population**

Seat Design

The seat should be able to be positioned fore and aft, up and down, and the backrest tilted if desired, so that the design criteria for operating the aeroplane are achieved: the eyes in the design eye position, and all vital controls within reach and capable of being moved to the full extent of their travel without undue stretching by the pilot.

Adjust your seat, and lock it.

The seat, having been designed to be moved and altered in shape to suit a wide range of pilots, must then be capable of being locked into position so that it cannot move in flight. Some accidents have occurred as a result of the pilot seat slipping back on its rails during the take-off acceleration – the tendency is for the pilot to pull himself forward again using the control column, perhaps causing the aeroplane to become airborne prematurely with the pilot in no position to control it. You should **check that the seat is securely locked** prior to every take-off and landing.

Adjust the rudder pedals.

With the seat adjusted so that your eyes are in the design eye position, you should now adjust the rudder pedals. You can do this while parked, but you may not be able to check full left and full right movement until taxiing, since in many aircraft moving the rudder pedals not only moves the rudder but also the nosewheel. The control column should be checked for full movement to ensure that it will not strike your knees or stomach. In some aircraft, other controls may also have to be positioned – for instance, a control column that may have to be swung over from right seat to left seat, or moved forward or back, although this is rare.

The Seat-Belt

The harness or seat-belt is a major protector of the pilot in turbulence, during aerobatic manoeuvres, or in an emergency, such as during heavy braking or (and let us make sure that it never happens) during an impact with the ground or some other object.

There are different seat-belt designs, but for any of them to be effective they must be fastened correctly. The simplest is a lap belt, often used for airline passengers, where the belt should be fastened firmly over the hips with the buckle kept away from the soft abdomen if possible, so that bone structure and not soft body parts carry the strain. The belt should be flat and not twisted, so that it will not cut into the body under the pressure of deceleration or turbulence.

Fasten your seat belt.

Many light aircraft have a lap belt for the occupants of the pilot seats, with an inertial reel shoulder strap that comes across one shoulder and fastens into the buckle, which should be positioned to the side of the hip and not over the soft abdomen. The inertial reel allows the pilot to lean forward under normal conditions, but under conditions of rapid acceleration or deceleration, such as in turbulence, the shoulder strap locks and holds the upper body of the pilot very firmly in position. Usually pilots lock the shoulder strap before commencing aerobatics or before entering unavoidable areas of known turbulence. You should test the inertial reel prior to use by pulling sharply on the shoulder strap and checking that it locks.

Larger aircraft usually have lap belts for the pilots, with a groin belt to hold the lap belt down and also to prevent the pilot from slipping under the lap belt, plus an inertial reel shoulder harness over each shoulder. During turbulence the shoulder strap can be locked. It is common during normal cruise in smooth flying conditions to remove the shoulder harness, but to have it fastened during take-off and climb-out, and during descent, approach and landing.

Checks of seat-belts in the cockpit should include:
- **belts attached securely** to aircraft structure;
- **no fraying** or chemical attack on the belt, as this will weaken it;
- **inertial reel locks** when tugged;
- **no twisting** of the belt, to prevent it from cutting into the body;
- **belt fastened,** with buckle correctly positioned.

■ Figure 9-5
Seat-belt designs

Remember to check that your passengers have their seat-belts fastened during take-off and landing, and whenever you expect turbulence. Use the seat-belt sign if you have one, or inform them verbally.

Design of the Controls

The cockpit contains many controls, such as the flight controls which are manipulated by the pilot to control the flightpath of the aeroplane, the engine controls, the flap control, the undercarriage control, the knob to adjust the pressure setting in the subscale window of the altimeter, radio frequency selectors and a transmit button, heating and cooling controls, switches for the electrical system, lighting controls, and many more.

Getting used to the controls can be quite a handful for a beginning pilot or a pilot converting to a new type, but by using a certain degree of standardisation and good design, the task is made somewhat easier. There has to be some flexibility of design available to the aeroplane manufacturer, however, otherwise there would be no progress.

Some general principles of control design for all aeroplanes are:
- **controls should be within reach** of the pilots and capable of being moved to their full extent without obstruction or without undue force being required;

- controls should be standardised where possible, so that controls in one aircraft resemble those in another, and are placed in similar positions;
- controls for different functions should be different enough to avoid confusion, so that the throttle is not confused with the propeller pitch control, or the flap lever with the landing gear lever;
- controls should be logically designed and placed, especially when they are to be used simultaneously or sequentially; and
- controls should not be prone to failure.

The Control Column

Most aircraft have a fairly standard control wheel placed centrally in front of the pilot. It is used to manipulate the elevator for pitch control by fore-aft movements, and to manipulate the ailerons for roll control by rotational movements. The standard control wheel is also known as the control column or yoke, and may have additional features in more advanced aircraft as mentioned before, such as a radio transmit button, a trim control, and an autopilot disconnect button.

There are other designs, however, involving totally different shapes such as the ram's horn in the *Concorde,* the joystick in older aeroplanes and some aerobatic aeroplanes, and the sidestick in the *Airbus 320* and *340* placed not directly in front of the pilot, but to the side as its name suggests. The sidestick is not just the province of modern airliners – the *Victa Airtourer* (and later development, the *CT-4*), a light aircraft designed in the 1960s, had a sidestick placed between the two pilots seated side-by-side; however, it was mechanical rather than electronic. The Cirrus series of modern composite light aircraft also employ a sidestick.

Traditional yoke

Sidestick

■ ✎ *Figure 9-6* **Some variations in design for the same control**

Converting from one type of control to another as you change aircraft types will take a little time, but is made much easier by the fact that all operate in a logical sense – fore-and-aft for pitch, and sideways or rotation for roll.

The Throttle

The throttle (or throttles, on multi-engined aircraft) controlling engine power, is usually placed forward and to the right of the pilot occupying the captain's seat, which is traditionally on the left.

The throttle is designed so that a forward movement will add power, and a rearward movement will reduce power.

Similarly, on aircraft with a constant-speed propeller, the rpm control (or pitch lever) is moved forward to increase rpm, and rearward to reduce rpm. The idea of moving a control forward for increase, and rearward for decrease, is a general design principle.

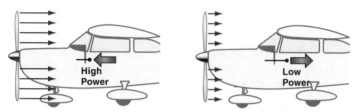

■ ✎ Figure 9-7 **Forward to increase, back to reduce**

Other Engine Controls

Aircraft with piston engines and constant-speed propellers have quite a few engine and propeller controls: throttle, propeller rpm (pitch) lever, mixture control, carburettor heat control (or alternate air control, if fuel injected), and cowl flaps control. On the four-engined *DC-4* (now rare), this meant 20 levers, plus an assortment of fuel control and fire switches.

It would be nice if there was an industry standard with respect to relative position of the engine controls, but unfortunately there is not, and sometimes you will find the rpm levers to the left of the throttles, and sometimes to the right. You must become very familiar with the control positions in any new aeroplane that you fly. On modern jets, an engine that is running is controlled by the throttle alone – much easier!

Fuel Tank Controls

Fuel tank switching has a notorious history, with many engines having stopped through fuel starvation while there was still plenty of fuel remaining. Faulty switching is often a result of poor design, and if you look at a variety of light aircraft you are sure to see a variety of fuel tank switches. Some aircraft have all tanks in use at the one time, others have left, then right, some have all tanks off with the switch forward, others with it aft. Always make sure that you know how yours works, as you may have to reach down and operate it at a stressful time in a darkened cockpit while you are trying to control the aeroplane.

Know your fuel system.

It is good airmanship to check that the fuel distribution system is indeed working correctly before setting out over an ocean where fuel from various tanks might be required. If an engine on a twin fails, the aeroplane will slowly go out of lateral balance limits unless cross-feeding from the tanks occurs. Fuel starvation could eventually be the result, even though the tank in the opposite wing contains fuel.

■ ✎ Figure 9-8 **Different designs of fuel tank switches**

Control Functions and Differentiation

Controls used for associated functions should be grouped together – for instance, the engine controls (throttle and pitch lever) should be near each other, but in an unambiguous manner that does not lead to confusion as to which control is which. Associated instruments should be nearby and, where possible, aligned with the control.

If certain controls are used for associated but different functions, and especially if they are located near each other, they need to be differentiated one from the other as much as possible. For instance, the throttle must look and feel different from the pitch lever, as must the mixture control and the carburettor heat control. This differentiation can be designed into the controls by using different shapes and different textured-surfaces (to provide a different feel), and different colours (but this may not be all that effective, especially at night). Throttles often have a rounded black knob, propeller pitch controls are often blue, mixture controls are often red, and carburettor heat controls are often white.

Know your cockpit.

Two controls that have been frequently misused by pilots in the past are the landing gear lever and the flap lever – a 'pilot error' to be sure, but one induced by poor design. In some older aircraft, the two controls were of similar shape and size, placed side by side, with the different colours not seeming to help fatigued pilots in darkened cockpits late at night.

Raising the flaps in flight immediately after take-off (reducing lift) instead of raising the landing gear (thereby retaining high drag instead of reducing it) could have disastrous consequences. An unexpected loss of lift instead of an expected reduction in drag is not conducive to a safe climb-out. There have also been incidents on the ground following a successful landing when the pilots retracted the landing gear instead of the flaps.

In more modern aircraft, the flap lever and the undercarriage lever are easily distinguishable, and are not placed side by side. The undercarriage (or 'gear', for landing gear) lever has a knob that resembles a wheel, and is moved up or down; the flap lever has a knob that resembles a flap, and may be moved through a series of slots to select the desired flap position.

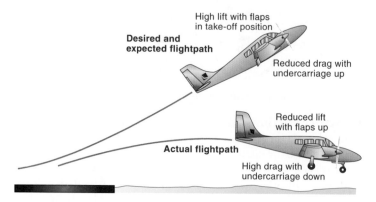

■ ✎ Figure 9-9 **Results of poor design leading pilots to misuse controls**

The use of logically associated symbols – such as a wheel for the undercarriage – both in controls and on displays, can help a pilot significantly.

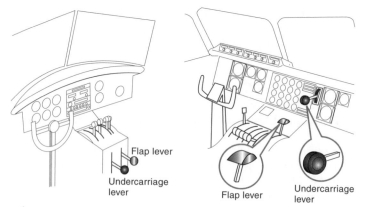

■ ✎ Figure 9-10 **Design – the old and the new**

NOTE Be very vigilant if flying a mixture of different aircraft that you do not confuse the controls of one with the controls of another. Some pilots fly several types on the one day.

Some cockpits are well designed to enable a pilot, having a limited number of hands and feet, to perform more than one function simultaneously. The rudder pedals, for instance, allow the pilot to move both the rudder and the nosewheel, and apply differential braking. Some advanced yokes, as well as controlling movement of the elevator and ailerons, allow a pilot (still using only the one hand) to operate the elevator trim control, a radio transmit button, or the autopilot disconnect button.

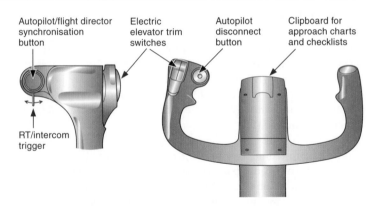

Autopilot/flight director synchronisation button

Electric elevator trim switches

Autopilot disconnect button

Clipboard for approach charts and checklists

RT/intercom trigger

■ ✎ Figure 9-11 **Simultaneous operation of various controls made easier by good design**

Design of Cockpit Displays

The function of cockpit displays (or instruments) is to pass information to the pilot. This information needs to be presented in a clear, unambiguous manner, where it can be easily seen. A well-designed display needs to be:

- **easily seen;**
- **placed in a logical position,** ideally near any associated control;
- **standardised;**
- **reliable,** and not prone to failure, but clearly indicating when it has failed;
- **easy to interpret** (and difficult to misinterpret).

These points will now be discussed with reference to flight instruments, engine instruments, and others, with comments on new developments which are helpful to pilots, and which we are now seeing in some basic training aeroplanes.

NOTE The coverage of cockpit displays includes some detail on more advanced features; whilst these are not examined in Private Pilot *Human Performance and Limitations,* the discussion is not complicated and will be of interest to many newer pilots who may be planning on making their career as professional pilots.

Standardisation of Displays

If particular displays are standardised in design and have a standard position in all cockpits, it helps a pilot. Of course this is not totally desirable if it rules out further development and improvement. We therefore have to expect some variations from the ideal.

The 'Basic-T' Layout of the Flight Instruments

In the old days, instruments were scattered around the cockpit, sometimes in a haphazard manner, as if providing information to the pilot was an afterthought. Critical instruments, such as the attitude indicator (AI), were placed in out-of-the-way positions, difficult to see and well away from associated instruments such as the airspeed indicator (ASI), the altimeter, and the compass or direction indicator (DI).

> The basic-T is standard.

It was a big advance when designers decided to arrange the main flight instruments in a standardised pattern, known as the *basic-T* pattern, on the panel in front of each pilot. The aim was to place the very important attitude indicator in a central position, since this is the instrument which pilots spend most time looking at. The other important flight instruments are placed to either side of and beneath the attitude indicator, forming a T-shape. Slightly less important flight instruments are placed diagonally beneath it.

■ ✎ *Figure 9-12* **Basic-T – old-style and new-style**

The Attitude Indicator

The attitude indicator (AI) is sometimes called the *artificial horizon* (AH) but in fact the AH is merely a component of the AI. It is a most important display, since it informs the pilot of pitch attitude and roll attitude relative to the horizon. It should therefore always occupy a central position on the instrument panel. It is an analogue (pictorial) display, showing the attitude of the wings and nose of the aeroplane relative to the horizon.

Often the sky above the horizon is represented by the colour blue, and the ground beneath the horizon by black or brown. Usually the blue of the sky is above the brown of the earth, indicating that the aeroplane is flying right side up. In a good instrument, the reverse would be the case if the aeroplane was inverted – and this can happen even in airliners, in extreme turbulence or following mishandling.

■ *Figure 9-13*

Attitude indicator

Less-than-perfect AIs topple when the angle of pitch or bank is too great, but a really good AI would give correct indications even when an aeroplane is in an unusual attitude. Unfortunately, many lives have been lost in the past when pilots have followed AIs that have toppled.

Modern instruments are more reliable, but never forget that indications from one instrument, if doubtful, can usually be confirmed or contradicted by indications from other instruments. Instrument-rated pilots will be familiar with the additional training that goes under the name of *limited panel*, which is necessary to cope with failure, complete or partial, of the primary flight instruments.

The same attitude information that is shown on a standard AI could be presented on a digital (numerical) display, but a pictorial representation of attitude seems to convey the information more efficiently and more quickly to a pilot than just numbers. 'P+3 R25L' is not as informative as a picture of the nose pitched 3° up, indicated by '**Pitch +3**', and the wings banked 25° to the left, indicated by '**Roll 25 left**'.

Analog display

Attitude indicator showing
3° pitch up, 25° left bank

Digital display

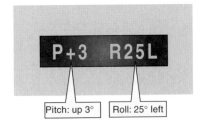

■ ✎ *Figure 9-14* **Analogue versus digital – which do you prefer?**

Personally, I prefer analogue displays, with one exception – the altimeter. There is more to follow on this shortly.

The AI is closely linked to the control column that the pilot uses to change pitch attitude and bank attitude, and so the AI is usually positioned directly in front of it. In normal flight, moving the control column back raises the nose; moving it to the left rolls the aeroplane to the left – movements relative to the horizon that are replicated on the AI. However, there are different AI designs that display the pitch and bank attitudes in quite different ways. It seems that once pilots get used to a certain attitude display, it is quite difficult to train them off it onto another.

On the standard AI, the artificial horizon moves, while the index aircraft remains fixed within the instrument. As the aircraft pitches up, the index aircraft and the AI dial move with it, and the artificial horizon moves down within the instrument to stay aligned (symbolically) with the real horizon. As it rolls from wings-level into a left bank, the index aircraft and the AI dial move with the real aircraft, and the artificial horizon remains horizontal in space and aligned with the real horizon. Bank angle can be determined from the angle that the wings of the model aircraft make with the artificial horizon, or from the bank pointer at the top of the instrument. The AI can be thought of as a porthole through which the attitude of the aircraft in relation to the horizon can be seen.

Know your instruments.

Unfortunately, even within the basic standard design of the AI there are variations. For instance, some designs of bank pointers give a clearer picture than others. Although we are used to a basic standard design of the AI, with its fixed index aircraft and moving artificial horizon, there are AIs in which the artificial horizon remains fixed in the instrument, and the model aircraft moves. This gives the pilot a view of the aircraft's attitude as if standing upright behind it as an observer.

In this instrument, however, the artificial horizon does not remain aligned with the real horizon in a banked turn, nor does the wing of the model aircraft remain aligned with the wing of the real aircraft. This sort of AI is common in Russian-designed aircraft, and the pilots like it. I have recently experienced the difficulties that pilots used to this instrument have had in converting onto standard Western AIs; this is very significant, considering how vital the AI is.

On other AIs, not only the model aeroplane moves, but also the artificial horizon – the index aeroplane moving quickly to indicate the change of attitude, and the horizon moving a little later to indicate the change of flightpath.

Most pilots seem to like the attitude indicator that they were trained on.

The AI is perhaps an instrument which may be replaced in the future, possibly by a predictive flightpath vector. At present, to determine the flightpath you have to integrate in your mind information obtained from the attitude indicator, the altimeter and VSI, the airspeed indicator and the direction (or heading) indicator – quite a task, as instrument trainees know.

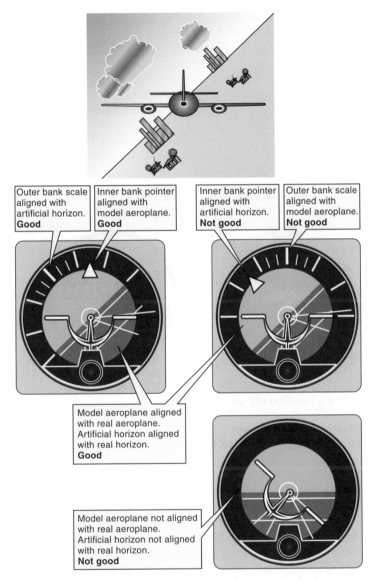

Outer bank scale aligned with artificial horizon. **Good**

Inner bank pointer aligned with model aeroplane. **Good**

Inner bank pointer aligned with artificial horizon. **Not good**

Outer bank scale aligned with model aeroplane. **Not good**

Model aeroplane aligned with real aeroplane. Artificial horizon aligned with real horizon. **Good**

Model aeroplane not aligned with real aeroplane. Artificial horizon not aligned with real horizon. **Not good**

■ ✎ Figure 9-15 **Differently designed AIs all displaying a 45-degree banked turn to the right**

Direction Indicators

The modern direction indicator (DI) (also called *heading indicator,* HI, *gyro horizon* or *directional gyro,* DG), which is placed directly beneath the attitude indicator in the basic-T layout, is an easy instrument to interpret and to use instinctively (or intuitively).

It is obvious to most pilots that to change heading from 360° to 340°, and further to 320°, a left turn is required. The desired heading is to the left of the current heading, both in reality and on the DI.

The direction indicator is based on a gyroscope which maintains its direction in space (ideally having been aligned with magnetic north by the pilot), and gives an accurate indication of heading during turns and accelerations.

Periodically check the alignment of the DI against the magnetic compass.

In contrast, the predecessor of the modern DI pictured in Figure 9-16, the original directional gyro (DG), was not an instinctive (or intuitive) instrument to use (Figure 9-17).

Turn left to take up heading 320°

Turn *left* to take up heading 320°; ... but indication of 320° is *right*

■ *Figure 9-16* **The modern DI is an easy instrument to use**

Figure 9-17 **The older DG display**

The Magnetic Compass

The magnetic compass is the *primary* heading reference in an aeroplane, therefore it is the magnetic compass, and not the DI, that initially provides us with the direction of magnetic north.

Why then do we not just use the magnetic compass for heading information, and do away with the DI? The reason is that, because of its design, the compass has certain indication errors, and also a non-instinctive relationship between its display and the necessary direction of turn to take up a new heading.

Indication errors will occur on the compass during any acceleration, deceleration or turning, with the degree of error being different on different headings, and reversed in the northern hemisphere compared with the southern hemisphere. Instrument pilots know the frustration of having to apply "undershoot when turning through north, overshoot when turning through south", by greater amounts at higher latitudes compared with lower latitudes near the equator, and then totally reversed when in the southern hemisphere. As if the pilot did not have enough to think about!

■ *Figure 9-18*
The magnetic compass
has a non-instinctive
display

The non-instinctive display of the magnetic compass derives from its construction, and the fact that the pilot is really viewing the compass card from behind, and not from ahead or above. The card remains oriented in space, and the pilot moves the aeroplane around it, the pilot's view being confined to viewing the most rearward face of the compass card.

On heading 360°, 340° will be to its *right* on the compass card, even though a *left* turn is required to take up heading 340°. This requires some thinking activity from the pilot if the intention is to turn in the correct direction – brain time that could perhaps be used on other problems.

Mental gymnastics are required from the pilot if wanting to turn in the correct direction (because of the non-instinctive display), and then roll out exactly on the correct heading (having allowed for turning errors during and shortly after the turn). For this reason, the usual technique of using the direction instruments is to:

• **allow the magnetic compass to settle down** in steady straight-and-level flight; then

• **align the DI with it,** and adjust heading according to the DI.

Modern instruments on some aircraft have direction indicators that *automatically* align with magnetic north, but in *all* aircraft, including the most sophisticated modern airliners, you will find an old-fashioned magnetic compass as a standby – it needs no power other than the earth's magnetic field, and has few moving parts that can fail.

Even though it is a simple instrument, the magnetic compass is difficult to use well, and pilots used to flying on the most modern glass instruments need practice to use the old, but faithful, magnetic compass (the same could be said of the practice needed to use the simple ADF well).

The Airspeed Indicator

Aerodynamic performance depends on indicated airspeed.

The airspeed indicator (ASI) displays the very important aerodynamic quantity *indicated airspeed* (IAS), upon which the flying capability of all aeroplanes depends. The pilot often needs to check IAS with a quick glance – for instance, when on approach to land – the indication must be clear and unambiguous.

Traditionally, IAS has been displayed on a circular dial, with the pointer moving clockwise to indicate an increasing airspeed, and anticlockwise to indicate a decreasing airspeed. Colour codes for various limiting airspeeds, such as maximum operating speed, stall speeds, and flap speed, are shown on the ASI, but only for maximum weight.

Some older ASIs may be graduated in mph or km/hr instead of the usual knots – always check this when flying a new aeroplane. Flying at 80 km/hr (50 knots) because you are used to seeing 80 knots in your familiar aeroplane could be dangerous.

Recent advances with 'glass' instruments (i.e. on small TV-like screens) have made it possible to display airspeed on a vertically oriented *speed tape* that moves behind a fixed pointer. Limiting speeds and advisory speeds can be shown on the electronic tape for the actual weight and configuration, such as flap limit speed, stall speed, and buffet boundary.

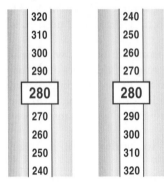
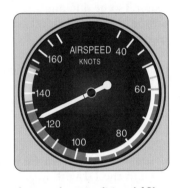

■ ✎ *Figure 9-19* **Two designs of the speed tape, plus a traditional ASI**

There is a design choice to be made with regard to the speed tape: should the high speeds be at the top of the tape (as would be traditional), or should the high speeds be at the bottom of the tape, encouraging a pilot to lower the nose of the aircraft to increase speed? Both designs are in use, even though a common standard would be preferable. It seems that pilots get used to the speed tape that they use consistently. Some older pilots even admit to referring to the traditional airspeed indicator that is often included in modern aircraft as a standby, and neglecting the tape.

A disadvantage of the speed tape is that the whole speed range is not always in view, but a compromise can be achieved in the glass cockpit by having vital speeds that are out of range printed above or below the tape until they come into view – for instance, the 'V₂' safety speed that is set for take-off by the pilot.

The Altimeter

The altimeter is a vital instrument, and misuse of it, by failing to set the correct pressure setting in the subscale or, more commonly, by failing to read its indications accurately, has led to many tragic accidents.

Setting Mean Sea Level Pressure (QNH)

With the current QNH pressure setting on the subscale, the altimeter reads altitude, the height above sea level (at least approximately). QNH is therefore the correct setting when operating at low altitudes where terrain could be a problem. It is set for take-off and landing, and when operating below what is called the transition altitude.

Setting the correct QNH is vital.

The mean sea level pressure varies from place to place, and from hour to hour, as pressure patterns move across the earth, so a pilot has to be aware of the current value of QNH, and have it set in the subscale, for the altimeter to provide good information.

Flying above the transition altitude, the standard pressure 1013.2 millibars (or hectopascals, hPa) – (or 29.92 inches of mercury in the USA) is set on the subscale (on the assumption that terrain is no longer a problem). Aircraft operating in the same airspace, however, need to have the same altimeter pressure setting to ensure vertical separation from one another. The level at which this change in pressure setting is made varies from country to country (3,000 feet at most UK aerodromes; 18,000 feet in the USA; 10,000 feet in Australia). Unless pilots are orderly and carry out consistent cross-checks, the wrong pressure can sometimes be set on the altimeter subscale, significantly reducing air safety for themselves and others.

In Figure 9-20, one pilot has 1013 mb set and is flying so that 11,000 feet (Flight Level 110) is indicated on the altimeter. The other pilot has mistakenly set 990 mb instead of 1013 mb, and is flying with 10,000 feet indicated on the altimeter. With 990 mb set instead of 1013 mb, this mistake of 23 mb will translate into a height indication error of $23 \times 30 = 690$ feet. He is 10,000 feet above the 990 mb pressure level, which means he is 10,690 feet above the 1013 mb pressure level. He *thinks* he is 1,000 feet below the first aircraft, but in fact is only 310 feet lower. This is a dangerous situation for both aircraft, and for the people on the ground beneath them!

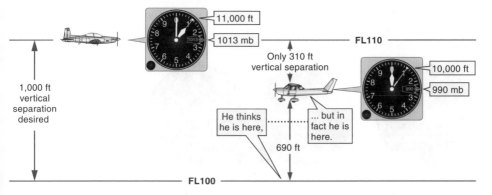

■ ✎ Figure 9-20 **Vertical separation compromised by an incorrectly set altimeter**

Flying a precision instrument approach to a decision height of 200 feet above ground level (agl) when the altimeter pressure window has not been reset from standard pressure 1013 to the current QNH could be lethal. If the QNH was in fact 1006, but this value had not been set in the pressure window, the altimeter would indicate 210 feet agl when in fact the aeroplane was **at** ground level (assuming 1 mb to be equivalent to 30 feet).

A pilot not becoming visual before reaching what is expected to be the decision height of 200 feet agl would most likely make unexpected contact with the ground. This potential for serious error must be addressed by each pilot, who must maintain adequate discipline and ensure that standard operating procedures are followed and checklists completed.

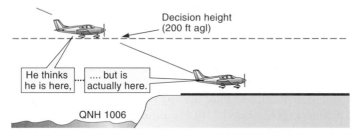

■ ✎ Figure 9-21 **Flying an ILS with an incorrect QNH set is dangerous**

Another aspect of the altimeter that can trap a pilot is caused by poor design on some instruments. We expect that clockwise rotation of a knob will bring an *increase* in the subscale reading, and that the scale bearing the pressure-setting numbers will move in the same direction as the nearest part of the knob. This is not the case for all altimeters – on some, a clockwise rotation of the knob brings a *decrease* in the pressure setting, something that many of us would consider a design weakness. Check your altimeter, and always check and recheck that you have the correct pressure setting for your current stage of flight.

Good design   Poor design

■ ✎ Figure 9-22 **Good and poor designs for the altimeter subscale and setting knob**

There has not been an altimeter designed that can automatically set the pressure subscale to 1013, or to current QNH, because of all the variations, but there are some devices that can help avoid altitude problems, such as:

- **the altitude alert system,** a light or sound that activates as you approach or depart a selected altitude, and that helps prevent incorrect altitudes being flown;
- **the radar altimeter,** or radio altimeter, and the associated *ground proximity warning system* (GPWS), that warn of impending ground contact;
- **the traffic alert and collision avoidance system (TCAS),** that shows potential conflicting traffic on your map display.

Reading or Misreading the Altimeter

Misreading the altimeter has led to many fatal accidents. Why should such a simple instrument as the altimeter be so dangerous? There is no doubt that the traditional three-pointer altimeter, whilst it works well technically, is often difficult to read correctly. Accidents caused by misreading it could be judged, at least to some extent, to be *design-induced errors*, even though the human pilot made the final mistake.

One safety magazine, in an attempt to improve the performance of pilots, showed a series of photographs of three-pointer altimeters, and challenged pilots to read them all correctly – and remember, just *one* mistake could be fatal! The pilot performance was not all that good, but the truly disturbing feature was that when the answers were published in the next issue of the magazine, some of them were wrong and had to be corrected. And these were answers that were prepared by people sitting in cosy offices and not in the cockpit of an aeroplane in flight. This is an indictment of the three-pointer altimeter!

Many errors have occurred with the 10,000-foot pointer – the altitude being misread by 10,000 feet or more – making it a particularly dangerous instrument for high-flying pilots descending in cloud or at night.

Know your instruments.

Some pilots have hit the ground at 3,000 feet when they thought that their altimeter was reading 13,000 feet – the altimeter was in fact reading 3,000 feet – they just did not know how to read it. It cannot be emphasised too much that any pilot who uses a three-pointer altimeter must really know how to use it – know which is the 10,000-foot pointer, which is the 1,000-foot pointer, and which is the 100-foot pointer – it is not obvious from the design.

A   B   C

■ ✎ *Figure 9-23* **Can you read these three-pointer altimeters?** *(Answers shown below.)*

NOTE On three-pointer altimeters, to assist pilots to know whether they are above or below 10,000 feet, designers incorporated a small striped sector which appears below the centre of the altimeter when the reading is less than 10,000 feet. This is labelled in Figure 9-24.

Some Better Designs

A *digital* altimeter read-out consisting only of numbers is a possibility. 13,430 feet is quite easy to read, and difficult to misread as 3,430 feet (as has occured with three-pointer *analogue* (pictorial) altimeters).

Disadvantages of a pure digital read-out, however, show up when climbing or descending; it is easier to judge the *rate* of altitude change from a moving pointer on an analogue altimeter than from a series of changing numbers on a digital read-out. It is also easier to maintain a constant altitude using a pointer and keeping it fixed rather than just by numbers!

Digital display   **Analogue display**   **Digital/analogue display**

10,000 ft sector that is striped when below 10,000 ft

■ ✎ *Figure 9-24* **The digital, analogue, and combined digital/analogue altimeter displays**

A well thought-out design improvement on older style altimeters was to keep the 100-foot pointer, where one complete rotation around the dial equals 1,000 feet, and to replace the 1,000-foot pointer and the 10,000-foot pointer with digits. This

---

Figure 9-23 **Altimeter A** *7,300 feet* **B** *2,900 feet* **C** *11,750 feet*

retains the advantage of the pointer for maintaining altitude or estimating rate of climb or descent, but removes the possibility of misreading altitude by 10,000 feet. This modification has resulted in a successful and easy-to-use instrument.

Instrument design is improving.

It is also possible to have a vertical altitude tape rather than the traditional altimeter dial, and this is often the case in 'glass' cockpits, with higher altitudes towards the top as is logical, and lower altitudes towards the bottom.

Rate-of-change of altitude can be judged by the speed at which the tape is moving behind the index mark (as well as from the VSI, of course), and *actual* altitude can be read from the numbers behind a pointer or displayed in an altitude box.

Important altitudes or flight levels, such as selected cruising level, can be displayed digitally above or below the tape as appropriate until it comes into range.

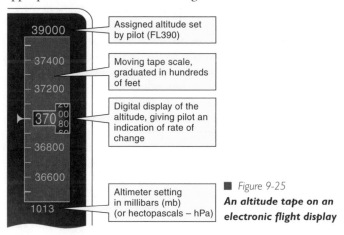

Assigned altitude set by pilot (FL390)

Moving tape scale, graduated in hundreds of feet

Digital display of the altitude, giving pilot an indication of rate of change

Altimeter setting in millibars (mb) (or hectopascals – hPa)

■ *Figure 9-25*
An altitude tape on an *electronic flight display*

The Vertical Speed Indicator

The typical VSI is an analogue display, with a pointer indicating rate of climb or descent against a static scale. On a glass display, the VSI may sometimes be associated with the altitude tape. It is easy to read, and has been a design success.

■ *Figure 9-26*
Traditional VSI display

The traditional VSI is operated by static pressure, but often lags or shows a move initially in the wrong direction when altitude is changed, before settling down and indicating correctly.

A small accelerometer removes the lag in modern instruments, known as the *instantaneous VSI* (IVSI).

Vertical speed indicators in very expensive airliners are operated, not by variations in static pressure, but by vertical accelerations measured by laser gyros.

The Turn Coordinator

The turn coordinator in most modern light aircraft shows the wings of an index aeroplane which can move only in a rolling sense, with the nose fixed. Whilst the real aeroplane is rolling into a turn, the wings of the index aeroplane move in the appropriate direction to indicate *rate of roll*.

Once the aeroplane is in a steady turn, the position of the wings indicates the *rate of turn*. The scale is marked with a '1' to indicate a rate-1 turn of 3°/second (360° in 2 minutes), and possibly with a '2' to indicate a rate-2 turn of 6°/second. Rate 1 is usual in instrument flying.

There is also an older instrument, the turn and slip indicator, which uses a 'bat' to indicate rate of turn – it does not indicate rate of roll.

The turn coordinator is an instinctive instrument for a pilot to use. It can be used in a turn to maintain the desired rate of turn – for instance, by keeping the indication on rate 1, and it can be used when straight-and-level to keep the wings of the real aeroplane level by not allowing any roll rate to develop, i.e. by keeping the wings of the turn coordinator's index aeroplane level, while keeping the balance ball centred. Normally, of course, the attitude indicator would be used for this purpose, but (on rare occasions) the AI has been known to fail. In such a situation, the turn coordinator is very useful.

■ *Figure 9-27*
The turn coordinator (top), and the older turn indicator

It is very important not to confuse the index aeroplane of the turn coordinator with the index aeroplane on the typical attitude indicator, which remains fixed while an artificial horizon moves behind it to give an indication of pitch attitude and roll attitude. To remind you of this, many turn coordinators are marked with the words 'no pitch indication', or something along these lines. Having to remind a pilot what the instrument does *not* do is a design weakness – any suggestions?

Know your instruments.

The coordination ball which is usually found with the turn coordinator is a simple pendulum-type indicator that lets a pilot know if the aeroplane is flying efficiently, with the tail following the nose, or if it is skidding or slipping. If the aeroplane is coordinated, or *balanced,* then the ball is in the centre. If not, it is out to one side, and the pilot can remedy this by applying same-side rudder pressure to centralise the ball.

Some instruments are simple and good.

The coordination ball is a very good and simple instrument, and is found in all aeroplanes, even the largest and most modern. These aeroplanes, however, may not have a turn coordinator, its functions having been taken over to some extent by a *flight director* incorporated into the attitude indicator.

The Flight Director

The flight director (FD), sometimes called the *flight director indicator* (FDI), is a device superimposed over the attitude indicator display to provide the pilot with guidance in pitch and bank attitude. It does not tell the pilot what the pitch and bank attitude is (which is the function of the underlying ADI), but what should be done with pitch and bank attitude to achieve the desired flightpath. It can therefore be used as a *predictive* instrument. By placing the aeroplane in this attitude, you should achieve the desired flightpath.

The flight director receives inputs from various sensors, and integrates them into a simple guidance indication for the pilot. Some features are automatic and the pilot can programme some in according to how it is desired to use the flight director. It can also be selected off, so that its symbology disappears from view and the basic attitude indicator remains.

Two typical designs of flight director are:
- **flying wings:** the pilot manoeuvres the aeroplane so that the index aeroplane on the ADI is tucked into the flying wings of the flight director; and
- **crossbars:** the pilot uses the controls to place the nose of the index aeroplane directly beneath the intersection of the two crossbars.

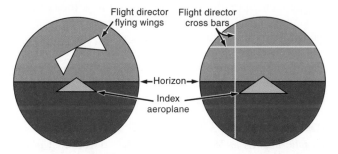

■ ✎ *Figure 9-28* **The two types of flight director presentations**

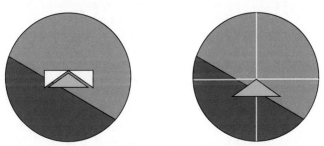

■ ✎ *Figure 9-29* **Instrument indications when the pilot has positioned the aeroplane attitude according to the flight director commands**

The flight director commands as shown in Figures 9-28 and 9-29 could be for an entry to a climbing left turn. How the instrument responds to the pilot (or autopilot) control input depends upon its design but, in the typical ADI found in most aeroplanes, the index aeroplane remains fixed in the ADI and the artificial horizon moves to remain aligned with the real horizon outside. The flight director command indicator moves within the instrument and, when the pilot has achieved the commanded pitch and bank attitude, it then overlies the index aeroplane.

The pilot can usually programme the flight director indicator to provide many types of commands, as desired, such as:

- **maintain or change heading** (by connecting the flight director to a bug on the direction indicator which the pilot can move);
- **maintain or achieve a selected airspeed** (by connecting the flight director to the airspeed system);
- **maintain altitude,** or achieve a selected rate of climb or descent (by connecting the flight director to the altitude system); and
- **maintain a localiser track and a glideslope** (by linking the flight director to the electronic *instrument landing system,* ILS).

Modern flight directors are so good that a pilot can easily become dependent upon them, but, like everything, they can fail. Many strenuous flight simulator exercises have resulted from the simulated failure of the flight director. As a result, the pilot has to revert to basic instrument attitude flying, using the basic AI and other flight instruments, and the basic radio navigation instruments, instead of relying on the flight director. This is known as flying on *raw data.*

> Be prepared to revert to basic instruments.

The ADF and the RMI
The *automatic direction finder* (ADF) is simply a needle that points towards a ground-based *non-directional beacon* (NDB). Older style ADFs have a fixed card to indicate relative bearing to the NDB, such as 30° left of the nose; this meant that a pilot had to use the direction indicator (or magnetic compass) in conjunction with the ADF if wanting to intercept and maintain a particular track to or from an NDB. Mental gymnastics were required, especially in strong winds when drift became a factor.

A major design advance was made when the two instruments, the ADF and the DI, were combined, with the ADF pointer (or pointers in a twin-ADF installation) now placed over a compass card. This instrument is called the *radio magnetic indicator* (RMI). An earlier version has the ADF pointer backed by a manually rotatable card and aligned with the compass or direction indicator.

> Combining instruments sometimes improves them.

The RMI combines the ADF and DI. Another improvement for the instrument pilot is the ability to select either needle of the RMI to point to a VOR station tuned on the VHF-NAV. This enables the pilot to have a better idea of the position in relation to a VOR without having to alter the course selection on the VOR display itself. The tail of the RMI needle indicates the aircraft's radial from the VOR, irrespective of the aircraft's heading.

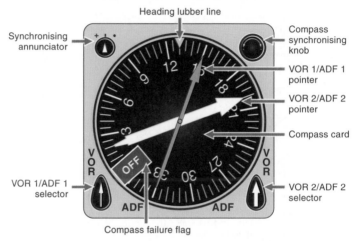

Heading lubber line

Synchronising annunciator

Compass synchronising knob

VOR 1/ADF 1 pointer

VOR 2/ADF 2 pointer

Compass card

VOR 1/ADF 1 selector

VOR 2/ADF 2 selector

Compass failure flag

■ ✎ *Figure 9-30* **A 'two-needle' radio magnetic indicator**

Two illustrations on page 178 show tracking to an NDB on a simple ADF indicator (Figure 9-32) and on an RMI (Figure 9-33).

The VOR and the HSI

2 dots right of the 062 radial from the tuned VOR station (no heading information)

■ *Figure 9-31*
The early VOR display, or course deviation indicator

The original VOR display that almost every pilot uses shows angular deviation from a selected VOR radial, but it is *not* heading sensitive. If you have the inbound course selected on the *omni bearing selector* (OBS), and you are flying inbound to the radio beacon on a heading close to that track, the course deviation information from the aid is instinctive.

Similarly, if you have an outbound course (known as a *radial)* selected, and you are flying outbound from the beacon on a heading close to that course, the information is again instinctive. If these conditions are not met, the older style VOR, while still being usable, is confusing to a beginner because it is not instinctive, i.e. CDI needle left – so course is left.

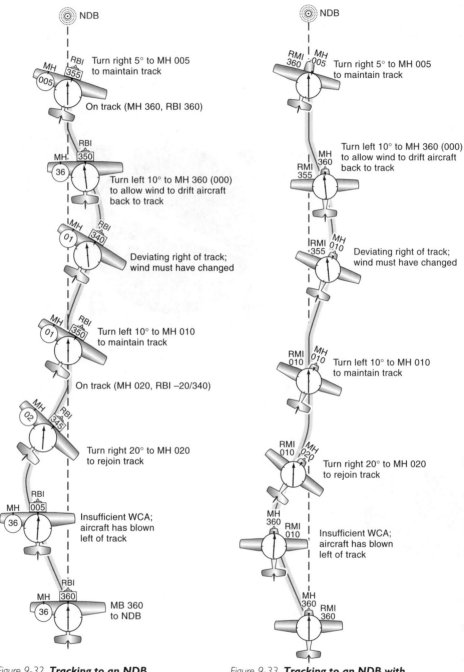

Figure 9-32 **Tracking to an NDB with a fixed-card ADF and DI**

Figure 9-33 **Tracking to an NDB with an RMI**

The HSI combines the VOR and DI.

A big design advance was made when the VOR display was superimposed upon the direction indicator, the new instrument being called a *horizontal situation indicator* (HSI). This means that the VOR display is a command instrument at all times, and the graphic design of the HSI makes it a very good instrument. As well as VORs, you can also select ILSs onto the HSI, and a glideslope needle will appear as well as the course bar. (When flying an ILS, you also use the marker lights and sounds to check the glideslope altitude at particular points along the localiser track.)

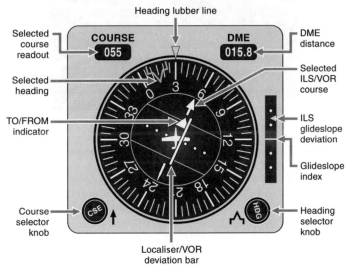

Heading lubber line

Selected course readout
COURSE
055
DME
015.8
DME distance

Selected heading
Selected ILS/VOR course

TO/FROM indicator
ILS glideslope deviation

Glideslope index

Course selector knob
Heading selector knob

Localiser/VOR deviation bar

■ ✎ *Figure 9-34* **A horizontal situation indicator**

Modern navigation displays in 'glass' cockpits usually can be switched into a VOR or ILS mode for instrument approaches, with the familiar HSI design appearing – proof that it is a design success.

The 'Glass' Navigation Display

Electronic flight instrument systems (EFIS) are usually two small computer monitors that display attitude and navigation information.

Map displays make visualisation easy.

The navigation display can be used in various modes, including VOR and ILS, but is generally operated in MAP mode whilst en route. In this mode, it shows the programmed route between waypoints in magenta, the track being made good in white (which should overlay the desired route), the heading, and the wind. Some displays are *heading-up* (with the direction of the nose of the aeroplane at the top), others are *track-up* (with the direction of travel relative to the ground at the top).

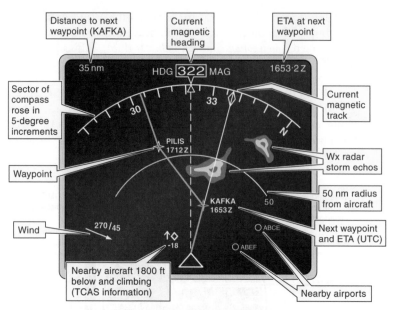

■ ✎ *Figure 9-35* **Example of an electronic navigation display**

Many other items can be brought up if desired, including nearby adequate airports, VORs, ETAs at waypoints, a weather radar display, and TCAS information (potential collision threats detected by the *traffic alert and collision avoidance system)*. Predictions of horizontal (turning) performance and vertical (climb or descent) performance can also be displayed, as shown in Figure 9-36.

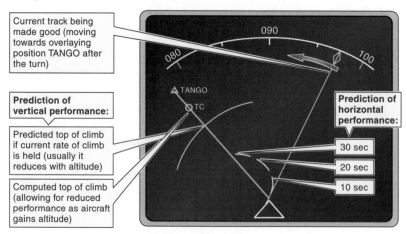

■ ✎ *Figure 9-36* **Predictions on the navigation display**

Head-Up Displays

A head-up display (HUD) is an instrument display that is projected ahead of the pilot so that instrument indications can be read while viewing through the windscreen. This is in contrast to the conventional head-down display, where the instruments are down on a panel, forcing the pilot to direct the eyes downwards from the windscreen to read them.

HUDs generally use a transparent screen, or block of transparent material, placed between the pilot's eyes and the cockpit window onto which images are projected to indicate various flight parameters to the pilot, such as airspeed, attitude, altitude and rate of change of altitude.

The original idea was to focus the images at infinity, on the basis that this was the natural focal length of the eyes as they looked out of the window (a faulty assumption), so that refocusing to read the instruments was not necessary.

There have been problems with HUDs, such as affecting the natural focal length of the resting eyes (which is much closer than infinity) and causing distortions of the outside view, as well as with finding suitable symbology to represent clearly the flight parameters.

HUDs are good, but not yet generally used.

Most applications for HUDs are in military aeroplanes, but a French civil airline has used them for many years with great success in achieving landings in very limiting meteorological conditions of low cloud and poor visibility. Similar success is now being achieved by conventional head-down instruments with good autopilots capable of performing autolands and roll-outs, and this seems to be the current trend. HUDs, however, have now been included in the B787 Dreamliner.

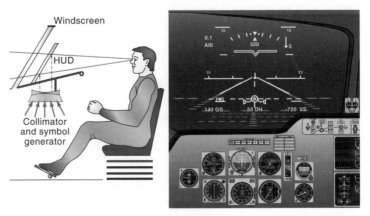

■ ✎ Figure 9-37 **A head-up display (HUD)**

Cockpit Checklists

Checklists are a vital part of modern day operation. In the old days, it was possible to commit to memory the few checks that were needed, including normal checks, such as the *Pre-Take-Off* and *Pre-Landing* checks, as well as *Emergency* checks to cope with engine fires and other emergencies. Nowadays, the complexities of aircraft, as well as the fairly intense operating environment and the ever-changing crew members, make checklists very important. Having a good checklist to assist in performing a certain task should reduce the difficulty of that task.

Humans are often better at remembering the generalities whilst forgetting the particulars. It is easier to remember the general rule to do the *Downwind* checklist on the downwind leg than it is to remember the particular items on the Downwind checklist for that particular aeroplane type.

Checklists ensure that the particulars are indeed actioned. In some drills, forgetting one item can have very serious consequences, both in emergency checklists and in normal operating checklists. For instance, some years ago an aircraft was destroyed because fuel was not cut off to a burning engine as the checklist required; and more than one aeroplane has landed wheels-up because the *'gear down'* item on the Final Approach or Pre-Landing checklist was not actioned.

Checklists are vital.

Checklists, if properly used, ensure that particular items are not missed.

One human characteristic that we need to guard against when using checklists is not to see what we want to see, but to **see what really exists.** For instance, with the *'gear down'* or *'wheels down'* call, we all want to see three green lights to confirm normal operation. On occasions, pilots have been known to respond, "Three greens", when in fact that was not the case, resulting in an unwanted wheels-up landing. Never respond to a checklist item automatically; always consider your response before giving it, even if it is an everyday, routine checklist that you are completing.

Actually check your response.

Another human failing with checklists is to skip items accidentally. This can happen with written checklists if you let your finger slip past one or two of the items – easy to do especially if the checklist is interrupted. It is good airmanship *not* to interrupt checklists unless absolutely unavoidable – this often requires cockpit discipline.

Do not interrupt checklists, or skip items.

For maximum efficiency, checklists should be:
- **easily found and easily read;**
- **concise; and**
- **very clear.**

All checklists should be located handily. Many checklists are contained in booklets or on cards located conveniently in the cockpit. Often, normal checklists are placed on a plate attached to the control column, allowing the pilot(s) to use them with very little distraction from instrument monitoring and scanning outside. Other aircraft have checklists that can be raised from the coaming panel, with small plates that can be moved across or down to cover the items as they are actioned.

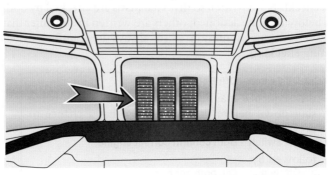

■ ✎ Figure 9-38 **Checklists should be accessible**

Checklist booklets should have thumb tabs alongside the index to simplify and speed up location of the precise checklist, bearing in mind that you might have to do this in a smoke-filled cockpit or in extreme turbulence (or both). Some aircraft also have electronic checklists that can be displayed on a screen, but this is often backed up by a conventional written checklist in case of electrical failure.

Some good and bad examples follow. These are taken from a multi-crew cockpit where one pilot monitors the action of the other. In a single-pilot cockpit, you have to monitor your own actions.

Checklists should be very easy to read. This means large, clear lettering, but not necessarily capital letters, as these are often more difficult to read than lower case.

Checklists should be written so that the meaning of each item is very clear, not only in the challenge, but also in response. Challenge-and-response checklists are one of the foundations of the well-functioning multi-crew cockpit. Some vital items need the response of both pilots, sometimes before the action is taken. Good checklists are written so that vital items are checked by both pilots before they are actioned; others are written in a manner that can lead to some confusion – so always be cautious when actioning checklists.

Checklists must be clear.

Fuel Cut-Off Switch – Off; Both – Confirm
- this sequence may lead to the wrong engine being shut down before the second pilot has a chance to prevent it; whereas:

Fuel Cut-Off Switch – Both confirm correct engine
- followed by:

Fuel Cut-Off Switch – Off, both confirm
- could prevent this.

■ ✎ *Figure 9-39* **Checklists need careful attention**

Fire Switch – *Pull* or, not as good: **FIRE SWITCH *PULL***

■ ✎ *Figure 9-40* **Checklist items should be easy to read**

It is important also that the items on a checklist are concise, something which is usually achieved by having short, sharp challenges with short responses. Long explanations of the 'whys and wherefores' should be confined to other documents which the pilot can read at leisure, such as in the aeroplane flight manual. These explanations are important so that the pilot understands the logic underlying the checklist, but in the cockpit, say during an emergency, is not the time to read through this information for the first time – the well-trained pilot will have read through it during initial training, and at periodic intervals thereafter.

Checklists must be concise.

The Scan Approach to Checklists

Many operators complete a check in two stages:
- **a scan** where the eyes and hands follow a flow pattern around the cockpit, noting and actioning the appropriate items; then
- **reading** the checklist to verify the items.

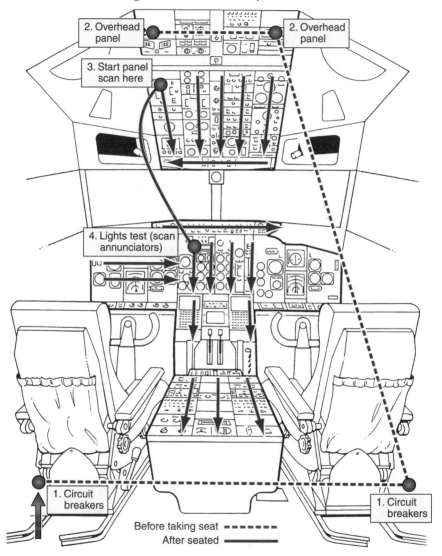

■ ✎ *Figure 9-41* **A scan pattern for the initial acceptance check (Boeing 737), which would be followed by completion of the appropriate checklist**

Manuals

Most of the information that a pilot needs to operate the
aeroplane is found in a manual. A common problem in even the
newest manuals, however, is that the information is often difficult
to find, is often spread around various parts of the manual, and is
often written in engineering terms. Bearing in mind these
difficulties, it is vital that a pilot becomes familiar with the
manuals for the aircraft type.

Know your manuals.

The requirements for a good manual, or set of manuals, are
similar to the requirements for a good checklist, other than that
there is no need for a manual to be concise. The manual is the
place for clear and full explanations and additional information,
both for new pilots and for experienced pilots, whereas the
checklist is a challenge-and-response action list for the qualified
pilot. For maximum effect, manuals should be:

- easily found;
- easily read; and
- very clear.

Standard Operating Procedures

In a multi-crew situation, each member of the crew should know
what the others are doing, or what they should be doing. This
means that the *standard operating procedures (SOPs)* specified by the
company should be adhered to whenever possible, which is
generally pretty well all of the time. This is not to say that pilots
are locked into a totally rigid system, but rather that they
participate in an easily controllable operation with no sudden
unexpected happenings.

*Adhere to standard
operating procedures.*

Most airline operators have a way out for pilots to improvise if
they feel they need to, often by using words such as "Non-
standard, I intend doing ....", which may be a slightly unusual
visual pattern to avoid a known area of turbulence, or it could be
a faster and steeper descent to circuit altitude to make up time, and
so on. The main thing is that each pilot knows what the other has
in mind before it actually happens.

External Visual Aids

There are many external visual aids designed to assist the pilot,
some which do so admirably, and others which are less successful.
Typical external visual aids are:

- taxiway and runway markings and lighting;
- wind direction indicators;
- aerodrome beacons;
- approach slope aids;
- parking aids;
- aerodrome notices and signs.

Aerodrome Notices and Signs

Know your signs.

Signs should be large, with colour or lighting being used to distinguish them. Often they will use contrasting colours, such as black against a yellow background, for good contrast. Typical signs include: runway entry points (e.g. **Runway 27 Taxiway G**), parking positions (e.g. **B23**), or taxi guidance information (e.g. **Runway 27 ↑**, and **Taxiway F →**).

Taxiway Markings and Lighting

Taxiway markings usually consist of yellow painted lines (as against white painted lines on runways), with the yellow standing out well against the dark bitumen of the taxiway, but maybe not quite so well against the white of a concrete taxiway. Dashed lines mean you can cross, full lines generally mean you should not cross without some prior thought (e.g. obtain a clearance to enter a runway).

Know your taxiway and runway markings.

The markings may be used to show the extent of the taxiway so that you do not allow the wheels of the aircraft to roll onto a soft surface, or they may run along the centre of the taxiway as guidelines for a pilot, which is particularly useful when manoeuvring large aeroplanes around corners or into a parking position; this is accomplished by keeping the lines beneath the pilot's eyes – the lines being positioned so that the aeroplane's wheels follow a safe path.

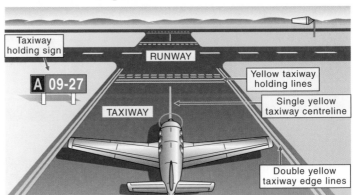

■ ✎ Figure 9-42 **Taxiway markings**

Taxiway lighting usually consists of either blue sideline lights, green centreline lights, or a mixture of both.

Know your taxiway and runway lighting.

With a complicated network of taxiways – for instance, at a large international airport – the pattern of blue lights seen from an angle may appear quite confusing, and you need to taxi slowly and check that you are indeed going between the intended two rows of blue lights.

Green centreline lights are in general easier to follow – just keep your eyes above them and the wheels should follow a safe path. Limits should be shown by red or amber lights, or well-lit signs.

■ ✎ Figure 9-43 **Taxiway lighting**

Now complete: **Practice Questions - The Flight Deck**

1. The question of ergonomics:

(a) *Describes the size of the area in which the pilot sits.*

(b) *Is the way that the environment is designed so that the pilot can act efficiently when operating the aeroplane.*

(c) *Is how the design of aeroplanes has evolved over time.*

(d) *Is the way the control wheel moves the flight controls.*

2. Design of fuel system controls:

(a) *Varies from aircraft to aircraft and a pilot should know his aeroplane design.*

(b) *Is common on any type of aeroplane to avoid accidental misuse.*

(c) *The 'Thin End' of the fuel lever shows the active part of the system that is selected.*

(d) *Is always designed the same way by each manufacturer.*

3. Design of controls:

(a) *Controls have always been shaped to help identify their function.*

(b) *Have evolved and shaped as a result of misuse.*

(c) *Are such that error is not possible.*

(d) *Have not reached the stage that improvement is not possible.*

4. Cockpit displays:

(a) *Vary from aircraft to aircraft and a pilot should know his aeroplane design.*

(b) *Design alters depending on the intended use of the aeroplane.*

(c) *Are always designed/laid out the same way by each manufacturer.*

(d) *The main 'Attitude Indicator' is central to the instrument panel and manufacturers lay out instruments depending on the intended use of the aeroplane.*

5. With reference to the design of the altimeter:

(a) *The design of the altimeter setting subscale has improved following accidents relating to mis-setting.*

(b) *Altimeter design has improved to such a degree that is is not possible to mis-set them.*

(c) *Have now reached the stage that design cannot be improved.*

(d) *Do not alter between manufacturers.*

Section **Two**

Safety, First Aid and **Survival**

Chapter 10

Safety and Care of Passengers 193

Chapter 11

First Aid 207

Chapter 12

Survival 215

Safety and Care of Passengers

The pilot is responsible for the safety of the aircraft and its passengers. As well as being properly prepared for the flight, the pilot must also ensure that the passengers are adequately briefed on safety matters.

Pilot Awareness

Passengers must have confidence in their pilot, and you, as pilot-in-command, can generate this. Passengers will feel more comfortable and less anxious if you, as their pilot and with their lives in your hands for the next few hours, are professional and confident both in your appearance and as you go about your duties. A scruffy looking pilot, running late, and agitated, will not inspire confidence; a well-dressed, well-organised pilot will.

No matter who the passengers are (parents or prime ministers), the pilot is in command during the flight, and the responsibilities of command begin well before the flight. Be aware of this, and conduct yourself in a manner that will inspire confidence.

As pilot-in-command, you are in command.

The normal order of authority may have to change during this period. A person who has authority on the ground, whether a parent or the boss or some dominant person, must subject himself or herself to the authority of the pilot-in-command once a flight commences – and a flight commences well before the aeroplane takes off. In reality, the sense of already being under way may commence much earlier, during the flight planning stages the night before, or on the drive to the airport.

It is important for you to be aware of this, and to assume the mantle of command right from the beginning, no matter how young or inexperienced you are. Passenger safety and the feeling of well-being should commence a long time before the flight.

Flight plan carefully.

Advise your passengers that you will need ten minutes without interruption to consider the weather forecasts and the other paperwork. They will respect this, and feel much better than if their proposed pilot bent to their every whim and did not pay attention to the other duties. Passengers will be aware of how you consider the preflight information and reach your 'go/no-go' decision; you should do this carefully, efficiently, and confidently. You should set the pace.

Prior to Boarding

As pilot you should inform the passengers that at various times throughout the flight you will have important duties to perform which will require your full attention. For this reason, you may occasionally request that there be no interruptions and no excessive conversation during the periods while you are concentrating on 'vital actions'.

Correct clothing is important to passenger comfort. Most aircraft cabins can be kept warm (or cool) in flight. Overcoats and other very heavy clothing need not be worn, although they should remain accessible in the event of an emergency evacuation. Passengers are forbidden to fly when drunk and should not fly if sick or affected by an upper respiratory complaint such as a cold.

Pressure changes will occur as the aeroplane climbs and descends and, if the ears do not automatically adjust, chewing, yawning or holding the nose whilst blowing with a closed mouth may assist. Blocked nasal passages can hinder this process. The higher noise level and possible turbulence may be a little disconcerting. Passengers should be reminded that there are no toilet facilities on board.

Baggage should be checked to ensure that it is not overweight and does not contain dangerous goods such as aerosol cans, pressurised cigarette lighters and matches, none of which should be carried.

Always check baggage.

It is inadvisable to smoke or have any naked flame near aircraft, especially if refuelling is in progress. Normally, passengers should remain well away from the aeroplane as a precaution while refuelling is in progress, since the fire risk is somewhat greater. It is advisable to wash your hands after refuelling because the smell of fuel or oil, or indeed any other unpleasant smells, in the cockpit can be annoying.

Passengers should be warned to remain well clear of propellers, since even a stationary propeller can spring to life, and a rotating propeller may hardly be visible. For this reason, children must be very closely supervised. The safest approach to an aeroplane is from the left and behind with passengers remaining in a single group under the supervision of the pilot.

Supervise your passengers.

Various attachments on the aeroplane, such as the pitot tube and radio aerials, are fragile and should not be used for support. Care should be taken when entering the aeroplane not to step where the wing or any part of the aeroplane structure could be damaged.

Preflight Check of Emergency Equipment

A vital part of any preflight check by the pilot is to ensure that the required emergency equipment is on board and serviceable. The emergency equipment carried will of course vary according to the nature of the flight about to be undertaken, the requirements for a trip across the Sahara being different from those for a trip over northern waters in the middle of winter.

Check emergency equipment.

The basic emergency equipment, such as emergency checklists and safety belts, will of course be on board at all times. Additional emergency equipment carried may include such items as a torch, fire extinguisher, emergency locator transmitter (ELT), life-jackets and life-raft for long overwater flights, survival kits, emergency flares, first-aid kit, and so on.

On Board

Make your passengers comfortable.

Ensure that your passengers are comfortably seated and confirm that the front-seat passenger will not restrict full movement of any control with bags, cameras or legs. Any metallic or magnetic objects should be stored well away from the magnetic compass.

Seat-belts will consist of a lap-strap and sometimes a shoulder harness. The lap-strap should be fastened and adjusted until it is firm but comfortable, followed by the shoulder harness if one is fitted. The passengers must be shown how to fasten, adjust and release their seat-belts.

The passengers should know how to close, lock and then open the **doors and windows** or canopy. Once a door is closed by the pilot, the position of the lock and handle should not be altered.

Aircraft cabins can become stuffy, so ensure that there is **adequate ventilation** and each passenger knows how to adjust the appropriate vent to maximise personal comfort.

The **intercom,** if one is to be used, should be explained. The radio volume should be adjusted to a comfortable level.

Passengers need not be passive, but can actively assist in some aspects of flight, such as maintaining a good **look out** for other aircraft and for landmarks.

Passenger Briefing

An important duty in taking care of your passengers is to brief them on the use of their safety belts, and on any relevant emergency procedures. This would form the basis of your standard passenger briefing. Additional items could be added to this standard briefing when appropriate.

Brief your passengers professionally.

If about to fly over an expanse of water, for instance, you would include in your briefing an explanation of how to don the life-jackets. If the expanse of water was great enough for you to be carrying a life-raft, then you would also brief on how to remove the raft from its pack and inflate it, making sure it does not drift away from the aircraft. If you were about to fly at high altitudes, you would also brief on the use of the supplemental oxygen system.

If you give the briefing in a friendly but confident manner, the passengers will be impressed by your professionalism, and be more relaxed. **A typical standard briefing follows.**

STANDARD PASSENGER BRIEFING

Seat-Belts

Remove any sharp articles from your pockets (such as keys, pocket knives, nail files, cigarette lighters).

Position your seat and ensure it is locked in position so that it cannot move.

To fasten your seat-belt, lengthen the strap if necessary, insert the belt link into the belt buckle, and tighten the belt by pulling the free end until you have a snug fit across your hips. If it is too tight, you will be uncomfortable; if it is too loose you may not be held firmly enough in your seat if we meet unexpected turbulence.

To release your seat-belt, pull upward on the top of the buckle.

The shoulder harness can also be fitted into the buckle. It has an inertia reel that allows you lean forward, but will lock you firmly in position with any sudden deceleration.

Your seat-belt must be fastened for every take-off and landing, but I recommend that it remain fastened throughout the flight.

Emergency Exits

In the rare event of having to leave the aircraft quickly, the exit to use is _____.

Move away from the aircraft, and keep well clear of the propeller at all times.

Smoking

You must not smoke on the tarmac area, nor during take-off or landing. I would prefer no smoking in flight, because we also have non-smokers aboard and because it introduces the unnecessary risk of fire.

Radio

If you wish to listen in to the flight radio, we can use the cockpit speaker or you may use a headset which should make the communications clearer. The volume control is here _____, and we can also use the intercom (test if possible).

Planned Route

We will taxi out and use Runway _____, which means a take-off into the (N, S, E or W), followed by a (right/left) turn.

We will be tracking overhead _____ and _____ to our destination _____.

The weather we expect en route is (good/may be a little bumpy).

STANDARD PASSENGER BRIEFING

Doors, Windows and Ventilation

Ensure your seat-belt is not hanging out, then close the door firmly and lock it.

The window may be open for additional ventilation while taxiing.

Normal vents are located _____, and you can adjust them by _____.

If you happen to feel unwell in flight, which I do not expect to be the case, advise me early on so that I can try to avoid bumpy areas or tight manoeuvres.

Now we are ready for engine start and radio communication.

End of passenger briefing.

Keep your passengers informed.

If you change your plans in flight, or if you have to carry out any unusual manoeuvres, then a quick briefing to your passengers will put them at ease.

Handicapped passengers may need special attention, and a modified briefing to explain how they should leave the aeroplane in the case of an evacuation.

Life-Jackets

Before flying over any expanse of water (e.g. the English Channel) in a single-engined aircraft, all occupants should don life-jackets. There are various types and the pilot must be familiar with their use. Most life-jackets are designed to be worn uninflated inside the aeroplane so that their bulk is minimised, both for comfort and for ease of departing the cabin.

The pilot should explain how to don the life-jacket, which is usually by fitting it over your head with the main part of the jacket in front of your body, then passing the straps around your back and tying them in front. Some jackets may require a different fitting technique for children.

Passenger knowledge of life-jackets is necessary for overwater flights.

The passenger must understand how to inflate the life-jacket and use any attached items such as a light or whistle. It should be emphasised that it is best to inflate the life-jacket *after* having exited from the cabin so that the evacuation is unhindered.

Inflation is generally achieved by pulling a release on a small gas cylinder attached to the front of the life-jacket. If the gas pressure provides insufficient inflation, there is a tube through which the passenger can blow and further inflate the life-jacket.

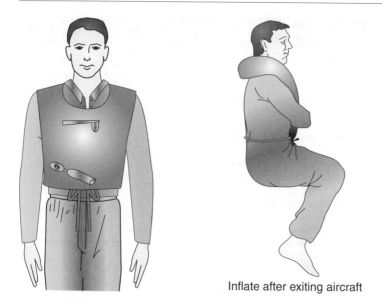

Inflate after exiting aircraft

■ ✎ Figure 10-1 **Follow the instructions in use of a life-jacket**

Life-Rafts

Immersion in the seas surrounding the UK could result in death within a few hours – within a few minutes in extreme temperatures and winds. Whilst life-jackets are useful for flotation, they will not protect the body from icy water. For this reason, it is prudent, on overwater journeys, to carry a life-raft in which the occupants can be sheltered from exposure and remain fairly dry.

If you carry a life-raft, know how to use it.

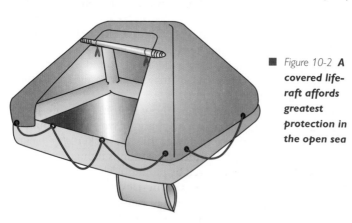

■ Figure 10-2 **A covered life-raft affords greatest protection in the open sea**

Most life-rafts suitable for light aircraft are stored in a small bag and weigh 10–15 kg. The raft must be inflated outside the aircraft, usually by removing it from its bag, ensuring that its cord is firmly held and placing or throwing the uninflated raft into the water. It may be advisable to swim a short distance from the aircraft before inflating the life-raft to avoid any danger of holing it.

Pulling the release cord should then activate the gas cylinder and inflate the raft. A sea anchor (bucket) can be used to prevent the raft drifting too far from the aircraft, which will assist in the search.

The raft will have associated equipment such as paddles, a canopy (very important in minimising exposure) ropes, knife, dyes, flares, light, first-aid kit and possibly emergency rations.

If necessary because of space constraints (and for faster evacuation of the aircraft), passengers should be instructed not to take luggage with them into the raft.

The Air Navigation Order (ANO), Schedule 6, Scale K lists the equipment that a life-raft should contain.

Oxygen Equipment

For high-altitude flights, brief your passengers on oxygen masks.

If you are going to be flying at high cabin altitudes, then the passengers should be briefed on the use of the on-board oxygen equipment. This will involve instructions on:

- **removing** fatty materials from facial areas exposed to the oxygen (such as face cream or cosmetics) since they could be combustible;
- **no smoking** when oxygen is being used because of the risk of combustion;
- **how to don the mask** and achieve a satisfactory oxygen flow; and
- **the time of useful consciousness,** which is only a few seconds at very high cabin altitudes, but longer at lower cabin altitudes.

The use of oxygen should be considered at cabin altitudes over 10,000 feet.

Fire

Fire is a hazard to aviation and is to be avoided at all costs. Three things are necessary for a fire to occur:

- **a fuel** (e.g. Avgas, oil, papers, fabric, cabin seating, etc.);
- **oxygen** (present in the air);
- **a source of ignition** (cigarettes, matches, electrical sparks, etc.), but bear in mind that once a fire is burning it is itself a source of ignition.

Prevent fires.

Prevention is by far the best cure, and pilots are advised to pay attention to items and situations that are a potential cause of, or contributor to, fire. Any possible **fuel** and any possible source of **ignition** should be kept separate. For example, when refuelling ensure that no person is smoking in the vicinity, that the aeroplane and refuelling equipment are adequately grounded to avoid the possibility of a static electricity build-up causing a spark, and that no fuel is spilled. As a precaution when refuelling, a suitable fire extinguisher should be readily available.

In flight, if the pilot permits any passenger to smoke, then he must ensure that no hot ash or cigarette butt comes in contact with papers or even the cabin seating, which may smoulder or burn, possibly unnoticed for some time.

Cigarettes can cause fires.

The risk of fire, as well as the detrimental effects of carbon monoxide in the blood, is another reason to discourage smoking in aircraft.

Cockpit fires can also be caused by faulty electrical circuits, which can often be recognised by a peculiar smell. Further development of an electrical fire may be prevented by switching off the electrical power (master switch OFF, or pulling the appropriate circuit breaker).

Extinguishing a Fire

The usual method of extinguishing a fire once it is burning is to eliminate one or more of these items (fuel, oxygen, source of ignition), e.g. blanketing a fire with dry chemical from a fire extinguisher to starve the fire of oxygen. If it appears that a fire has not yet started but is imminent, and the fuel and ignition source cannot be separated, it may be advisable to starve the area of oxygen by using an extinguisher.

Extinguish any fire quickly.

Fire Extinguishers

The CAA requires that Public Transport aircraft carry fire extinguishers; however, for Private Category aeroplanes this is only a recommendation and not a requirement.

Know your fire extinguishers.

Many light aircraft are indeed fitted with a small fire extinguisher that is securely stowed where the pilot may reach it in flight. The usual extinguishants contained in these are BCF (halon) and dry chemical, both of which are capable of handling most types of fires. Other extinguishants in use include carbon dioxide, water and foam.

Paper, wood, textiles

There is a standard graphic code and/or colour to differentiate between the suitability of fire extinguishers in fighting certain types of fire, and this is usually displayed on the extinguisher with an indication of its suitability for the specific categories.

Inflammable liquids & gases

Typically, a stored gas pressure discharges the extinguishant when a trigger is pressed. Each particular brand of fire extinguisher may have special requirements (such as to break a seal by twisting a handle, or by releasing a handle, or by breaking a lockwire), so the pilot should read the instructions and become familiar with the extinguisher that he might have to use at short

Live electrical equipment

■ *Figure 10-3*

Graphic code in use on many fire extinguishers

notice. Some of the more common types of fire extinguishers are discussed below.

Some fire extinguishers are re-usable either by recharging the cylinder or by placing the trigger and head mechanism onto a new cylinder, whereas others may have to be discarded once used.

A serviceability check of the fire extinguisher may require checking pressure on a gauge which may be colour-coded, or on an indicator disc which, if it can be pressed in, indicates that the pressure is low and the fire extinguisher unserviceable.

There may also be a weight check to determine that no extinguishant has been lost, but this check is more likely to be done by a maintenance engineer during the periodic inspections.

BCF (Halon) (coloured or labelled green)

BCF extinguishers contain Halon 1211 (bromochlorodifluoromethane), and are often found in light aircraft. BCF is a very versatile extinguishant and is capable of combating most types of fires, including fuel, fabric and electrical. BCF is stored as liquefied gas, which comes out as a fine jet of fluid and develops into a spray. Its toxicity is low (so will not poison the pilot or passengers) and can be safely used in the cockpit, although it is advisable to avoid inhaling excessive amounts of fuel and smoke.

Bearing in mind that the BCF extinguishant gas will exclude oxygen to some extent, **the cabin should be well ventilated once the fire is extinguished.** A significant advantage of BCF is that (unlike *dry chemical*) it does not leave any residue, and so the cabin and instruments will not require cleaning after its use.

BCF is now recognised as a 'greenhouse gas' and is slowly being phased out worldwide.

Dry Chemical (coloured or labelled blue)

A dry chemical fire extinguisher contains dry powder and carbon dioxide. It is very effective against most types of fire, including electrical and fuel, but is less effective than BCF against material fires (paper, textiles, wood).

Unfortunately, dry chemical has several disadvantages. During its use it may restrict visibility in the cockpit and cause breathing difficulties, so **ventilating the cabin is important once the fire is out.** After it has been used, a powdery residue will remain which is corrosive to aluminium alloys and can be damaging to instruments, so thorough cleaning is necessary after dry chemical has been used.

CO_2 Fire Extinguishers (coloured or labelled black)

Carbon dioxide fire extinguishers contain liquefied CO_2 which can be discharged as a gas and used to combat electrical fires, engine fires on the ground and other fires. When sprayed at the base of the fire, the CO_2 blankets the fire and starves it of oxygen.

A typical CO_2 fire extinguisher will have a trigger with a lock-wire that must be broken before use (an intact lockwire is also a check for serviceability), and a nozzle that should be raised before the CO_2 is discharged with the trigger. The nozzle pipe should not be held with the bare hands, since it will become extremely cold as the gas vaporises, and skin could be frozen to it. CO_2 will cause breathing difficulties and is best not used in the cockpit unless oxygen masks are available.

Water Fire Extinguishers (coloured or labelled red)

'Wet' water fire extinguishers generally contain distilled water with an anti-freeze agent to retain serviceability at low temperatures and a 'wetting' agent. Water is suitable for extinguishing material fires (e.g. a smouldering cabin seat), but definitely should not be used for electrical fires or fuel fires.

Foam Fire Extinguishers (coloured or labelled red)

Foam fire extinguishers are generally designed for outside use. One common type is inverted just prior to use, causing chemicals to mix and form foam under pressure which can then be directed at the base of the fire.

NOTE Some older fire extinguishers may not comply with international colour coding, e.g. BCF extinguishers may also be red.

Using a Fire Extinguisher

The instructions on how to use a particular fire extinguisher will normally be found on it, but in general the procedure is:
- **hold** the extinguisher by its handle in a vertical position;
- **remove** any safety locks or safety wires;
- **from a distance** of about 1 to 1.5 metres, direct the nozzle at the base of the fire, depress the trigger and hold it down;
- **release** the trigger when you want to stop the discharge.

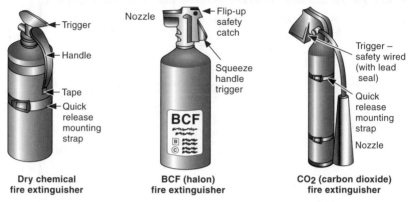

Dry chemical fire extinguisher   **BCF (halon) fire extinguisher**   **CO2 (carbon dioxide) fire extinguisher**

■ ✎ Figure 10-4 **Typical fire extinguishers in aviation use**

Now complete: **Practice Questions - Safety & Care of Passengers**

1. Prior to boarding:

(a) Always make sure that the passengers' needs are catered for as a priority.

(b) Do not make the passengers feel worried about the flight by studying the weather for a long time.

(c) Inform your passengers that pre-flight preparation is part of the flight and at times you will not be able to 'chat'.

(d) Try not to make passengers feel uncomfortable by briefing them on emergency procedures.

2. Pre-flight check of emergency equipment:

(a) Is checked by the person doing the first flight of the day

(b) Is part of the engineers'/club mananger's responsibility.

(c) The emergency equipment on aeroplanes is provided for all flight requirements.

(d) It is the responsibility of the commander to check the required equipment is on board and in date.

3. Passenger briefing:

(a) Is found on a large airliner for their passengers.

(b) Is the responsibility of the commander of any aeroplane.

(c) Covers the use of seats and seat belts on single engined aeroplanes.

(d) Needs only to be done when flying over water.

4. Fire extinguishers:

(a) A halon extinguisher is standard equipment on a single-engined aircraft.

(b) A dry chemical extinguisher is standard equipment on a single-engined aircraft.

(c) A CO_2 extinguisher is standard equipment on a single-engined aircraft.

(d) A foam extinguisher is standard equipment on a single-engined aircraft.

5. Survival equipment:

(a) *The most important equipment when a forced landing is imminent is the radio and transponder.*

(b) *The emergency locator transmitter should be tested before each flight.*

(c) *Parachute flares can be used before the aeroplane has landed in a field during a forced landing.*

(d) *Inflate life jackets as soon as a ditching is imminent.*

First Aid

First aid is what its name suggests – the initial care of the sick or injured. It can preserve life, protect the unconscious, prevent worsening of a condition and promote recovery. First aid lasts until medical aid (doctor, nurse or ambulance officer) arrives or until the casualty recovers.

First aid is useful knowledge for all citizens, but is especially useful for those who may find themselves in remote areas well away from medical aid (e.g. following a forced landing in an aircraft). The St. John's Ambulance Association specialises in first aid and is highly recommended for its manuals and courses.

First aid knowledge can be very useful.

Minor Problems that may Occur In Flight

Minor medical problems may occur in flight and can often be handled without difficulty. It is most important, however, that this does not distract you from flying the aeroplane and adequately controlling its flightpath, which is your principal responsibility.

Airsickness and Nausea

Airsickness (a form of *motion sickness*) may occur in flight, especially if the person is passive, in a hot stuffy cabin and is experiencing unusual motion, such as in manoeuvres or turbulence. Generally, passengers are more passive than the pilot, although it is not unknown for a pilot to become airsick. The affected person may feel poorly, 'hot and cold' and nauseous, but will often feel better after having vomited.

To manage a person who feels airsick (ensuring that you, as pilot, do not neglect your prime responsibilities in controlling the flight path of the aeroplane):

- loosen clothing;
- ensure plenty of fresh air;
- lay the patient down or recline the seat;
- place a cool cloth on the forehead;
- comfort and reassure;
- have a 'sick bag' handy in case of vomiting.

Fainting

Insufficient blood reaching the brain may cause a person to faint and possibly lose consciousness temporarily. A temporary disturbance of the nervous control of the blood vessels can be caused by nervous shock (such as a fright or a horrifying sight), an injury, being passive in a hot stuffy environment or by a sudden postural change (like standing up after having been sitting for a long period). It can also occur in an unfamiliar or physically (e.g. vibration) or mentally (e.g. fear) stressful environment.

A person who is about to faint may feel weak and giddy, 'hot and cold', and have a pale, clammy skin, experience blurred vision and have a desire to yawn.

To manage a person who has fainted, or is about to faint:
- lay the casualty down if possible, with the legs raised; otherwise recline the seat;
- loosen clothing;
- ensure plenty of fresh air;
- allow the casualty to rest;
- have a sick bag handy in case of vomiting;
- place a cool cloth on the forehead; and
- if hyperventilating, have them breathe into a paper bag.

Nose Bleeding
Nose bleeding may result from injury, high blood pressure or excessive blowing of the nose. It usually occurs from just inside the nose on the central cartilaginous partition below the bone.

Instruct the casualty:
- not to blow the nose;
- to breathe through the mouth;
- to apply finger and thumb pressure on the flaps of the nostrils (just below the bony part of the nose) for at least 10 minutes;
- to sit up, with the head slightly forward and loosen any tight clothing; and
- to keep cool with a good supply of fresh air and with cold towels on the neck and forehead.

More Serious Problems that may Occur In Flight
Anything that prejudices the health and well-being of the pilot in flight may end in disaster. **Food poisoning**, for instance, can totally disable a pilot quite quickly, even though symptoms may not appear until several hours after an ill-prepared meal. Also, the onset of symptoms, when they do appear, can be quite sudden! Diarrhoea is certainly not helpful to safe flight. Passengers, as well as the pilot, can experience medical problems (fainting, heart attack, stroke, etc.).

Eat carefully to avoid food poisoning.

It is up to the pilot to decide how to manage the problem, either in flight or on the ground following a landing (ideally at an aerodrome, but in a nearby field if urgency demands it). It may be necessary to make a MAYDAY or PAN call to ensure that assistance is available on the ground.

First Aid Following an Accident

The pilot is responsible for the safety of the aeroplane and its occupants at all times. On rare occasions, accidents do occur and the pilot must be capable of managing subsequent events adequately. The welfare of the group must take precedence over that of any individual and, if possible, the safety of the flight (whilst it lasts) should not be prejudiced.

Prevention is the Best Cure

Preventing an accident or incident is of course best. Food poisoning, for instance, can be avoided by careful choice of food. Pilot welfare is best achieved by staying on the ground if someone has diarrhoea or nausea, or if an upper respiratory or hearing complaint is being experienced.

Some good points of airmanship (common sense) in *prevention* are as follows:

- have the seat-belts fastened;
- do not allow careless smoking; and
- guard against fumes and carbon monoxide in the cabin by ensuring a good supply of fresh air.

If an Accident Occurs and Passengers are Injured (*Note)

In the event of an accident actually taking place do everything in your power to stop the situation worsening. Secure the aeroplane and evacuate uninjured passengers, taking any useful emergency equipment and supplies. Consider the welfare of injured passengers and whether or not they should be moved. Do not forget the welfare of the non-injured members of the party.

◀ Figure 11-1
The recovery position

If an unconscious passenger is evacuated, then it should be done gently and firmly, with the casualty being placed in the recovery position. Techniques can be learned on how to do this correctly. This is a comfortable position that aids blood supply to the brain and allows any vomit to escape without blocking the breathing passages.

NOTE Removal from the aircraft may not be appropriate e.g. if they may have a spinal injury. If they must be moved e.g. fire or water hazard - keep spine in position.

Head Injuries

Head injuries are potentially very serious as they can result in brain damage, altered consciousness, spinal injury, bleeding, breathing difficulties, vision and balance difficulties. Even mild head injuries should be treated seriously.

Indications of head injury may include headache, nausea, memory loss, blurring of vision, weakness on one side of the body, wounds, bleeding, bruising, clear fluid escaping from the nose or ear, twitching, noisy breathing, incoherent speech, congestion on the face, vomiting, dilated pupils or pupils becoming unequal in size, strange behaviour and abnormal responses of the injured person to commands and to touch.

Treat someone suffering head injury the same as for being unconscious. Consider placing the victim in the *recovery position* so that any bleeding, discharge or vomit will not block the airway. An open airway is vital. Ensure that the tongue or dentures do not obstruct the passages. Breathing should be monitored and assisted if necessary. Be alert for possible concussion.

Bleeding

Bleeding is loss of blood from the blood vessels and may be either internal or external. In either case blood is lost from the circulation and the ability to carry energy-giving oxygen around the body and to the brain is reduced. Blood loss can lead to faintness, dizziness, nausea, thirst, a weak and rapid pulse, cold and clammy skin, and rapid breathing.

Fortunately, bleeding will often stop of its own accord but, if it does not, severe bleeding can lead to shock and eventually to death. Shock *(see next page)* is inadequate blood supply to the body tissues (including the brain). This is not the same as "being shocked" i.e. frightened. Severe bleeding, therefore, is extremely serious and must be controlled before less serious injuries are attended to.

External bleeding is best controlled by placing a bulky dressing (or your hand if nothing more suitable is available) over the wound and applying firm pressure until it stops or help arrives. Raise the injured part and rest it to decrease the blood flow.

Profuse bleeding may be reduced by pressing the sides of the wound together by hand pressure to block the blood flow through the arteries (say above the elbow or knee). This should be a last resort and the pressure should be released every 10 minutes or so to ensure some blood supply to the area.

Bleeding from the palm of the hand may be serious and can best be treated by clasping a firm pressure pad (e.g. a bandage roll, a handkerchief wrapped around a stone, or two or three fingers of the other hand) and elevating the hand above the head to reduce the blood flow to it.

Internal bleeding may result in pain, tenderness, tight stomach muscles and the above-mentioned signs of blood loss. To manage internal bleeding, lie the casualty down. Elevate the legs comfortably (if not broken), loosen tight clothing and allow no food or drink. Seek urgent medical assistance.

Fractures

A fracture is a broken or cracked bone. There will be bleeding, either internally or through an open wound, causing a loss of blood to the circulation. The area where the break has occurred may be painful, tender, mis-shapen or swollen, bruised and unable to be used normally.

In managing a casualty with a fracture:

- **Control bleeding and cover wounds** with a sterile or clean dressing.
- **Immobilise and support the fracture** with a sling, bandage or splint, and preferably support the injured limb in an elevated position.
  - **Splints:** use any suitable material that is long, wide and firm enough to give support and to immobilise the joints above and below the fracture. Use can be made of the upper body to splint a fractured arm and of a good leg to splint a fractured leg.
  - **Padding:** may protect the skin and bony points and may allow the splint to fit snugly.
  - **Bandages:** in general should be broad and supportive.
- **Check frequently** to ensure that blood circulation to a fractured limb is not impaired, that bandages have not loosened, and that splints are still supportive, and look for signs of shock.

Burns

Burns are a serious injury. Extensive burns to the body or to the respiratory tract (due to breathing hot air or fumes) are potentially dangerous and may be fatal.

To manage a casualty with burns, first extinguish the fire if possible and/or remove the casualty from danger, making sure that you do not become a burns casualty yourself.

- **Put out burning clothing** by smothering with a non-inflammable blanket or jacket, or possibly a dry chemical fire extinguisher (directed away from the eyes).
- **Remove or cut away any clothing** near the burnt area unless it is stuck to it, in which case leave it alone. Remove any rings, bracelets, watch bands, etc., before swelling starts. Cool the injured area if possible under cold, gently running water – (cooling make take up to 10 minutes).
- **Do not prick blisters and avoid touching** the burnt area. Do not apply any lotions, ointments, oily dressings or fluffy material. Apply a sterile non-stick dressing and bandage lightly.

A conscious casualty seriously burnt should be given frequent small amounts of water, weak tea or milk (about $\frac{1}{2}$ cup every 10 minutes) to minimise the effect of fluid loss from the burnt tissues. Do not give alcohol. Seek medical aid urgently.

Shock

Insufficient circulation of blood to the brain and other body tissues may lead to a collapse of the circulatory system and death. It can be caused by bleeding, burns or spinal injury.

Shock is progressive and may take some hours to become obvious and the symptoms should be carefully watched for. A casualty experiencing shock may be faint or dizzy, restless and apprehensive, nauseous and thirsty. The pulse may be very weak and rapid. The face and lips may be pale and the skin pale and clammy, the extremities becoming bluish. Breathing may be rapid and the casualty may become dull, drowsy, apathetic, confused or unconscious.

To Treat a Person In Shock:

- **Increase the blood supply** to the brain if possible by laying the patient down with the head low and feet elevated.
- **Control any external bleeding,** dress any wounds or burns, immobilise any fractures and loosen any tight clothing.
- **Keep the casualty warm,** but do not overheat him as this draws blood away from the vital organs.
- **If thirsty,** moisten the lips.
- **Monitor breathing and pulse.**
- **If breathing is difficult,** or vomiting likely or if consciousness is lost, lay the casualty on the side with the mouth slightly down.
- **Seek urgent medical assistance.**

First-Aid Kits

Although aeroplanes flying for a purpose other than commercial air transport (e.g. for training or for private flights) are not required to carry a first-aid kit, (whereas commercial air transport aircraft are required to do so), it is good airmanship for the operator of the aeroplane to provide one.

Keep your first-aid kit well-stocked.

Scale A

(iii) First-aid equipment of good quality, sufficient in quantity, having regard to the number of persons on board the aircraft, and including the following:

Roller bandages, triangular bandages, adhesive plaster, absorbent gauze, cotton wool, (or wound dressings in place of the absorbent gauze and cotton wool), burn dressings, safety pins;

Haemostatic bandages or tourniquets, scissors;

Antiseptic, analgesic and stimulant drugs;

Splints, in the case of aeroplanes the maximum total weight authorised of which exceeds 5700 kg;

A handbook on first aid.

■ ✎ Figure 11-2 **Air Navigation Order (ANO) Schedule 6, Scale A provides a guide to the contents of a suitable first-aid kit**

Survival

Before venturing over dangerous terrain or over water, especially if well away from civilisation, it is good airmanship to consider survival aspects in case an unplanned landing or ditching becomes necessary, and to carry additional survival equipment. The basic aims in survival are:

- **let people know where you are** so that rescue time can be shortened; and
- **have sufficient emergency equipment** and supplies on board and sufficient knowledge to sustain life until rescue is achieved.

Lodge a Flight Plan

If the territory you plan to cross is dangerous, then you should submit a flight plan with Air Traffic Control so that you receive a high level of search and rescue protection. This is advisable if you plan to fly:

- **more than 10 nautical miles from the coast;**
- **over a remote or hazardous area** (e.g. Northern Scotland, or the west coast down to Cornwall); or
- **in an aircraft not fitted with a suitable radio.**

Survival chances are greater if people know where you are.

Quick and effective response by search and rescue organisations can be vital in an emergency, and this is best achieved by you protecting your flight by filing a flight plan. The chance of surviving a ditching in the icy-cold North Sea, for instance, diminishes with every passing minute.

Maintain Body Core Temperature

Maintaining body temperature is critical to survival. Normal body core temperature (core temperature being that of the inner body) is slightly under 37°C, and any change of more than about two degrees, either up or down, can seriously affect bodily functions, including brain and heart function. Unconsciousness will occur if body core temperature falls about 4°C to 34°C. Temperatures above 37°C are called a fever, and in a high fever where the core temperature rises about 4°C to 41°C, delirium and convulsions might occur. The brain needs to be functioning well if people are to act to survive, and so body core temperature control is vital.

Keeping body core temperature up, since the environmental temperature is usually more than 10°C cooler, uses most of the energy produced by the body. This production of heat energy is fairly constant, with body core temperature being controlled by heat loss, mainly convection as air carries excess heat away from the skin.

In *low* environmental temperatures, heat loss from the skin by convection is reduced by clothing. This insulates the body from circulating air by trapping a layer of air that is warmed by the body but not carried away. If body temperature still drops, extra heat is generated by muscular contractions that we call *shivering*. Shivering uses a lot of energy and can lead to premature exhaustion.

Keep warm ...

You can be exposed to a severe heat loss:
- **following sudden cabin depressurisation** at high altitude;
- **in extremely cold conditions** on land or at sea; or
- **during immersion in water** below 20°C following a ditching.

In *high* environmental temperatures, light and loosely fitting clothing allows the circulation of air across the skin to carry heat away. If this heat loss by convection is insufficient, the body sweats, and the evaporation of this sweat from liquid to vapour absorbs additional heat energy from the skin. Sweating means that the body is losing fluids, and these have to be replaced by drinking if dehydration or overheating is to be avoided.

... but not too warm.

Survival Equipment

The survival equipment to be carried will depend upon the nature of the terrain or water to be crossed, and upon the climate and expected weather conditions. Some survival equipment is useful in all conditions (including your communications radio, an emergency locator transmitter (ELT), optical signals such as signal mirrors and flares, waterproof matches, a compass, a large knife, rope, a whistle, etc.), whereas other survival equipment (such as a life-raft) is more specific.

The Radio and the Transponder

If a forced landing or ditching is imminent, then you should make use of all means at your disposal to inform someone who can activate the search and rescue organisations. You could:
- **broadcast a Mayday call** on the frequency in use or on the emergency frequency 121·5 MHz which is monitored by ground stations and by many aircraft; and
- **squawk 7700 on your transponder** – this will bring attention to and emphasise your aircraft on any radar screen (provided that you are within radar coverage).

Most airliners will be using one VHF-COM set for normal air traffic control purposes, and will be listening out on 121·5 MHz on their second VHF-COM, enabling them to pick up any voice messages transmitted on this emergency frequency or any signals emitted by an ELT. If you ever find yourself in trouble and out of radio range from a ground station, transmit a voice message on 121·5 MHz – some other pilot or ground station may hear you and may be able to pass on your message to the authorities or provide some other sort of assistance.

Communicate your emergency:
• radio (frequency in use or 121·5 MHz)
• transponder (7700)

If you transmit early enough while you are still at altitude, an airport with *VHF direction-finding* (VDF) capability may have time to determine the direction from which your voice signals are coming, which will considerably simplify search procedures.

The Emergency Locator Transmitter (ELT)

The emergency locator transmitter is one of the best means of locating a downed aircraft. It is an electronic, battery-operated transmitter which emits a very distinctive radio signal.

Activate your ELT.

When activated, either by impact following hard contact with the ground or water, or by pilot-activation following a successful forced landing or ditching, the ELT transmits a *wailing* signal on the international emergency frequencies (civil 121·5 MHz, military 243 MHz). Other aircraft and ground stations will be listening out on these frequencies.

Land and sea survival beacons known as *emergency position indicating radio beacons* (EPIRBs) also transmit on 121·5 MHz.

The ELT is also known as the *emergency locator beacon* (ELB), the *radio beacon,* the *VHF survival beacon* (VSB), and by various other names. A PLB (personal locator beacon) is a smaller version of the ELB and is registered to an individual rather than a vessel. In the absence of an ELT fitted to your aircraft, an individual PLB may be carried to satisfy the requirements of Part-NCO.

Receiving Stations

Aircraft and ground stations monitor the emergency frequencies 121·5 and 243 MHz. The intensity of the ELT signal gives an indication of the proximity of the listening station to the downed aircraft. Searching aircraft can measure variations in signal strength as they fly a search pattern, with strengthening signals leading them towards the downed aircraft.

There is now a global satellite system known as COSPAS/ SARSAT (C/S) which uses four near-polar orbital satellites to detect and localise signals from ELTs. In the UK, a local user terminal at Lasham processes C/S satellite information and passes it to the UK Mission Control Centre which is co-located with the Plymouth Rescue Coordination Centre (RCC).

The maximum waiting time between ELT activation and satellite detection should not exceed 90 minutes, and will usually be shorter.

Listen out for others in trouble.

It is good airmanship to listen out on the emergency frequency 121·5 MHz if you have a second VHF-COM radio set. Any ELT signals that you hear should be reported – it could be from a downed aircraft (although on rare occasions it could be a false alarm caused by a pilot accidentally activating the ELT).

Your report should include your position and altitude, and:

- **when you first heard,** and last heard the signal; and
- **any bearing obtained.**

It is also useful to advise when the signal was at maximum strength.

Activating an ELT

Most ELTs will be activated by impact in the case of heavy contact with ground or water. In the case of a successful forced landing or ditching where no significant impact occurs, some ELTs are activated by a switch, and others are activated by insertion in water or some other fluid. The antenna, if fitted, should be extended vertically for best transmission. Instructions will be found on the ELT unit itself.

The ELT may be activated in its installed position in the aircraft, or it may be removed, depending upon the situation. It is more important for the ELT to be with the survivors, who might be drifting in a raft or hiking through the jungle, than to remain with an abandoned aircraft.

After a ditching, a buoyant ELT with its antenna vertical should be attached by a lanyard to the raft so that the ELT does not become separated from the survivors, and a searching aircraft locate the ELT but not the survivors. The water surface will act as a reflector and effectively increase the ELT's transmitting strength. Hoisting the ELT up a mast would degrade the transmission, since it would eliminate reflection of the signals from the water surface.

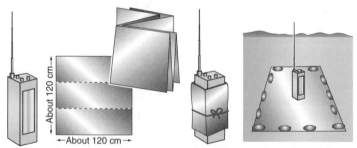

About 120 cm

←About 120 cm→

1. Prior to departure, join strips of household aluminium foil, to make a 120 cm (4 feet) square 'earth mat'.

2. Carefully fold the earth mat to a convenient size.

3. Tie or tape the folded earth mat to your ELT.

4. If you need to activate your ELT clear of the aircraft, unfold the earth mat and place it on the ground in a clear area away from obstacles, with rocks or earth to hold it down.

5. Turn the ELT on and place it on the mat so that the aerial is vertical.

6. Remain clear of the ELT.

■ ✎ *Figure 12-1* **Operating an ELT**

After a forced landing on land, the ELT can be activated in its installed position in the aircraft, or it can be removed and operated on the ground or on an *earth mat,* which is simply a reflecting surface made from something like household aluminium foil formed to the size of small sheet. If the ELT is removed from the aircraft, place it in a clearing on high ground near the survivors, away from trees, rocks, etc., which could distort or weaken the signal. Some ELTs need to be inserted in a fluid to be activated, even on the ground, and this can be achieved by placing it in a plastic bag containing fluid, and making sure that it remains upright with the antenna extended vertically. Placing the ELT on the wing of the aircraft or some other reflecting surface will also increase its effectiveness.

If possible, secure the ELT in a position so that its antenna remains vertical, using tape, rocks, sticks, etc. Once the ELT is activated, you should keep persons and objects clear of it since they could distort its signals.

When Should You Activate the ELT?

Following an impact, the ELT will activate immediately. Following a smooth touchdown, however, it will not activate automatically, and the pilot-in-command must decide when to activate it.

If you are near a ground station or within 100 nautical miles of a busy air route, or if you have already alerted others to your predicament (say with a Mayday call and by squawking 7700 on your transponder), then activate the ELT *immediately.* Also, if anyone is injured or if conditions for survival are poor, then switch it on immediately.

Some ELTs can be switched off and used only intermittently, others operate continuously until their batteries run flat after 48 hours or more. Some can be temporarily deactivated with a switch, others can be deactivated by removing them from their vertical position and laying them horizontally.

If you are in a remote area with no air routes within 100 nautical miles, then you might decide to conserve the ELT and activate it at a time when you think someone might hear it. This could be at or after your expected arrival time when Flight Service, or friends and family, might be starting to question your overdue arrival. It might be appropriate to switch it on at dusk, or at first light the following morning, or whenever you think it might be heard.

Optical Signals

Know your safety equipment.

There are various devices that can be used to help search aircraft visually to determine your position, including signal rockets, hand flares, flashlights, signal mirrors, and sea dye markers.

Signal Mirror

The signal mirror (or heliograph) is a small, light and cheap device that can be extremely useful in sunlight. Reflecting sunlight towards a search aircraft, which will probably see it as a series of very bright flashes, can be most effective at distances up to 25 nautical miles. The signal mirror is simply a metal or glass reflecting surface.

One way of using a signal mirror is:

1. **Hold it close** to your face so that you can look through the small hole in the reflecting surface (but not at the sun, which would do damage to your eye).

2. **Hold a** *target* at arms length (the target could be attached to the mirror, or it could be your finger or a pencil) and align it visually between your eye and the aircraft you want to alert.

3. **Move the mirror** so that the sun's rays are reflected onto the target, which means that they will be directed at the aircraft.

Another method of using the mirror, as illustrated in Figure 12-2, involves viewing the aircraft through the mirror and adjusting the angle of the mirror so that the spot of light from the sun that falls on your face, hand or shirt disappears through the hole while you have the aircraft in view through it.

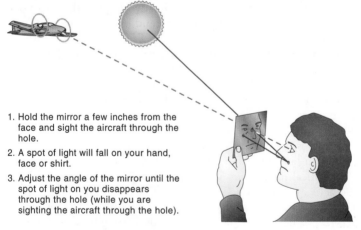

1. Hold the mirror a few inches from the face and sight the aircraft through the hole.

2. A spot of light will fall on your hand, face or shirt.

3. Adjust the angle of the mirror until the spot of light on you disappears through the hole (while you are sighting the aircraft through the hole).

■ ✎ *Figure 12-2* **Using a signal mirror**

The target aircraft will spot a *flashing* signal more easily than a steady signal, however there is no need for you to rock the mirror to cause flashing – the natural movement of your hand will be sufficient. If no aircraft or ship is in sight, continue to sweep the horizon using the signal mirror, just in case.

Signal Rockets (Parachute Flares)

There are some signal rockets available which can shoot up a red fireball which then sinks slowly beneath a small parachute. This should only be used when you think that someone will spot it, with the fireball being most effective at night.

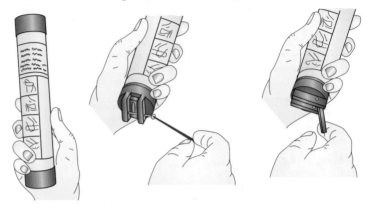

1. Unwrap when ready for use.	6. Firing lever falls down.
2. Read instructions.	7. Point rocket.
3. Remove top and bottom caps.	8. Bend lever up alongside and parallel to the firing tube, and squeeze.
4. Firing mechanism is in the base.	
5. Pull string to remove safety pin.	

■ ✎ Figure 12-3 **Firing a signal rocket**

The instructions should be read carefully. They will advise that the signal rocket tube should be held firmly, well away from the body, and pointing in the shooting direction, which should be near-vertical in a downwind direction to avoid any contact with your body or anyone else's, before the mechanism is activated.

Hand Flares

Hand flares provide a coloured flare or smoke that lasts for 30 seconds or more, which can draw the attention of searchers to your position.

You should read the instructions carefully before using a hand flare. They will probably advise you to hold the hand flare firmly, well away from the body, and pointing in the shooting direction, which should be near-vertical in a downwind direction to avoid any contact with your body or anyone else's, before ignition. Flares that produce a flame (usually red) are effective at night or in daylight; those that produce smoke (usually orange) are only useful by day.

1. Unwrap when ready for use.	7. Ignite by grinding striker across
2. Read instructions.	top of flare.
3. Unwrap top sealing tape.	8. Hold clear immediately ignition
4. Remove top card and discard.	occurs.
5. Unwrap bottom tape.	9. Smoke is locally dense but is
6. Remove bottom cap incorporating	dispersed with the breeze.
striker.	

■ ✎ *Figure 12-4* **Igniting a hand flare**

Flashlight or Spotlight

A strong flashlight can be used both to assist you getting organised at night, and also to send emergency signals in the direction of anyone who might see them. Typical signals that can draw attention are:

* **a wide circling motion;** or
* **the SOS emergency signal:** 3 short flashes, 3 long flashes, 3 short flashes – and then repeated:

(· · · — — — · · ·   · · · — — — · · ·   · · · — — — · · ·   etc.)

Sea Dye Marker

Sea dye marker, when released into the sea, spreads out and forms a very brightly marked area (usually bright green) that can be seen for many miles in daylight hours. It lasts for several hours. The bag containing the dye should be fastened to the outside of the raft so that the dye is released in the vicinity of the raft. In strong winds, the raft might drift away from the dyed area, so it would be advisable to delay the use of the dye until a search craft is in sight.

Ground-to-Air Visual Signals for Search and Rescue

The following ground-to-air visual signals can be used, as appropriate, to inform searchers with whom you have no radio contact what your needs are and what your actions will be. Make the symbol as large as possible (preferably 6 metres or so long, but at least 2 or 3 metres), using materials that contrast with the background. The materials could be clothes or sleeping bags which are held in position by stones, or you could use tree branches, etc.

You could also lay out a large **SOS** signal. It has been known for airline passengers to spot SOS signals on the ground, whereas they may not have understood the significance of the other ground-to-air visual signals.

STANDARD GROUND-TO-AIR SEARCH AND RESCUE VISUAL SIGNALS		
No.	**Message**	**Symbol**
1	Require assistance	V
2	Require medical assistance	X
3	No or Negative	N
4	Yes or Affirmative	Y
5	Proceeding in this direction	↑

Flags

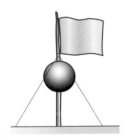

■ Figure 12-5
Fly a flag and ball

Flying anything in the form of a flag will help to attract attention. If possible, fly a ball or something resembling a ball directly beneath the flag or above it, which is an international distress signal.

Fires and Smoke

Fires can be seen well at night, and dense smoke can be seen well by day. Lighting two or three fires 20 metres apart, and possibly in the shape of a triangle, may help draw attention to your position. Using dry wood at night will produce the brightest flames; using damp wood with lots of green leaves by day will produce lots of smoke, as will adding engine oil. Waterproof matches are worthwhile having in any survival kit.

Acoustic Signals

If the aircraft has come down in a jungle or heavily wooded area, it may not be visible from the air or from the ground. Ground searchers may be assisted in wooded areas or at night if you can make a lot of noise, by blowing whistles or by calling out. The Australian bush call 'coo-ee' has saved many lives.

Written Notes

If for any reason you leave the vicinity of the downed aircraft, then leave a written or scratched note stating your intentions, in case searchers find the aircraft before they find you.

Survival at Sea

A forced landing into water is known as a ditching. Some ditchings have been made into lakes, dams, and wide rivers, and others have been made into oceans.

The initial problem following a ditching is to ensure that everyone leaves the aircraft safely, and is able to float and avoid drowning. This is achieved by the use of life-jackets and/or rafts.

The next, and major, problem is to avoid death or injury by exposure. Some oceans are quite warm, for instance those surrounding Hawaii and Northern Australia, where survival might have less to do with water temperature and more to do with sharks. In and around the UK, however, where water temperatures are very cold, the major factor in surviving a ditching is **avoiding hypothermia**. Hypothermia is caused by a loss of heat, leading to a reduction in the core temperature of the body, i.e. not just the skin temperature, but the internal temperature of the body and its organs.

The early stages of hypothermia can lead to a serious reduction in mental and physical performance; a *severe* case of hypothermia can result in death. Therefore, time is of the essence in rescue following a ditching! Rescue must occur before hypothermia sets in.

Fit Life-Jackets before Touchdown, and Fasten Seat-Belts

It is good airmanship to wear life-jackets when flying for extended periods over water in a single-engined aircraft, because you may not have time to fit them in an emergency situation. In the case of a ditching, make sure that everyone has a life-jacket on, and that seat-belts are fastened firmly. Instruct the passengers not to inflate the life-jackets prior to leaving the aircraft, as this could hinder, or even prevent, exit.

Use your life-jackets.

A quick briefing is appropriate, warning everyone to brace for one or two impacts following touchdown on the water surface, possibly with very strong deceleration forces.

Cushions and other soft materials may be used to protect some of the passengers from the impact forces, but they must not interfere with the controls. In some aircraft, the cushions also act as flotation devices.

If Possible, Ditch Close to Rescuers

Ditching is usually a last resort, and it should be performed as close to a shore or to a ship as possible to reduce the time needed for rescue.

Ditch In Smooth Water if Possible ...

Ditching in calm seas is of course preferable, but this option is not always available. On a calm water surface, it is probably best to touch down into-wind to have the lowest groundspeed on contact with the water.

The wind direction can be determined from your drift angle over the surface, or from wind streaks on the surface. There could be sufficient smooth water on the lee side of a ship (i.e. out of the wind).

... Otherwise on the Crest or Back Side of a Swell

In water that is not calm, it is advisable to avoid landing into the swell (i.e. the rows of widely-spread waves coming from a long distance away); it may be better to land along the swell, even if you have to accept some crosswind, preferably touching down on the crest or on the back side of the swell. In a confused sea, try to land on the crest or on the back side of a wave, and avoid landing in its face.

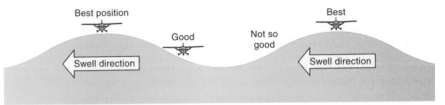

■ ✎ Figure 12-6 **Suggested ditching places in water that is not calm**

The wind direction in a confused sea can be determined from wind streaks on the surface and from *whitecaps* which fall forward with the wind, but are then over-run by the wave producing the effect that the foam in the whitecap is sliding backwards.

Touchdown should be as slow as is possible, with a low rate of descent, and with the nose held in a high attitude. Flying at about 10 knots above the stall, power can be used to hold a low height until a smooth patch of water is found, and touchdown can be made near stalling speed on the crest or back side of a swell.

Do not stall the aircraft before touchdown, as this could lead to a heavy drop into the water if you have misjudged the height, which is easy to do above water, especially if it is smooth. There may be one or two impacts, but the slow speed should prevent the aircraft from bouncing back into the air and coming down for a second and less-controlled touchdown. After impact with the water, there is little that the pilot can do to control the aircraft.

If the ditching is as a result of the **loss of power,** then you do not have the luxury of holding off until you find a relatively smooth stretch of water. In this case, glide down at slightly higher than normal approach speed, and then flare early, leaving you some airspeed to bleed off as you feel for the surface. Preferably touch down on the crest or back side of a swell.

Vacate the Aircraft and Enter the Raft

The time the aircraft may float for is quite variable, so plan for an immediate evacuation, using a life-raft if available, and with everyone having their life-jacket inflated before entering the water.

The welfare of the raft occupants will depend upon the skill, knowledge and leadership qualities of the raft leader (usually the pilot-in-command unless incapacitated). Items of importance are:

- **strengthen the will** to survive;
- **issue clear orders** in a calm but firm manner;
- **account for all the survivors** – those in the water can best be brought on board backwards by lifting them under the armpits;
- **take as much emergency equipment** on board as possible in the time available (ELT, drinking water, flares, flashlights, survival kits, first-aid kits, clothing, blankets, sleeping bags, etc.);
- **assign a person to maintain watch** for possible search aircraft or for ships or fishing boats.

Disconnect the raft from the aircraft in case it sinks quickly, and move a short distance away. Deploy a sea anchor (e.g. a bucket attached to the raft) to avoid the raft being blown away from the ditching position, which might delay the rescue. Search and rescue activities will always start at the reported ditching position.

Delegation of Duties

Assign tasks to others to offload yourself, and to keep them busy, which will increase their initiative and their will to survive. Initially the tasks can be immediate survival ones – look for survivors, collect emergency equipment, wring out wet clothing, bail out the raft, etc. Later, it can be the more long-term tasks, such as taking duty with the signal mirror, keeping watch, shading sleeping occupants, etc.

Organise the survivors.

Prevent Hypothermia

The colder the water, the faster the body loses heat. Being immersed in water at 20°C, the body would lose a critical 4°C in about 2 hours, probably leading to unconsciousness. In water at 5°C, such as in the northern waters surrounding the UK in winter, this could occur in a few minutes. Also, the extremities, such as the hands, will cool very quickly, making climbing into a raft or grasping anything much more difficult. It is vital to leave cold water quickly and climb into a raft. It is even better if you can enter the raft directly from the aircraft and avoid immersion completely.

Keeping warm is vital.

After coming on board a raft following a ditching, wear dry clothing and stay out of the wind. If possible, wet clothing should be removed and replaced with dry clothing, otherwise wrung out and put on again in a drier state. The evaporation of water absorbs a lot of heat, and could speed up the onset of hypothermia.

Any wind will also increase the rate of evaporation and will lower body temperature, so try to shelter all occupants from the wind, or use warm blankets if available. Some food and drink will provide a source of energy to help in internal warming. Alcohol should definitely *not* be used, since it dilates the vessels near the skin and leads to an even greater heat loss.

The symptoms of hypothermia are skin that is cold to touch, and a slow pulse with slow and shallow breathing. Elderly people and children are especially vulnerable to hypothermia.

Seasickness

If seasickness tablets are available, try to distribute them immediately after things have settled down on the raft, as a preventive measure. Even people not prone to seasickness under normal conditions can become sick quite quickly in a raft. Being seasick causes a loss of food and fluids, wastes a lot of energy, and can weaken the will to survive. Typical dosage is two tablets immediately, and then every 12 hours until rescue.

Emergency Signals

The raft leader should determine when the emergency signals should be used. Normally the ELT will be activated immediately if the raft is near land or near a shipping lane or air route, but it may be advisable to delay using flares, pyrotechnic signals, or sea dye until a ship or aeroplane is in sight, or unless they can possibly attract the attention of people on land. The signal mirror should be used continuously in sunlight. Whistles and other loud noises may attract the attention of people on nearby ships or land, especially at night.

Frostbite

Avoid frostbite.

In cold climates, the extremities with large surface areas (toes, fingers, ears, nose) are subject to frostbite (freezing). The affected parts become pale and numb, possibly appear shiny, and sometimes blisters will form. Ice forms in the tissues and may destroy them, making later amputation necessary.

As a preventive measure, the body should be kept warm, by wearing sufficient clothing and gloves or by placing the hands in the warm area under the armpits, or by the occupants huddling together on the floor close to each other and with their legs pulled up in order to warm each other. The body can be kept warm by light exercise to stimulate blood circulation, but **suspected frostbitten parts should not be rubbed,** since there will be no blood circulation in the tissues – warming using tepid water, if available, is preferable.

Skin Irritation

Exposure to cold and salty water for long periods can lead to skin irritation, stiffness, swellings, and sores. This can be prevented by keeping the body covered and as dry and warm as possible in the circumstances. Bailing out the raft and keeping its floor dry is a priority. The body can be kept warm by light exercise to stimulate blood circulation.

Sunburn

Sunburn is a distinct risk if the sun is shining, even if there is some cloud cover and even if the temperature is low. Use some sun-protection cream and sunglasses if available, and keep in the shade where possible. If temperatures are high, then heat exhaustion or hyperthermia (exceptionally high body core temperature) may occur, causing weakness, dizziness, vomiting, and possibly unconsciousness. Applying moist cloths or shirts to the body may increase cooling.

Avoid sunburn.

Emergency Rations

A person can survive for 30 days or more without food, but only for a day or two without water, so the rationing of water is top priority for long-term survival.

Water should not be rationed out until there is a distinct need for it, which may be after 24 hours, or earlier if a person is in distress or injured. Until then, the body will be functioning on previously consumed fluids. Drink only in small quantities to avoid vomiting up the precious water, which can happen if a large amount is gulped down after a prolonged period of thirst.

Fresh water is vital.

Take every opportunity to collect rainwater, using plastic sheets, plastic bags and buckets if available.

Never drink sea water – it causes vomiting, diarrhoea, and possible mental damage. Do not drink alcohol, but keep it for possible disinfection purposes.

Food rationing could commence after 24 hours. Fishing is a possibility, but only eat raw fish if plenty of drinking water is available, since the salt in fish will increase the need to drink fluids. Do not throw food scraps overboard, especially in warm waters, as this may attract sharks.

Raft Hygiene

Try to keep the raft as clean as possible, with the floor dry.

Behaviour On Board When Rescue Is Imminent

Raft discipline must be maintained until the rescue is complete. Occupants should not leave the raft and swim towards the rescue ship, but should remain on board and await orderly rescue by the crew of the ship or boat.

Maintain survivor discipline.

If found by a search aircraft, the most likely happening will be the dropping of additional equipment, such as locator buoys, food, water, and medical supplies, and the dispatch of a rescue ship. The retrieval of these items must be very orderly to avoid upsetting the raft. There could still be some hours before rescue.

Immersion In Water

If no raft is available in the aircraft following a ditching, then immersion in water for a long period is a possibility. The time for which a person can survive depends to a large extent upon the water temperature. People with a layer of fat and people used to being in water for long periods generally have a greater tolerance and can last a bit longer. Immersion times that people can survive vary greatly, but as a guide, if the water temperature is near 0°C, about 1 hour or less (even a lot less – maybe just a few minutes) is all you can expect. With 12°C, the time could be 4 hours; with 20°C, it could be 12 hours or more.

Heat loss can be prevented by wearing a flotation device that eliminates the need for muscular movement (and hence heat loss) to remain afloat. Clothing, even though wet, will slow the rate of cooling, although the weight of it may prove a disadvantage.

Bunching up under the water will also protect the chest, groin, and arms, and reduce heat loss from these areas. A group of survivors could huddle together to reduce heat loss, and provide mutual support (mental and physical).

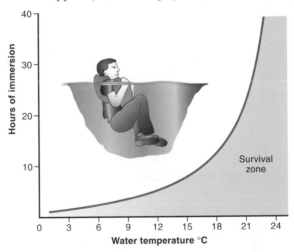

■ ✎ Figure 12-7 **Bunch yourself up (or huddle together in a group) to preserve heat**

Survival in Very Cold Climates

If flying in remote icy regions, then a polar survival kit should be carried to assist in immediate survival, which has mainly to do with keeping warm in a very hostile environment.

Wear Warm Clothing and Shoes

It is essential to survival in a very cold climate that the body is kept warm and dry, hence the wearing of sufficient clothing, shoes, gloves, and a head cover is important. The head is in fact where most heat loss occurs because there are many blood vessels near the surface of the head. Thick layers of loose, dry clothing will provide the best insulation and help retain body heat, with the outer layer of clothing acting as protection against the wind.

Wear the clothing loosely. Clothing that is too tight may hinder blood circulation and lead to frostbite later on. Do not wear too many socks or tight shoes that may hinder blood circulation in your feet. If wearing oversized shoes, however, then they can be packed with handkerchiefs or dry grass or some other stuffing to provide insulation. If shoes are not available, then wrap the feet in clothing. If gloves are not available, do the same, or keep the hands in pockets.

Avoid sweating if possible, as it could lead to frostbite later when you have finished the activity. If working hard, temporarily open the clothing at the neck and wrist, or remove some, but return it to the full warmth position after the work is done and you are cooling down a little.

Keep warm, but avoid sweating.

Keep the clothing as dry as possible. Snow should be brushed off before entering a shelter or approaching a fire which could melt the snow and make the clothes wet. If the clothes are very wet, say from falling in water, rolling in dry snow will help dry them. The dry snow will absorb a lot of the moisture like blotting paper. Wet clothing should then be dried at a fire if possible, but make sure that clothing and shoes do not burn.

If possible, use additional clothing around the shoulders and hips when sleeping, for comfort and warmth.

Gather Survivors and Allot Duties

The leader (normally the pilot-in-command unless incapacitated) should allot duties to fit survivors, such as:

Organise survivors.

* gather other survivors;
* assemble emergency equipment, first-aid kits, rope, etc.;
* activate the ELT if so decided, or fire off flares if help is nearby;
* have a person stay by the aircraft and use the radio if possible;
* prepare ground-to-air signals;
* collect warm clothing and food and water supplies;

- **commence construction** of a shelter;
- **search for firewood** or other combustible material (such as oil from the engine) and start a fire;
- **prepare hot drinks;**
- **select a toilet area** some distance from the proposed shelter, but itself sheltered if possible;
- **have a person maintain watch** for possible search aircraft;
- **rotate duties periodically** to provide some variety, to maintain interest, and to ensure that everyone is involved and getting some exercise.

Take Shelter

Immediate shelter in a polar environment is vital. If there is no risk of fire in the aircraft (i.e. no fuel vapours, etc.), then it may be used as shelter against wind, rain, snow, and low temperatures. If the aircraft cannot be used for shelter, then other shelter has to be quickly found or constructed.

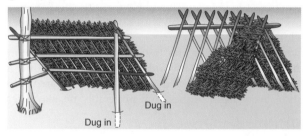

■ ✎ Figure 12-8 **Construct a shelter (or use the aircraft)**

Injured survivors can rest on seat cushions as insulation while fit survivors construct the shelter.

Take shelter.

In a polar environment, construct a shelter near trees if possible, or somewhere that is naturally sheltered against wind and snowdrifts, such as mounds or small hills. Keep away from areas where snowfalls or avalanches are possible, such as the base of high cliffs.

Canvas sheets supported by tree branches or the wing of the aircraft and held down by rocks can provide good shelter. In the long term, a snow hut or snow holes will provide good shelter, but ensure that someone remains on watch for searchers, because snow is a very good sound insulator and may muffle the sound of search aircraft.

Ensure that there is sufficient ventilation for smoke and other fumes to escape from the shelter, and reduce the risk of carbon monoxide poisoning. Drinking water can be obtained from melting ice or snow – ice is better, since it is often cleaner and it also produces more water for less heat input.

■ ✎ Figure 12-9 **Excavating a snow cavity against a small hill for shelter**

The toilet area, some distance from the main shelter, should be the only area used for these purposes for reasons of hygiene. Personal cleanliness can be maintained by wiping the body with a damp cloth. Teeth can be kept clean with a small amount of water or a damp cloth.

If the environment is not icy, for instance in a tundra region in summer, then flies, mosquitoes, and other insects may be a significant problem. Construct the shelter in an elevated and windy position away from bushes, and preferably near a water supply.

Avoid Frostbite

Frostbite is a possibility in icy and windy conditions that remove more heat from the body than it can produce. Reduced blood flow in the extremities can lead to frostbite, even at temperatures above freezing if the clothing is wet.

Prevent frostbite by keeping the extremities warm with clothing if possible, or by covering them with warm hands. Exercise lightly by doing such things as moving, chewing, and contracting muscles.

Neighbours should observe each other for signs of frostbite, such as pale, cold and unfeeling skin, the tip of the nose becoming red, skin turning blue or black (a final stage). **If frostbite is suspected, do not rub the area** or try to remove frozen gloves or shoes; this may do further damage to the skin, as would muscular movement. Try to gradually warm the area with body heat from other people, or use warm water or clothing.

Snow Blindness

Snow blindness is caused by glare from very white and reflective snow. It causes inflammation and burning in the eyes, tears running from the eyes, headaches, and reduced vision.

Prevent the onset of snow blindness by wearing sunglasses or by making improvised eye protectors, say by using cardboard strips with small slits to restrict the amount of light entering the eyes.

Fires and Other Signals

Alert rescuers.

Signal fires should be lit on a solid base (e.g. rocks) to prevent the fire melting the snow or ice and extinguishing itself.

Rescue signals can be laid out in the snow using canvas sheets held down by rocks, or by digging shallow trenches in the snow and laying branches or grass in them, or around the edges of the trench to enlarge the signal and make it stand out.

■ ✎ *Figure 12-10* **Prepare visible ground-to-air signals**

The aircraft itself may be very visible from the air if you can keep its upper surfaces clear from snow, especially if the aircraft is brightly coloured. For this reason, many aircraft that regularly operate in Arctic or Antarctic environments are painted bright red or orange.

Survival in a Hot, Arid Climate

Survival in a desert region depends mainly upon the body retaining and obtaining sufficient fluids to avoid dehydration and overheating.

After touchdown and coming to a stop, it is important to remove water and other rations and the emergency equipment from the aircraft as quickly as possible because of the increased risk of fire, and then to find cool and shady protection. As many articles as possible should be taken from the aircraft, including seat cushions and blankets (to be used as cooling insulation from the hot ground by day and for warmth at night).

When the environmental temperature is above 30°C, the greatest loss of water is caused by sweating, which is the natural cooling mechanism of the body when heat loss by convection is insufficient. The evaporation of moisture on the skin absorbs heat (the latent heat of vaporisation), and so cools the skin and the rest of the body. The initial aims of survival in very hot and dry weather are therefore to:

Minimise sweating.

- **reduce body heat** and minimise sweating; and
- **find water** (possibly in the cool of the night).

Gather Survivors and Allot Duties

The leader (normally the pilot-in-command unless incapacitated) should allot duties to fit survivors, such as:

Organise survivors.

- **gather other survivors;**
- **assemble emergency equipment,** first-aid kits, rope, etc.;
- **activate the ELT** if so decided, or fire off flares if help is nearby;
- **have a person stay by the aircraft** and use the radio if possible;
- **prepare ground-to-air signals;**
- **collect clothing** (desert areas can be cold at night);
- **gather food and water supplies** (especially water);
- **begin construction** of a shady and open-sided shelter;
- **search for firewood** or other combustible material;
- **select a toilet area,** some distance from the proposed shelter; and
- **have a person maintain watch** for possible search aircraft.

Activate the appropriate emergency signals, or plan when to activate them. If the radio in the aircraft is usable, and there is no risk of fire, then it can be used to broadcast Mayday calls, either on the local frequency most likely to be used, or on the emergency frequency 121·5 MHz. Conservation of the battery should be considered, and the radio only used at times when it is likely to be most effective.

Fires laid out in a clearing can also generate a lot of smoke by day that will be visible for many miles by day, and with flames that may be visible by night. Perhaps three fires laid out 5 or 10 metres apart in an unusual and unnatural triangle would attract attention more easily than just one large fire. Oil drained from the engine could also be added to increase the amount of smoke.

Fires should be lit in a cleared and open area – away from overhanging trees – as the risk of setting fire to the entire area of vegetation around you would be high in hot and dry climates, especially if it is windy.

Clothing

Protect the body.

Light clothing is the best protection against sunburn and heat exposure, especially if all parts of the body can be covered, including the back of the neck and the head. This will also reduce the need for water, especially if sweating is kept to a minimum, and provide protection against sand and insects. A single layer of loosely worn clothing will minimise any heat gain, and maximise the amount of heat lost through sweating.

The cooling benefit of any sweating will be maximised by light clothing worn loosely.

Good shoes should be worn as protection against the hot ground and also as protection against insects, spiders, snakes, scorpions and other inhabitants of desert regions. Shoes and clothing should be shaken and checked clear of insects, spiders, etc., before being put on.

If there is a lot of dust or sand in the air, which will be the case in duststorms or sandstorms, use a handkerchief or shirt to protect the mouth, nose and eyes.

Find Shade and Set Up Camp

It is important to minimise the increase in body temperature and the loss of fluids. Finding a cool and shady place is vital! Solid shade is better than leafy or intermittent shade.

Do not consider travelling by day unless a copious water supply is guaranteed. Set up camp near the aircraft if possible (i.e. within some hundreds of metres from it), since the aircraft will probably be very visible to search aircraft. If you move further away than this, leave arrows indicating the direction of where you have gone to set-up camp. There have been cases where abandoned aircraft and cars have been found, but no survivors – they had wandered away and perished in the desert.

Take shelter.

Any enclosed space such as the cockpit of the aircraft, even though it may provide shade, will very quickly heat up as a result of heat soaking in the sun, and may even become much warmer than the outside air temperature. A naturally shaded area, for instance in the shade of a tree (preferably near water), or in the shade of a rock face, generally provides the coolest and shadiest protection against heat and the sun.

The surrounding ground that has been shaded will also be relatively cool, whereas if you shelter in the shade of the aircraft wing the ground is likely to be very warm. A cooling breeze of fresh air is also helpful so, if you have a tent, keep the sides or door flaps open during the day.

Avoid sitting or lying on hot ground. Sitting or lying a foot above the warm ground, on cushions or life-jackets or on a bed constructed from branches, may reduce the temperatures that the body is exposed to by some 10–12°C and significantly reduce the loss of fluid through sweating. If moving around is inevitable, then move slowly to conserve energy and avoid sweating.

Consider the risks of setting up camp in a dry river bed – flash floods are possible, with water rushing down from storms miles away.

Be careful of using river rocks to surround a camp fire as they could possibly explode with the heat.

Protect the Eyes and Prevent Sunburn

Wear sunglasses, or make an eye protector from cardboard with small slits to see through, which should prevent the intense sunlight and reflection from the desert surface straining or damaging the eyes.

Being fully covered by clothing and a hat will be some protection against sunburn, but sun-protection cream should also be used to protect exposed parts of the body, such as the face, hands, and neck.

Find Water

In hot, arid areas, the human body requires about 4–5 litres of water a day to remain healthy, and even more if the person is exposed to the sun or is over-energetic in the conditions and perspires a lot.

The need for regular water is much greater than for solid foods – survival may be possible without food for 30 days, but for only a few hours or a day without water in an extreme desert environment. If food is available, only carbohydrates should be eaten as they require little water to be digested, whereas proteins and fats require more water to excrete the wastes formed during their metabolism.

One of the first tasks delegated to one of the survivors should be to retrieve any water or other drinking fluids on board the aircraft. Alcohol should not be consumed, and very sweet drinks are vastly inferior to plain water. Rainwater from any showers can be collected using plastic sheets, or caught in containers as it runs off the aircraft wings. Dew can also be collected at night if it is allowed to form on plastic sheets, canvas, the metal surfaces of the aircraft, plants, stones, etc. – up to a litre per hour can be collected in good conditions for the formation of dew.

Fresh water is vital.

With luck, there might be a running stream in the vicinity, but in desert areas this is unlikely, and a search for underground water might be required. Terrain, vegetation, birds, insects and animal tracks can sometimes provide clues as to where water might be found. Be aware of running towards shimmering mirages in the distance which can give the illusion of an expanse of water, and which have led some survivors to their death.

Fresh water can often be found if a hole is dug in the sand of a dry river bed. Water may be found sometimes just under the surface, but sometimes the hole may have to be a metre or more deep before any dampness is found. Even if the sand in the bottom of the hole is only slightly damp, water may gradually trickle in and accumulate over a period of time. Digging too deep may lead to salty water, which should not be drunk.

Fresh water can also sometimes be found in rock pools, even on stony hills. Ayers Rock in the middle of the Australian desert has rock pools permanent enough to contain fish. Some desert plants and trees also contain water.

Water transpirator bags designed for collecting water in desert environments are commercially available, and these are recommended for desert survival kits.

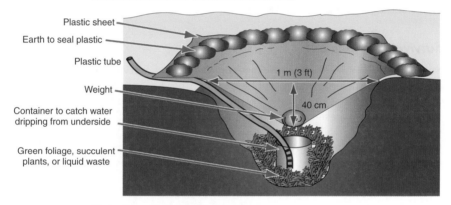

■ ✎ *Figure 12-11* **Procuring water**

Conserve Energy and Ration Water

Conserve energy.

Do not consider trying to hike out of the desert area by day unless there is absolute certainty of a water supply. Moving around under a hot sun may reduce survival time by half, compared with resting in a shady area. Travelling in the cool of the night, if travelling is considered necessary, is a much better proposition.

Monitor the condition of the survivors for any signs of dehydration, and ration water accordingly. The colour of urine is a good test of the need for water, with very dark yellow urine indicating some level of dehydration. Extreme thirst, headache, dizziness and disorientation are also indications.

Water is the best fluid to drink. Alcohol should not be consumed, and tea and coffee should be avoided, since they are diuretics, i.e. cause the loss of more fluid than is consumed. Control the activities of the survivors to conserve energy and to minimise the loss of fluids through sweating. If moving is inevitable, then move slowly.

People suffering heat exhaustion may have a flushed face at first, which might then go pale. They may sweat a lot even though their skin might feel cool, eventually becoming delirious or unconscious. They should lie down on their backs in a well-shaded area, and drink some water, possibly with a little salt added. If shivering, keep them warm with a blanket and a hot drink. Heat convulsions may occur in the leg and stomach muscles. A cool drink, possibly with some salt added, plus resting on the back in a cool area is the best remedy.

In an extreme case, a person might suffer heat stroke – indicated by a red face, hot and dry skin with no sweating, the pulse rate increasing and perhaps being very strong, and possible unconsciousness. The person should be laid on the back in the shade, the clothes loosened, and the body cooled with moist cloths and by fanning air.

Survival in a Jungle

Survival in a jungle depends first on making a survivable touchdown, which preferably will be in a clearing, but may have to be in the treetops. If in the unfortunate position of having to land in treetops, you should approach at the lowest possible flying speed.

An aircraft in the centre of a clearing, or suspended in the treetops, should be visible to searching aircraft. An aircraft that has fallen down through the trees, however, may be completely covered by foliage and not be visible from the air.

Gather Survivors and Allot Duties

The leader (normally the pilot-in-command unless incapacitated) should allot duties to fit survivors, such as:

Organise survivors.

• **gather other survivors**;
• **assemble emergency equipment**, first-aid kits, rope, etc;
• **activate the ELT** if so decided, or fire flares if help is nearby;
• **have a person stay by the aircraft** and use the radio if possible;
• **prepare ground-to-air signals**;
• **collect warm clothing** and food and water supplies;
• **commence construction** of a shelter;
• **search for firewood** or other combustible material and start a fire;
• **prepare hot drinks**;
• **select a toilet area** some distance from the proposed shelter, but itself sheltered if possible;
• **have a person maintain watch** for possible search aircraft.

If the aeroplane is hidden from the view of searching aircraft, then set up camp in a nearby clearing or on a peak visible from the air. Finding water and food in a jungle may be straight forward

– the greatest difficulty will probably be the searchers locating you, so make yourself visible.

Jungle Clothing

Protect the body. Remain fully clothed, with trousers tucked into the socks, as protection against insects, leeches, sharp blades of grass, etc., and always wear shoes. Take the usual protection as described earlier to protect against sunburn if appropriate. Cover all exposed parts including your face, especially during the periods of dusk and dawn, as protection against mosquitoes, which may carry malaria in some parts of the world (e.g. Africa). If no covering is available, smear your face and hands with mud, which will dry and provide some protection.

Try to keep your clothes clean and dry, to avoid skin problems developing. Wring out your clothes after going through water, and dry your body (check for any leeches) and shoes. Try to wash and dry your clothes periodically to keep them clean.

Any wound or infection should be cleaned and disinfected, and then covered, as serious infections can develop very quickly in a warm, moist environment.

Other Inhabitants of the Jungle

Jungles are a great home for all sorts of life, some of which is outright dangerous to humans, and some just of nuisance value.

Meat-eating animals such as tigers or crocodiles, or the piranha fish in some South American rivers, are a consideration, as are venomous or constricting snakes, and poisonous plants. Small animals and insects, such as wasps, bees, mosquitoes, ticks, leeches, spiders, centipedes, ants, and scorpions also need to be protected against. The mosquito can be very dangerous in the long term if it is carrying malaria. Malaria will not develop immediately, but some weeks or months after the victim has been bitten by the mosquitoes, with the effects possibly lasting for many years.

SNAKE BITE. Remember that not all snakes are poisonous. However it is wise to treat all snake bites as potentially dangerous. The modern treatment for snake bites is the *pressure–immobilisation* method:

- **Keep the victim lying down and resting;** this will localise the venom as much as possible.
- **Immediately apply a broad pressure-bandage** over the two puncture marks made by the fangs; the bandage should be as tight as you would apply to a sprained ankle.
- **Then extend the bandaging** by rolling the bandage firmly around as much of the limb as possible.
- **Do not remove the clothing,** as the movement will help the venom to circulate.

- **Leave the bandage in place** until medical facilities are reached.
- **Apply a splint to the limb** to immobilise it (if, as is most likely, the bite is on a limb).
- **If possible, transport the patient without panic** to the nearest hospital or medical clinic, preferably on a stretcher; otherwise keep the patient still and in shade, and reassure them until medical help arrives.
- **Should breathing begin to fail,** give artificial respiration.
- **Do not attempt to excise the venom** from the wound.

LEECHES, which attach themselves to the skin and then grow to a large size as they fill with blood, can best be removed by applying heat from a burning match. It is advisable to check for leeches every 30 minutes or so, as they can work their way through your clothing and on to your legs and arms without you noticing.

Use disinfectant, if available, on any bites or scratches.

Water

Water should be purified before drinking, either by sterilising it by boiling for five minutes or more, by using sterilising tablets, or by filtering it through a cloth. Near a muddy river or pool, clear water can sometimes be obtained by digging a deep hole a few metres away, and allowing water to seep in.

Fresh water is vital.

Coconut milk can also satisfy thirst.

Food

Food may be plentiful in a jungle area, but you need to be careful of disease in meat and poison in plants. Meat should always be well cooked to kill any parasites. Any plant food that irritates the skin or mouth should not be swallowed.

Shelter

Shelter may be needed at night or in rain, as protection against animal and insect life and the elements. Dry and rocky ground in a breezy area is preferable to a swamp. Try to keep above ground level, or separated from the ground by a plastic or rubber sheet, as protection against insects, leeches, and dampness.

Take shelter.

Attracting Attention

Make use of the radio and the ELT if available. If hidden from the view of searching aircraft by foliage, use smoky fires (using damp wood or adding engine oil will assist), or fire some flares when you hear an aircraft overhead.

Alert rescuers.

Index

A

acceleration, sensing 53
action
  feedback and 121
  information process, in 107
  judgement and 131
ADF *see* automatic direction finder
adrenalin 75
aerodrome notices and signs 187
agnosia 115
AH *see* artificial horizon
AI *see* attitude indicator
airmanship 141
Air Navigation Order
  first-aid kit contents 212
  life-raft equipment 199
airsickness 63
  avoiding 63
  first aid 207
airspeed indicator 167
  'glass' instrumentation of 168
  colour codes 167
  speed tape 168
alcohol 67
  alcohol-induced sleep 94
  flying after drinking 67
  visual acuity and 29
alertness 80, 93, 98
  body temperature and 98
altimeter
  10,000 ft pointer 171
  10,000 ft sector 172
  altitude alert system 171
  design 170, 172
  design-induced errors 171
  ground proximity warning systems 171
  misreading 171
  radar (radio) 171
  setting QNH 168
  subscale-setting designs 170
altitude, physiology and 3
alveoli 9
amnesia 119
analogue flight instruments 163, 168
analysis, in information process 106, 107
  reflexes 108
  thinking and flying 109

ANO *see* Air Navigation Order
anxiety 82
  symptoms 82
approach
  black-hole approach 44
  night approach 43
  perspectives on 43
  slope guidance 43
  using a PAPI 43
  white-out approach 44
arousal
  levels 76
  optimum level 77, 114
  performance and 114
  stress and 76
artificial horizon 162
ASI *see* airspeed indicator
astigmatism 47
atmosphere 11–12
attention and motivation 113
  divided attention 113
  selective attention 113
attitude indicator 162
  analogue versus digital 163
  different designs 165
attitudes, psychological
  to avoid 133
  to develop 133
auditory nerve 51
auricle 49
autokinesis 36
automatic direction finder 176
autonomic nervous system 109
Aviation Medical Examiner 66

B

balance
  cupula 55
  mechanism 23, 50, 54
  orientation 57
  semicircular canals 54
  sensing 53
  spatial disorientation 57
barotitis 50
barotrauma 16, 52
basic-T flight instrument layout 162
bends, after diving 17
binocular vision 27, 29

black-hole approach 44
blackout 54
blind spot 27, 28
blood
    donation 67
bodily feel 57
body clock 99, 101
    adjustment with jet lag 102
    time zones and 101
body rhythms 96
    cycle 96
    natural 96, 102
    sleep routine and 96
    zeitgebers 96
body temperature 98
    alertness and 98
    performance and 99
    survival and 215
bone marrow, donation 67
brain 4
    decision-maker 106, 119
    disorder, agnosia 115
    interpreting patterns 37
breathing
    difficulties – hypoxia/hyperventilation 16
burns, first aid 211

C

carbon dioxide in air 12
carbon monoxide poisoning 18, 69
    dealing with 19
    symptoms 18
cardiovascular disease 70
ccc *see* crew coordination concept
checklists 182
    check items, examples 184
    design features 182
    human involvement with 182
    scan approach 185
ciliary muscles 24
circadian disrhythmia 101
circadian rhythms 76, 96, 98
circulatory system 5
closed-loop system 152, 153
cochlea 50
cockpit
    display, design 161
    early designs 151
    ergonomics 141, 151
    see also flight deck, flight instruments
cockpit resource management 133
    standard operating procedures 186
cognition 107

cold environment, survival in 230
colds and flying 19, 69
colour vision 32
command 136
    remaining in 138
cones, in eyes 25
control column 157
controls
    control column 157
    design 156, 159
    engine controls 158
    flap lever 159
    functions, differentiation 159
    ram's horn 157
    sidestick 157
    throttle 157
    undercarriage lever 159
    yoke 157
control wheel 157
coordination ball 174
cornea 24
COSPAS/SARSAT satellite system 217
crew coordination concept (ccc) 134–135
Crew Resource Management (CRM) 141
CRM *see* cockpit resource management
cupula, balance mechanism 55

D

decision-making 106, 119, 129
    overload 125
    requirements 130
decompression sickness 16
deep shock, first aid 212
depressurisation 14
depth perception 31
design 155
    airspeed indicator 167
    altimeter 170, 172
    checklists 182
    controls 156
    EFIS 179
    flight director 175
    horizontal situation indicator 179
    induced errors, altimeter 171
    radio magnetic indicator 176
    seat-belt 155
    seats 155
    turn coordinator 174
design eye position 153
design population 154
DG *see* directional gyro
DI *see* direction indicator
diarrhoea 209

digital flight instruments 163, 168
directional gyro 166
direction indicator 165
    VOR display and 179
disability, and pilot licence 66
distress signals
    acoustic 223
    optical 219
    written notes 223
ditching 224
double vision 26
drugs, flying and 66

E

ears 49
    auditory nerve 51
    balance mechanism 50, 54
    barotitis 50
    cochlea 50
    Eustachian tubes 50, 68
    inner ear 50
    ossicles 49
    outer ear 49
    pain in 69
    semi-circular canals 50
    static organ 55
    structure 49
    vestibular apparatus 50
EFIS *see* electronic flight instrument systems
ELB *see* emergency locator beacon
electronic flight instrument systems 179
ELT *see* emergency locator transmitter
emergency equipment, preflight check 194
emergency frequencies, civil and military 217
emergency locator beacon 217
emergency locator transmitter 217
    when to activate 219
emergency position indicating radio
        beacon 217
empty field myopia 26, 35, 36
engine controls, design 158
EPIRB *see* emergency position indicating radio
        beacon
ergonomics 153
    and flight deck design 141, 151
Eustachian tubes 50
    dangers of flying when blocked 19, 60, 69
    pressure vertigo and 60
external visual aides 186
    aerodrome notices and signs 187
    taxiway markings and lighting 187
extroverts 99, 132
eyes 23

accommodation 25
adaptation to darkness 33
binocular vision 27, 29
blind spot 27, 28
ciliary muscles 24
cones 25
cornea 24
depth perception 31
eye test chart 29
foveal region 25
glasses and contact lenses 45, 70
iris 24
lens 24
light-sensitive cells 25
normal functions 29
retina 25
rods 25
sensitivity 25
structure 28
see also vision

F

fatigue 87
    cure for 87
    flying and 71
    guarding against 71
    long-term, chronic 87
    noise, from 51
    short-term, causes 71
    sleep deprivation and 71
    symptoms 87
    visual acuity and 29
    workload and 86
FD *see* flight director
FDI *see* flight director indicator
fight or flight, response to stress 75
fire 199
fire extinguishers 200
    BCF (Halon) 201
    carbon dioxide (CO_2) 202
    carriage of 200
    dry chemical 201
    foam 202
    using 202
    water 202
first aid 207
    accident, following 209
    airsickness and nausea 207
    bleeding 210
    burns 211
    deep shock 212
    fainting 207
    food poisoning 208

fractures 211
frostbite 227, 232
head injuries 209
hyperventilation 16
hypothermia 226
injured passengers 209
nose bleeding 208
seasickness 227
shock 212
snow blindness 232
St. John's Ambulance Association 207
sunburn 228
first-aid kits 212
fitness to fly 65–71
flares
  hand-held 221
  parachute 221
flickering lights, effect on vision 31
flight deck
  altitude alert devices 171
  attitude indicator 162
  cockpit checklists 182
  cockpit displays,design 161
  control column 157, 161
  control functions and differentiation 159
  controls design 156
  design 151
  design eye position 153
  designing work space 153
  design population and 154
  early cockpits 151
  engine controls 158
  ergonomics 153
  fuel tank controls 158
  landing gear lever 159
  manuals 186
  seat-belts 155
  seats 155
  standardisation of displays 161
  standard operating procedures 186
  throttle 157
  undercarriage lever 159
  vertical speed indicator 173
flight deck see also flight instruments
flight director 175
  crossbars 175
  flying wings 175
  programmable modes 176
flight director indicator 175
flight instruments
  ADF
  airspeed indicator 167
  altimeter 168

altitude alert devices 171
attitude indicator 162
coordination ball 174
electronic flight instrument systems 179
flight director 175
head-up displays 181
horizontal situation indicator 177
instantaneous vertical speed indicator 173
magnetic compass 166
non-instinctive displays 167
rate of turn 174
RMI 176
standard layout 161
turn coordinator 174
turn indicator 174
vertical speed indicator 173
VOR display 177
flying at altitude
  barotrauma 52
  colds, sinus problems and 19
  decompression sickness 16
  glare, protection from 30
  hyperventilation 16
  hypoxia 13
  scuba diving, after 16
food poisoning and flying 69, 208
foveal region, eyes 25
fractures
  first aid 211
frostbite 227, 232
fuel tank controls 158

G

glare, protection from
  snow blindness 232
glasses and contact lenses 45
  for flying 47
'glass' navigation displays 179
g-loading 14
  vision and 26
GPWS see ground proximity warning system
graveyard spiral 59
greyout 54
ground proximity warning system 171
gyro horizon 165

H

hallucinations 114
harness design 155
head injuries
  first aid 209
head-up displays 181
hearing

frequency or pitch 51
loudness or intensity 51
hearing loss 52
  conductive 52
  minimising 53
  presbycusis 53
  sensory or noise-induced 53
heliograph 220
heading indicator *see* direction indicator
HI *see* direction indicator indicator
horizontal situation indicator 179
hot environment, survival in 233
HSI *see* horizontal situation indicator
HUD *see* head-up displays
hypermetropia 46
hyperopia 46
hyperthermia 77, 228
hyperventilation 16
  treating 16
hypnotics 90
hypoglycemia 80
hypothermia 78, 224
  after ditching 226
hypoxia 13
  anaemic hypoxia 15
  avoiding 15
  hypoxic hypoxia 15
  pressurised cabins 14
  time of useful consciousness 14
  visual acuity and 29

I

IAS *see* indicated airspeed
Illness and drugs, flying and 66
Illusions
  Coriolis 60
  information processing and 114
  the 'leans' 58
  oculogravic 61
  somatogravic 61
  vertigo 60
  vestibular 57
  visual 36
  visual, on approach 39, 41
ILS *see* instrument landing system
indicated airspeed 167
information processing 105
  action and feedback 121
  amnesia 119
  analysis 106
  anticipation 112
  attention and motivation 113
  autonomic activities 109

  conditioned reflexes 108
  conflicting information 125
  decision-making 119
  divided attention 113
  encoding 117
  episodic memory 118
  event memory 118
  excessive workload 125
  experience and expectation 111
  long-term memory 117
  meaning memory 118
  memory 115
  mental activity levels 107
  mental overload 124
  mental workload 123
  mind-set 112
  model 106
  motivation 114
  motor programmes 107, 120
  Pavlov's dogs experiment 108
  perception 111
  perception, abnormalities in 114
  perception, stress effect on 113
  precoding 113
  receptors 109
  rehearsing 117
  response time 120, 122
  selective attention 113
  semantic memory 118
  sensory confusion 112
  sensory memory 110, 115
  sensory nerves 110
  sensory threshold 110
  short-term memory 116
  stimulation, sensing and perception 109
  stimulus 106
  thinking and flying 109
  tunnel vision 123
  working memory 117
  workload 123, 124
insomnia 89
instantaneous vertical speed indicator 173
instrument landing system 176
international distress signal 223
introverts 132
iris 24
IVSI *see* instantaneous vertical speed indicator

J

jet lag 101
  body clock adjustment 102
  circadian disrhythmia 101
  travelling east or west 102

zeitgebers and 102
judgement 129
  cognitive 129
  making a decision 130
  perceptual 129
  personality and attitude influence 131
jungle survival 238

L

leadership
  qualities 135
  style 135
leans, illusion 58
lens, eyes 24
life-jackets 197
life-rafts 198
long-sightedness 46
lungs 11

M

magnetic compass 166
  indication errors 166
manuals in aircraft 186
mean sea level pressure, altimeter 168
medical checks, flying and 66
medication, flying and 66
melatonin 90
memory
  decision-making and 119
  encoding 117
  episodic memory 118
  event memory 118
  long-term memory 117
  meaning memory 118
  mental overload and 125
  semantic memory 118
  sensory memory 110, 115, 125
  short-term memory 116, 125
  spatial part 118
  working memory 117
mental activity, information processing 107
mental fitness 65
mental overload 124
mental workload 123
middle ear 49
mind-set 112
motion sickness 63
  avoiding 63
  first aid 207
motivation 114
motor programmes 105, 107, 120
  flying 120
myopia 45

empty field myopia 26, 35, 36

N

nausea, first aid 207
navigation displays
  analogue 162
  'glass' 179
NDB see non-directional beacon
nervous system 3, 105
  brain 106
night vision 33
  rods in eyes 25
nitrogen, in air 12
noise
  fatigue and damage from 51
  minimising effect of 53
  safe limits 79
non-directional beacon 176
NUTA – Notice, Understand and Think
  Ahead 142

O

OBS see omni bearing selector
oculogravic illusion 61
omni bearing selector 177
open-loop system 152
optical signals 219
optic nerve 23
  blind spot and 28
orientation 57
ossicles 49
otoliths, balance mechanism 55
oxygen equipment, in aircraft 199
ozone 12

P

PAPI see precision approach path indicator
passengers
  briefing 195
  care of 191
  clothing, for safety 194
  injuries, first aid 209
Pavlov's dogs experiment 108
perception 106, 111
  abnormalities in 114
  depth 31
  stress, effect of 113
performance
  airsickness, effect of 80
  –arousal relationship 114
  cycle 98
  psychomotor 99
  rhythms 100

peripheral vision 25
personality and attitude 131
PF *see* pilot flying
physical fitness 65
physiology, altitude and 3
pilot
   awareness 193
   capability versus workload 86, 123, 124
   –machine interface 153
   workload, excessive 125
   workload, mental 123
pilot flying 134
pilot-in-command 136
   attitudes to avoid 133
   attitudes to develop 133
   cockpit resource management 133
   leadership style 135
   qualities 135
   remaining in command 138
   responsibility for safety 193
pilot not flying 134
pinna, ears 49
PNF *see* pilot not flying
precision approach path indicator 43
precoding 113
presbycusis 53
presbyopia 47
pressurised cabins 14
proprioceptive sense 57

Q

QNH, altimeter setting 168

R

radar (radio) altimeter 171
radio magnetic indicator 176
rapid eye movement 91
rate of turn indication 174
RCC *see* Rescue Coordination Centre
receptors 109
recovery position 209
red-out 54
reflexes 108
   conditioned reflexes 108
   information processing and 108
REM *see* rapid eye movement
Rescue Coordination Centre 217
respiration 8
   problems 19, 60, 68
retina 25
RMI *see* radio magnetic indicator
rods, in eyes 25
rudder pedals, adjustment 155

S

safety 191
   awareness 191
   fire extinguishers 200
   fire prevention 199
   life-jackets 197
   life-rafts 198
   on board 195
   oxygen equipment 199
   passenger briefing 195
   prior to boarding 193
scan checks, of cockpit 185
scanning sky for aircraft
   daylight 33
   night 35
scuba diving, before flying 16
sea dye marker 222
search and rescue visual signals 222
seasickness 227
seat-belts 155
   checking 156, 196
   design 155
seats
   adjustment 155
   design 155
semicircular canals 54
sense organs 109
sensory nerves 110
sensory threshold 110
shock, first aid 212
short-sightedness 26, 37, 45
sidestick 157
signal mirror 220
signal rockets 221
sinus problems and flying 19, 69
Situational Awareness (SA) 141
skills 105, 120
   skill stress 80
sleep 88
   alcohol-induced 94
   body rhythms and 96
   body temperature and 98
   circadian rhythms and 98
   credits 88, 94
   deprivation and fatigue 71
   disorders 89
   fatigue cure 87
   jet lag and 101
   paradoxical 92
   rapid eye movement 91
   sleep/wakefulness rhythm 96
   slow-wave 92

stages of 91
strategies for getting good 89
zeitgebers and 96
sleeping drugs (hypnotics) 90
melatonin 90
sleep patterns 92, 97
disturbed, effect of 93, 95
high latitudes 98
performance cycle 98
shorter-than-normal 94
smoking, and flying 70
snow blindness 232
somatogravic illusion 61
somatosensory inputs 23
SOP see standard operating procedures
sound 51
frequency or pitch 51
loudness or intensity 51
typical noise levels 52
spatial disorientation 57
standard operating procedures 134, 186
static organ, ears 55
stimulus 106
arousal level and 76
misinterpretation 114
responding to 74
stress 73
anxiety 82
causes 73, 77–81
chronic stress overload 82
defence mechanisms against 85
emotional 81
management 73, 82, 83
non-physical stress 76
overload 74
perceived pressures 75
perception, effect on 113
physical stress 75
pilot workload and 85
psychological 81
self-imposed, avoiding 85
skill stress 80
unacceptable means of coping with 85
work-related 81
stressor 73, 77
acute 73
chronic 73
environmental or physical 77
psychological and emotional 81
survival 215
body temperature, maintaining 215
cold climates 230
ditching 224

emergency signals 219, 227, 233, 240
hot climate 233
international distress signal 223
jungle 238
search and rescue visual signals 222
shelter 231
UK Mission Control Centre 217
survival equipment
COSPAS/SARSAT satellite system 217
emergency locator transmitter 217
flashlight or spotlight 222
global satellite system 217
life-jackets 197, 198, 224
radio and transponder 216
sea dye marker 222
signal mirror 220
signal rockets 221
water transpirator bags 237

T

taxiway markings and lighting 187
TCAS see traffic alert and collision avoidance
    system
TDODAR 144
thinking and flying 109
Threat and Error Management (TEM) 141
Threat and Error Management TEM 145
throttle 157
time of useful consciousness 14
time-sharing 113, 119
traffic alert and collision avoidance system 171,
    180
transition altitude 169
transponder
emergency code 216, 219
emergency use 216
TUC see time of useful consciousness
tunnel vision 123
turn coordinator 174
turn indicator 174

U

UK Mission Control Centre 217
upper respiratory tract problems 19, 60, 68

V

Valsalva movement 19, 69
VASI see visual approach slope indicator system
VDF see VHF direction finding
vertical speed indicator 173
vertigo 60
flicker vertigo 60
pressure vertigo 60

vestibular illusions 57, 61
vestibular inputs 23
VHF direction finding 217
VHF survival beacon 217
vision
    acuity 29
    astigmatism 47
    binocular vision 27
    central and peripheral, difference 30
    colour vision 32
    dark adaptation 33
    double vision 26
    empty field myopia 26, 35, 36
    flickering lights 31
    glare 30
    glasses and contact lenses 45
    hyperopia 46
    long-sightedness 46
    monocular vision 26
    myopia 45
    night vision, protecting 33
    orientation 57
    peripheral vision 25
    presbyopia 47
    scanning for aircraft 33, 35
    short-sightedness 26, 37, 45
    snow blindness 232
    testing with eye chart 29
    see also eyes
visual acuity 29
    testing 29
visual aids, external 186
visual approach slope indicator system 43
visual illusions 36
    approach, while on 39, 41
    autokinesis 36
    black-hole approach 44
    false expectations 37
    false horizons 39
    interpreting patterns 37
    self-motion 36
    white-out approach 44
VOR display 177
VSB *see* VHF survival beacon
VSI *see* vertical speed indicator

W

water
    collecting at sea 228
    finding in hot, arid areas 236
    precautions before drinking 240
    transpirator bags 237
white-out approach 44

wind chill 78
    shelter against 231
workload
    excessive 125
    mental workload 123
    performance and 114
    pilot capability versus 86, 123

Y

yoke, control 157

Z

zeitgebers 96, 102

The Air Pilot's **Manual**

EASA Operational Procedures

Contents

Preamble 255

Chapter 1 – Operation of Aircraft...257
Definitions 257
Applicability 278
ICAO Annex 6, General Requirements 279
Practice Questions 287

Chapter 2 – Noise Abatement Procedures 291
Influence of the Flight Procedure 293
Runway Incursion Awareness 299
Aerodrome Signals & Markings 302
Light Signals (SERA Appendix 1 (EU Reg. 923/2012)) 310
Callsigns for Aircraft 327
Taxi Clearances 327
Practice Questions 331

Chapter 3 – Fire or Smoke 333
Cause 333
Carburettor Fire 335
Engine Fire 336
Fire in the Cabin and Cockpit 339
Smoke in the Cockpit and Cabin 344
Practice Questions 347

Chapter 4 – Windshear and Microburst 351

Effects and Recognition during Departure and Approach 351

The Effect of Windshear 351

Windshear 353

Overshoot and Undershoot Effect 356

Practice Questions 361

Chapter 5 – Wake Turbulence 363

Cause 363

List of Relevant Parameters 365

Actions taken when crossing traffic, during take-off and landing 367

Practice Questions 373

Chapter 6 – Emergency & Precautionary Landings 375

Definition 375

Cause 376

Passenger Information 378

Evacuation 380

Ditching in Water 381

Practice Questions 385

Chapter 7 – Contaminated Runways 389

Kinds of Contamination 389

Estimated Surface Friction & Friction Coefficient 392

Practice Questions 397

Abbreviations 399

Index 401

Editorial Team

Jonathan Shooter

Jonathan had his first trial lesson on his twelfth birthday before going on to gain his PPL with the help of an RAF flying scholarship. He went on to fly with the University Air Squadron before gaining airline sponsorship in conjunction with one of Europe's largest flying schools. He taught the PPL and associated ratings at Elstree aerodrome before gaining an internal promotion to teach the CPL and Instrument Rating at the commercial college at Cranfield aerodrome. In 2004 he was awarded a flying bursary from The Air League. After two years he joined his sponsoring airline and flew the Dash 8 Q400 throughout Europe. In 2005 he joined Europe's largest tour operator and flew the Boeing 757, 767, A320 & A321 both on short and long haul operations. He currently flies the 737NG and has over 7000 hrs with 1500 hrs instructional experience on commercial courses. He holds European, Canadian and American airline transport licences and is an authorised PPL examiner for both single and multi-engine aeroplanes.

Dorothy Saul-Pooley LLB(Hons) FRAeS

Dorothy holds an ATPL (A) and a CPL (H), and is both an instructor and examiner on aeroplanes and an instructor on helicopters. She is Head of Training for a school dedicated to running Flight Instructor courses at Shoreham. She is also a CAA Flight Instructor Examiner. In addition, having qualified as a solicitor in 1982, Dorothy acted for many years as a consultant specialising in aviation and insurance liability issues, and has lectured widely on air law and aviation insurance. This highly unusual combination of qualifications led to her appointment as Honorary Solicitor to the Guild of Air Pilots and Navigators (GAPAN).

Dorothy is a Fellow of the Royal Aeronautical Society, Past Chairman of the GAPAN Instructor Committee of which she was a founding member and the prime instigator of the Guild's Joint Forum with Central Flying School at RAF Cranwell for Senior Flying Instructors. She is a Past Chairman of the Education & Training Committee. After serving as a Warden on the Court of GAPAN for three years, she was appointed Master for the year 2014-2015 of the newly renamed Honourable Company of Air Pilots. She is also Chairman of the Professional Flying Instructors Association.

In 2003 Dorothy was awarded the Jean Lennox Bird Trophy for her contribution to aviation and support of Women in Aviation and the BWPA (British Women Pilots Association). In 2013, Dorothy received the prestigious award of a Master Air Pilots Certificate from GAPAN. In 2015 she was awarded the Brabazon Cup by the BWPA for her outstanding achievement in aviation. A regular contributor to seminars and conferences, Dorothy is the author and editor of a large number of flying training books and has published articles in legal and insurance journals and many in aviation magazines. A regular contributor to seminars, conferences and aviation publications. Dorothy is the author and editor of a number of flying training books and has published articles in legal and insurance journals.

Daljeet Gill BA(Hons)
Daljeet is the Head of Design & Development for Pooleys Flight Equipment and editor of the Air Pilot's Manuals, Pre-flight Briefing and R/T Communications as well as many other publications. Daljeet has been involved with the editing, typesetting and designing of all Pooleys publications and products since she joined us in 2001. Graduating in 1999 with a BA(Hons) in Graphic Design, she deals with marketing, advertising, exhibition design and technical design of our manufactured products in the UK. She maintains our website and produces our Pooleys Catalogue. Daljeet's design skills and imaginative approach have brought a new level of clarity and readability to the projects she has touched.

Acknowledgements
Thanks to Jo Shooter and all of my flying colleagues for helping to proof read this book.

Preamble

EASA Part-FCL.120 & 215 requires that applicants for the LAPL(A) and PPL(A) study a course of theoretical knowledge training and pass a theoretical knowledge examination in nine subjects, which is an increase on previous legislation.

The aim of this manual is to provide the required material to study for, and pass, the EASA Part-FCL LAPL(A) and PPL(A) Operational Procedures theoretical knowledge examination. The subject matter covered in Operational Procedures is common to other subjects in both the LAPL(A) and PPL(A) syllabus; therefore, it is recommended that this exam be taken once all of the other series of Air Pilot Manuals have been studied.

The EU Commission has implemented Regulation 923/2012 introducing the Standardised European Rules of the Air into the UK and as a result, UK Rules of the Air have been substantially modified (see Rules of the Air Regulations 2015).

INTENTIONALLY BLANK

Operation of Aircraft

Definitions

The following summarises definitions used in the ICAO Annexes pertinent to EASA Part-FCL. You should be familiar with these definitions because they are used in the PPL examinations. Not every definition has been included as they are not appropriate for PPL operations. The full list is contained in ICAO Annex Operation of Aircraft Part 2.

Acts of Unlawful Interference. These are acts or attempted acts such as to jeopardise the safety of civil aviation and air transport, i.e:

i. Unlawful seizure of aircraft in flight,

ii. Unlawful seizure of aircraft on the ground,

iii. Hostage-taking on board an aircraft or on aerodromes,

iv. Forcible intrusion on board an aircraft, at an airport or on the premises of an aeronautical facility,

v. Introduction on board an aircraft or at an airport of a weapon or hazardous device or material intended for criminal purposes,

vi. Communication of false information as to jeopardise the safety of an aircraft in flight or on the ground, of passengers, crew, ground personnel or the general public, at an airport or on the premises of a civil aviation facility.

Aerial Work. An aircraft operation in which an aircraft is used for specialised services such as agriculture, construction, photography, surveying, observation and patrol, search and rescue, aerial advertisement, etc.

Aerodrome. A defined area on land or water (including any buildings, installations and equipment) intended to be used either wholly or in part for the arrival, departure and surface movement of aircraft.

Aerodrome Operating Minima (AOM). The limits of usability of an aerodrome for:

a. Take-off, expressed in terms of runway visual range and/or visibility and, if necessary, cloud conditions;

b. Landing in precision approach and landing operations, expressed in terms of visibility and/or runway visual range and decision altitude/height (DA/H) as appropriate to the category of the operation;

c. Landing in approach and landing operations with vertical guidance, expressed in terms of visibility and/or runway visual range and decision altitude/height (DA/H); and

d. Landing in non-precision approach and landing operations, expressed in terms of visibility and/or runway visual range, minimum descent altitude/height (MDA/H) and, if necessary, cloud conditions.

Aeroplane. A power-driven heavier-than-air aircraft, deriving its lift in flight chiefly from aerodynamic reactions on surfaces which remain fixed under given conditions of flight.

Aircraft. Any machine that can derive support in the atmosphere from the reactions of the air other than the reactions of the air against the earth's surface.

Aircraft Operating Manual. An operator should provide operations staff and flight crew with an aircraft operating manual, for each aircraft type operated, containing the normal, abnormal and emergency procedures relating to the operation of the aircraft. The manual should be consistent with the aircraft flight manual and checklists to be used. The design of the manual should observe Human Factors principles.

Airworthy. The status of an aircraft, engine, propeller or part when it conforms to its approved design and is in a condition for safe operation.

Alternate Aerodrome. An aerodrome to which an aircraft may proceed when it becomes either impossible or inadvisable to proceed to or to land at the aerodrome of intended landing where the necessary services and facilities are available, where aircraft performance requirements can be met and which is operational at the expected time of use. Alternate aerodromes include the following:

Take-off Alternate. An alternate aerodrome at which an aircraft would be able to land should this become necessary shortly after take-off and it is not possible to use the aerodrome of departure.

En-route Alternate. An alternate aerodrome at which an aircraft would be able to land in the event that a diversion becomes necessary while en route.

Destination Alternate. An alternate aerodrome at which an aircraft would be able to land should it become either impossible or inadvisable to land at the aerodrome of intended landing.

> *Note.* — The aerodrome from which a flight departs may also be an en-route or a destination alternate aerodrome for that flight.

Area Navigation (RNAV). A method of navigation which permits aircraft operation on any desired flight path within the coverage of ground or space-based navigation aids or within the limits of the capability of self-contained aids, or a combination of these.

> *Note.* — Area navigation includes performance-based navigation as well as other operations that do not meet the definition of performance-based navigation.

Commercial Air Transport Operation. An aircraft operation involving the transport of passengers, cargo or mail for remuneration or hire.

Continuing Airworthiness. The set of processes by which an aircraft, engine, propeller or part complies with the applicable airworthiness requirements and remains in a condition for safe operation throughout its operating life.

Corporate Aviation Operation. The non-commercial operation or use of aircraft by a company for the carriage of passengers or goods as an aid to the conduct of company business, flown by a professional pilot(s) employed to fly the aircraft.

Dangerous Goods. Articles or substances which are capable of posing a risk to health, safety, property or the environment and which are shown in the list of dangerous goods in the Technical Instructions or which are classified according to those Instructions.

Note. — Dangerous goods are classified in ICAO Annex 18, Chapter 3.

Emergency Locator Transmitter (ELT). A generic term describing equipment which broadcasts distinctive signals on designated frequencies and, depending on application, may be automatically activated by impact or be manually activated. An ELT may be any of the following:

Automatic Fixed ELT (ELT(AF)). An automatically activated ELT which is permanently attached to an aircraft.

Automatic Portable ELT (ELT(AP)). An automatically activated ELT which is rigidly attached to an aircraft but readily removable from the aircraft.

Automatic Deployable ELT (ELT(AD)). An ELT which is rigidly attached to an aircraft and which is automatically deployed and activated by impact, and, in some cases, also by hydrostatic sensors. Manual deployment is also provided.

Survival ELT (ELT(S)). An ELT which is removable from an aircraft, stowed so as to facilitate its ready use in an emergency, and manually activated by survivors.

Engine. A unit used or intended to be used for aircraft propulsion. It consists of at least those components and equipment necessary for functioning and control, but excludes the propeller/rotors (if applicable).

Enhanced Vision System (EVS). A system to display electronic real-time images of the external scene achieved through the use of image sensors.

Extended Flight over Water. A flight operated over water at a distance of more than 93 km (50 NM), or 30 minutes at normal cruising speed, whichever is the lesser, away from land suitable for making an emergency landing.

Flight Crew Member. A licensed crew member charged with duties essential to the operation of an aircraft during a flight duty period.

Flight Manual. A manual, associated with the certificate of airworthiness, containing limitations within which the aircraft is to be considered airworthy, and instructions and information necessary to the flight crew members for the safe operation of the aircraft.

Flight Plan. Specified information provided to air traffic services units, relative to an intended flight or portion of a flight of an aircraft.

Flight Recorder. Any type of recorder installed in the aircraft for the purpose of complementing accident/incident investigation.

Flight Simulation Training Device (FSTD). Any one of the following three types of apparatus in which flight conditions are simulated on the ground:

A Flight Simulator, which provides an accurate representation of the flight deck of a particular aircraft type to the extent that the mechanical, electrical, electronic, etc. aircraft systems control functions, the normal environment of flight crew members, and the performance and flight characteristics of that type of aircraft are realistically simulated;

A Flight Procedures Trainer, which provides a realistic flight deck environment, and which simulates instrument responses, simple control functions of mechanical, electrical, electronic, etc. aircraft systems, and the performance and flight characteristics of aircraft of a particular class;

A Basic Instrument Flight Trainer, which is equipped with appropriate instruments, and which simulates the flight deck environment of an aircraft in flight in instrument flight conditions.

Flight Time — Aeroplanes. The total time from the moment an aeroplane first moves for the purpose of taking off until the moment it finally comes to rest at the end of the flight.

Note. — Flight time as here defined is synonymous with the term "block to block" time or "chock to chock" time in general usage which is measured from the time an aeroplane first moves for the purpose of taking off until it finally stops at the end of the flight.

General Aviation Operation. An aircraft operation other than a commercial air transport operation or an aerial work operation.

Head-Up Display (HUD). A display system that presents flight information into the pilot's forward external field of view.

Instrument Meteorological Conditions (IMC). Meteorological conditions expressed in terms of visibility, distance from cloud, and ceiling, less than the minima specified for visual meteorological conditions.

Large Aeroplane. An aeroplane of a maximum certificated take-off mass of over 5700 kg.

Maintenance. The performance of tasks required to ensure the continuing airworthiness of an aircraft, including any one or combination of overhaul, inspection, replacement, defect rectification, and the embodiment of a modification or repair.

Maintenance Programme. A document which describes the specific scheduled maintenance tasks and their frequency of completion and related procedures, such as a reliability programme, necessary for the safe operation of those aircraft to which it applies.

Maintenance Release. A document which contains a certification confirming that the maintenance work to which it relates has been completed in a satisfactory manner, either in accordance with the approved data and the procedures described in the maintenance organisation's procedures manual or under an equivalent system.

Meteorological Information. Meteorological report, analysis, forecast, and any other statement relating to existing or expected meteorological conditions.

Night. The hours between the end of evening civil twilight and the beginning of morning civil twilight or such other period between sunset and sunrise, as may be prescribed by the appropriate authority.

Note. — Civil twilight ends in the evening when the centre of the sun's disc is 6 degrees below the horizon and begins in the morning when the centre of the sun's disc is 6 degrees below the horizon.

Operational Flight Plan. The operator's plan for the safe conduct of the flight based on considerations of aeroplane performance, other operating limitations and relevant expected conditions on the route to be followed and at the aerodromes concerned.

Operations Manual. A manual containing procedures, instructions and guidance for use by operational personnel in the execution of their duties.

Operator. A person, organisation or enterprise engaged in or offering to engage in an aircraft operation.

Pilot-in-Command. The pilot designated by the operator or the owner as being in command and charged with the safe conduct of a flight.

Psychoactive Substances. Alcohol, opioids, cannabinoids, sedatives and hypnotics, cocaine, other psychostimulants, hallucinogens, and volatile solvents; whereas coffee and tobacco are excluded.

Repair. The restoration of an aeronautical product to an airworthy condition to ensure that the aircraft continues to comply with the design aspects of the appropriate airworthiness requirements used for the issuance of the type certificate for the respective aircraft type, after it has been damaged or subjected to wear.

Runway Visual Range (RVR). The range over which the pilot of an aircraft on the centre line of a runway can see the runway surface markings or the lights delineating the runway or identifying its centre line.

Safety Management System. A systematic approach to managing safety, including the necessary organisational structures, accountabilities, policies and procedures.

State of Registry. The State on whose register the aircraft is entered.

Visual Meteorological Conditions (VMC). Meteorological conditions expressed in terms of visibility, distance from cloud, and ceiling, equal to or better than specified minima.

The following summarises terms contained in the ICAO Annexes used in EASA Part-FCL. Whilst it is clearly impossible to memorise all of these terms you should at least be familiar with them as you will be asked questions on them in the theoretical knowledge exam. Typical questions asked are found in Chapter 1 Questions.

ICAO ANNEX TERMINOLOGY

Accident
Event associated with the operation of an aircraft in which the aircraft sustains significant damage, causes significant damage, or causes personal injury. Specifically, an event that occurs between the time any person boards the aircraft with the intention of flight and the time all persons have disembarked, where:

- a person is fatally or seriously injured as a result of:
  - being in the aircraft; or
  - being in direct contact with any part of the aircraft, including parts that have fallen off the aircraft; or
  - direct exposure to jet blast;

Note: Exceptions are when the injuries are from natural causes, self-inflicted or inflicted by other persons, or when the injuries are to stowaways hiding outside the areas normally available to passengers and crew (such as cargo bays).

- the aircraft sustains damage or structural failure which:
  - jeopardises the structural strength, performance or flight characteristics of the aircraft; or
  - would normally require major repair or replacement of the affected component;

Note: Exceptions are engine failure or damage (when the damage is limited to the engine, its cowlings or accessories), damage limited to propellers, wing tips, antennae, tyres, brakes, fairings, small dents or puncture holes in the aircraft skin.

- the aircraft is missing or is completely inaccessible.

Note: An aircraft is considered to be missing when the official search has been terminated and the wreckage has not been found.

Advisory airspace
Airspace of defined dimensions, or a designated route, within which air traffic advisory service is available.

Advisory route
Designated route along which air traffic advisory service is available.

Aerial work
Aircraft operations where aircraft are used for specialised purposes, such as agriculture, construction, fish-spotting, photography, surveying, search and rescue etc.

Aerodrome
Defined area of land or water used for the arrival, departure and surface movement of aircraft.

ICAO ANNEX TERMINOLOGY

Aerodrome beacon
An aeronautical beacon used to indicate the location of an aerodrome from the air.

Aerodrome control service
Air traffic control service for aerodrome traffic.

Aerodrome control tower
A unit established to provide air traffic control services to aerodrome traffic.

Aerodrome elevation
The elevation (height above sea level) of the highest point of the landing area at the aerodrome.

Aerodrome identification sign
A sign at an aerodrome that indicates the name of the aerodrome from the air.

Aerodrome reference point
Designated geographical location of an aerodrome.

Aerodrome traffic
All traffic on the manoeuvring area of an aerodrome and all aircraft flying in the vicinity of an aerodrome.

Note: An aircraft is considered to be 'in the vicinity of an aerodrome' when it is in, entering, or leaving an aerodrome traffic circuit.

Aerodrome traffic circuit
The specified path to be flown by aircraft operating in the vicinity of an aerodrome.

Aeronautical beacon
An aeronautical ground light visible from all directions, either continuously or intermittently, to indicate the location of a particular point on the surface of the earth.

Aeronautical fixed service (AFS)
A telecommunication service between specified fixed points provided primarily for the safety of air navigation and for the regular, efficient and economical operation of air services.

Aeronautical ground light
A light provided to aid air navigation (not a light on an aircraft).

Aeronautical Information Publication (AIP)
A document issued by a State that contains permanent aeronautical information essential to air navigation.

Aeronautical station
A land (or sea) station in the aeronautical mobile service.

Aeronautical telecommunication service
A telecommunication service provided for any aeronautical purpose.

Aeroplane
A power-driven heavier-than-air aircraft that derives its lift from aerodynamic reactions on fixed aerofoils, i.e. fixed-wing.

Airborne collision avoidance system (ACAS)
Aircraft system based on secondary surveillance radar (SSR) transponder signals which indicates to a pilot potential conflicting aircraft that are equipped with SSR transponders. ACAS operates independently of any ground-based equipment.

ICAO ANNEX TERMINOLOGY

Aircraft
Any machine that can support itself in the atmosphere, by means other than the reactions of air against the earth's surface.

Aircraft identification
A group of letters, numbers or a combination thereof which makes up the callsign of an aircraft.

Aircraft observation
A meteorological observation made from an aircraft in flight.

Aircraft proximity
A situation where minimum safe separation distances between aircraft in flight have been compromised.

Aircraft stand
A designated area on an aerodrome apron for the parking of aircraft.

Air-ground communication
Two-way radio communication between aircraft in flight and ground (or sea) stations.

AIRMET information
Information issued by a met office about weather conditions or expected weather conditions that may affect the safety of aircraft. Such information is in addition to previously issued forecasts.

AIRPROX
Code word used in an air traffic incident report to designate aircraft proximity.

Airship
A power-driven lighter-than-air aircraft.

Air-report
A report from an aircraft in flight containing specific information on position, operation and meteorological conditions.

Air-taxiing
Movement of a helicopter above the surface of an aerodrome, normally in ground effect and at a groundspeed of less than 20 knots.

Air traffic
All aircraft in flight or operating on the manoeuvring areas of aerodromes.

Air traffic advisory service
A service provided within advisory airspace to ensure separation in so far as practical between aircraft operating on IFR flight plans.

Air traffic control clearance
Authorisation for an aircraft to proceed under conditions specified by an air traffic control unit. This term is often abbreviated to 'clearance'.

Air traffic control instruction
A directive issued by air traffic control that requires a pilot to take a specific action.

Air traffic control service
A service provided (a) to expedite the flow of air traffic and (b) to prevent collisions between aircraft in flight and on the manoeuvring area, and between aircraft and ground obstructions.

Air traffic control unit
Aerodrome control tower, area control centre or approach control office.

ICAO ANNEX TERMINOLOGY

Air traffic service
Flight information service, alerting service, air traffic advisory service or air traffic control service.

Air traffic services airspaces
Airspaces of defined dimensions, alphabetically designated (Classes A to G), within which specific types of flights may operate and for which specific air traffic services and rules of operation apply.

Air traffic services unit
Air traffic control unit, flight information centre or air traffic services reporting office.

Airway
A corridor-shaped control area equipped with radio navigation aids.

Alerting service
Service which notifies appropriate organisations of aircraft that require search and rescue aid.

Alert phase
Where concern is registered regarding the safety of an aircraft and its occupants.

Alternate aerodrome
An aerodrome to which an aircraft may proceed if it becomes either impossible or inadvisable to proceed to or land at the intended destination aerodrome. Alternate aerodromes include the following:

* En-route alternate: an aerodrome at which an aircraft would be able to land after experiencing an abnormal or emergency condition while en route.

* Destination alternate: an alternate aerodrome to which an aircraft may proceed if it becomes

either impossible or inadvisable to land at the intended destination aerodrome.

Note: The departure aerodrome may also be an en-route or destination alternate aerodrome for the flight.

Altitude
The vertical distance of a point from mean sea level.

Approach control office
A unit established to provide air traffic control service to controlled flights arriving at, or departing from, one or more aerodromes.

Approach control service
Air traffic control service for arriving or departing controlled flights.

Approach sequence
The order in which two or more aircraft are cleared to approach to land at an aerodrome.

Appropriate ATS authority
The authority designated by a State as being responsible for providing air traffic services in its territory.

Appropriate authority
(a) Regarding flight over the high seas: the relevant authority of the State of Registry; (b) Regarding flight over the territory of a State: the relevant authority of the State that has sovereignty over the territory being overflown.

Apron
An area on an aerodrome where aircraft can be parked for the loading and unloading of passengers, mail or cargo, refuelling or maintenance.

ICAO ANNEX TERMINOLOGY

Area control centre
Unit which provides air traffic control service to controlled flights in control areas under its jurisdiction.

Area control service
Air traffic control service for controlled flights in control areas.

Area navigation (RNAV)
A navigation method where aircraft may operate on any flightpath within the coverage of station-referenced navigation aids or within the limits of self-contained aids, or both. Such systems avoid the need to overfly ground-based radio navigation aids.

Area navigation route
An ATS route for aircraft using area navigation.

Assignment, assign
Distribution of frequencies to stations or SSR codes to aircraft.

ATIS
Automatic terminal information service: continuous repetitive broadcast of current routine aerodrome information to arriving and departing aircraft.

ATS route
A route (airway, advisory route, arrival or departure route etc.) used as necessary for the provision of air traffic services.

Balloon
A non-power-driven lighter-than-air aircraft.

Blind transmission
A radio transmission from one station to another where the transmitter cannot hear the receiver, but believes that the transmission can be received.

Broadcast
An 'all stations' transmission of air navigation information.

Ceiling
The height above ground or water of the lowest layer of cloud below 20,000 ft covering more than half the sky.

Clearance limit
The point to which an aircraft is granted an air traffic control clearance.

Clearway
A defined rectangular area at the upwind end of a runway that is suitable for the initial climb-out of aeroplanes. Will be under the control of the aerodrome authority.

Control area
A controlled airspace extending upwards from a specified height above the earth's surface.

Controlled aerodrome
An aerodrome at which a control service to aircraft is provided.
Note: This does not necessarily imply that the aircraft is within a control zone.

Controlled airspace
An airspace of defined dimensions within which air traffic control services are provided to IFR and VFR flights.

ICAO ANNEX TERMINOLOGY

Controlled flight
Any flight subject to air traffic control clearances.

Control zone
A controlled airspace extending upwards from the earth's surface to a specified upper limit.

Cruise climb
An aeroplane cruising technique resulting in a net gain in altitude as the aeroplane mass decreases.

Cruising level
A level maintained during a significant portion of a flight.

Dangerous goods
Articles or substances that are capable of posing significant risk to health, safety or property when they are transported by air.

Declared distances
Declared distances at aerodromes are agreed by the relevant authority – in the UK this is the CAA, and the distances are published in the Aerodrome section of the AIP.

- **Take-off run available (TORA)**. The length of runway declared available and suitable for the ground run of an aeroplane taking off.

- **Take-off distance available (TODA)**. The length of the take-off run available plus the length of the clearway, if provided.

- **Accelerate-stop distance available (ASDA)**. The length of the take-off run available plus the length of the stopway, if provided.

- **Landing distance available (LDA)**. The length of runway declared available and suitable for the ground run of an aeroplane landing.

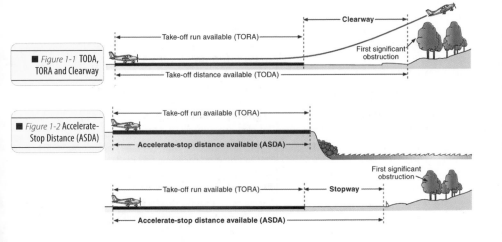

■ *Figure 1-1* **TODA, TORA and Clearway**

■ *Figure 1-2* **Accelerate-Stop Distance (ASDA)**

ICAO ANNEX TERMINOLOGY

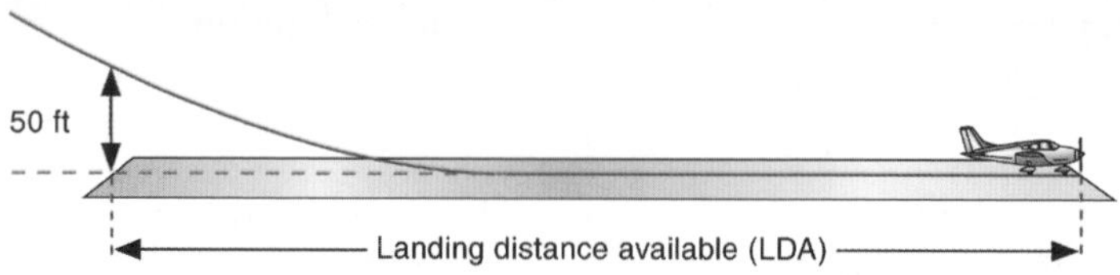

50 ft

Landing distance available (LDA)

■ *Figure 1-3* **Landing Distance Available (LDA)**

Distress phase
Where it is reasonably certain that an aircraft and its occupants require immediate assistance or are threatened by grave or imminent danger.

Ditching
The forced landing of an aircraft on water.

Elevation
The vertical distance between a point on the earth's surface and mean sea level.

Emergency phase
Generic term meaning either uncertainty phase, alert phase or distress phase.

Estimated elapsed time
Estimated time required to proceed from one significant point to another.

Estimated off-block time
Estimated time at which the aircraft will move 'off chocks' to begin movement towards take-off.

Estimated time of arrival (ETA)
For VFR flights, the estimated time at which the aircraft will arrive over the destination aerodrome.
For IFR flights, the estimated time at which the aircraft will arrive over a point defined by radio navigation aids, from which an instrument approach procedure will begin

(if the destination aerodrome does not have an associated navigation aid, ETA is the time at which the aircraft will arrive over the aerodrome).

Expected approach time
The time at which ATC expects an arriving aircraft that has been instructed to hold will leave the holding pattern to complete its approach for a landing.

Filed flight plan
A flight plan as submitted to an ATS unit without subsequent changes.

Fireproof material
A material capable of withstanding heat as well as, or better than, steel.

Flight crew member
A licensed crew member charged with duties essential to the operation of an aircraft during flight.

Flight Information centre
A unit that provides flight information service and alerting service.

Flight information region
An airspace of defined dimensions within which flight information service and alerting service is provided.

Flight information service
Service which provides advice and information useful to the safe and efficient conduct of flights.

ICAO ANNEX TERMINOLOGY

Flight level
A surface of constant atmospheric pressure which is related to a specific pressure datum, 1013.2 mb (hPa), and is separated from other such surfaces by specific pressure intervals. Flight levels are expressed in hundreds of feet, e.g. FL180 = 18,000 ft.

Flight Manual
A manual, associated with the Certificate of Airworthiness, containing limitations within which the aircraft is to be considered airworthy, and instructions and information necessary to the pilot for the safe operation of the aircraft. An aircraft Flight Manual is written by the manufacturer (e.g. Piper), approved by the State of Manufacture (in the US approval is given by the FAA) and supplemented if necessary by the State of Registration (for instance, by the UK CAA). The Flight Manual forms part of the Certificate of Airworthiness.

Flight plan
Specified information provided to air traffic services units about an intended flight or portion of a flight.

Flight time
The total time from the beginning of the take-off roll until the moment the aircraft stops at the end of a flight.
Note: This definition of flight time is synonymous with the terms 'block to block' or 'chock to chock'.

Flight visibility
Visibility forward from the cockpit of an aircraft in flight.

Forecast
A description of the expected weather conditions over a specified period of time for a particular area.

General aviation operation
An aircraft operation other than a commercial air transport flight or an aerial work operation.

Glider
A non-power-driven heavier-than-air aircraft that derives its lift from aerodynamic reactions on fixed aerofoils.

Ground visibility
Visibility at an aerodrome, as reported by a meteorological observer.

Gyroplane
A power-driven heavier-than-air rotorcraft that derives its lift from aerodynamic reactions on a freely-rotating rotor in the vertical axis. Powered by a propeller on the longitudinal axis.

Hazard beacon
An aeronautical beacon used to indicate a danger to air navigation.

Heading
The direction in which an aircraft is pointing, usually expressed in degrees from north (either true, magnetic or compass).

Height
The vertical distance between a point and a specified datum (such as sea level or ground level).

Heavier-than-air aircraft
An aircraft that derives its lift mainly from aerodynamic forces.

ICAO ANNEX TERMINOLOGY

Helicopter
A heavier-than-air rotorcraft that derives its lift and control from one or more power-driven rotors on substantially vertical axes.

Heliport
An aerodrome or a defined area on a structure for the landing, taking off and surface movement of helicopters.

Holding bay
A defined area at an aerodrome where aircraft can be held or bypassed without disrupting the flow of other traffic.

Holding point
A specified location, around which an aircraft flies a standard pattern until cleared to proceed with the flight.

Identification beacon
An aeronautical beacon that flashes a coded signal such that its location can be identified.

IFR flight
A flight made under the Instrument Flight Rules.

IMC
Instrument Meteorological Conditions.

Incident
An occurrence, other than an accident, which affects or could affect the safety of an aircraft operation.

Instrument Meteorological Conditions (IMC)
Meteorological conditions expressed in terms of visibility, distance from cloud, and ceiling, less than the minima specified for visual meteorological conditions.

Investigation
A process conducted for the purpose of accident investigation which includes the gathering and analysis of information, the drawing of conclusions, including the determination of causes and, when appropriate, the making of safety recommendations.

Landing area
The area on an aerodrome used for the landing or take-off of aircraft.

Level
A generic term relating to the vertical position of an aircraft in flight – referring to either height, altitude or flight level.

Lighter-than-air aircraft
An aircraft that is supported in flight mainly by its buoyancy in the air (e.g. a hot-air balloon).

Location indicator
A four-letter code assigned to the location of an aeronautical fixed station (could be either an aerodrome or a met station).

Manoeuvring area
The part of an aerodrome used for the taxiing, take-off and landing of aircraft, excluding aprons.

Marker
An object displayed above ground level to indicate an obstacle or boundary, e.g. the orange-and-white striped wedge-shaped markers that delineate an aerodrome boundary.

ICAO ANNEX TERMINOLOGY

Marking
A symbol or group of symbols displayed on the surface of the movement area to convey aeronautical information, e.g. the double white cross used to indicate gliding is in progress.

Meteorological information
Meteorological report, analysis, forecast or other statement relating to existing or expected weather conditions.

Meteorological office
An office that provides a meteorological service for international air navigation.

Meteorological report
A statement of observed weather conditions at a specific place at a specific time.

Mode (SSR)
Mode of operation of SSR transponder, e.g. Mode C (altitude reporting) or Mode A.

Movement area
The part of an aerodrome used for the taxiing, take-off and landing of aircraft, including the manoeuvring area and apron(s).

Night
The hours between the end of evening civil twilight and the beginning of morning civil twilight or such other period between sunset and sunrise as may be prescribed by the appropriate aviation authority.

Non-instrument runway
A runway for the use of aircraft using visual approach procedures only.

Non-radar separation
Separation distances between aircraft when position information is obtained from sources other than radar.

NOTAM
Notice to Airmen, which contains urgent information concerning the establishment, condition or change in any aeronautical facility, service, procedure or hazard.

Obstacle
Any fixed or mobile object (or part thereof) located on the surface movement area of an aerodrome that extends above a defined height.

Operator
A person, organisation or enterprise engaged in or offering facilities in aircraft operations.

Pilot-in-command
The pilot responsible for the operation and safety of an aircraft during flight time.

Pressure altitude
An atmospheric pressure expressed in terms of altitude which corresponds to that pressure in the standard atmosphere (i.e. 1013.2 hPa set in altimeter subscale).

Primary radar
Radar system that uses reflected radio signals.

Primary surveillance radar
Radar surveillance system that uses reflected radio signals.

ICAO ANNEX TERMINOLOGY

RADAR
Radio detection system which provides information on range, position and elevation of objects.

Radar approach
An approach to land where the final approach phase is directed by a radar controller.

Radar clutter
Unwanted signals displayed on a radar screen, caused by interference, static etc.

Radar contact
When the radar position of a particular aircraft is seen and identified on a radar display.

Radar control
Where radar information is used directly in the provision of air traffic control.

Radar controller
An air traffic controller qualified to use radar information.

Radar display
Electronic display (screen, monitor) which uses radar information to depict the position and movement of aircraft.

Radar identification
When the position of a particular aircraft is seen on a radar display and positively identified by the air traffic controller.

Radar monitoring
Use of radar to provide aircraft with information on their deviations from planned flightpath and deviations from air traffic control clearances.

Radar separation
Separation distances used when aircraft position information is provided by radar sources.

Radar service
A service provided by means of radar.

Radar unit
Part of an air traffic services unit that uses radar.

Radar vectoring
Where a radar controller issues heading instructions to aircraft, based on radar information.

Radio direction-finding station
A radio station that determines the relative direction of other transmitting stations.

Radiotelephony
A form of radio communication used mainly for the exchange of speech information.

Reporting point
A geographic location at which the position of an aircraft in flight can be reported.

Rescue coordination centre
Unit responsible for organising search and rescue operations within a certain area.

Rescue unit
A group of people trained and equipped to perform search and rescue operations.

Rotorcraft
A power-driven heavier-than-air aircraft that is supported in flight by reactions of air on one or more rotors.

ICAO ANNEX TERMINOLOGY

Runway
A defined rectangular area on an aerodrome used for the take-off and landing of aircraft.

Runway guard lights
A light system which alerts pilots or vehicle drivers that they are about to enter an active runway.

Runway visual range (RVR)
The distance along which the pilot of an aircraft on the centre-line of a runway can see the runway surface markings or lights.

Safety recommendation
A proposal made by the accident investigation authority of the State conducting an investigation, based on information derived from the investigation, with the intention of preventing accidents or incidents.

Search and rescue aircraft
An aircraft equipped to conduct search and rescue missions.

Search and rescue region
An area of defined dimensions within which search and rescue service is provided.

Search and rescue services unit
A generic term meaning either rescue coordination centre, rescue subcentre or alerting post.

Secondary radar
Radar system where an 'interrogating' radio signal transmitted from the radar station prompts a 'reply' signal to be sent from an aircraft transponder.

Secondary surveillance radar (SSR)
Radar system that uses transmitters/receivers (interrogators) and transponders.

Serious incident
An event that almost resulted in an accident.

Note: The only difference between an accident and an incident is the result: damage and/or injury = accident; could have been damage and/or injury = incident.

Serious injury
An injury sustained by a person in an accident which:

• requires hospitalisation for more than 48 hours (from within 7 days of the accident);

• results in a bone fracture (apart from simple fractures of fingers, toes or nose);

• involves lacerations which cause severe haemorrhage, nerve, muscle or tendon damage;

• involves injury to any internal organ;

• involves second or third degree burns, or any burns that affect more than 5% of body surface;

• involves verified exposure to infectious substances or harmful radiation.

SIGMET information
Information issued by a met office concerning weather conditions or expected weather conditions that may affect the safety of flights.

Signal area
An area on an aerodrome used for the display of ground signals.

ICAO ANNEX TERMINOLOGY

Slush

Water-saturated snow which, with a heel-and-toe slap-down motion against the ground, will be displaced with a splatter.

Snow (on the ground)

- **Dry snow.** Snow which can be blown if loose or, if compacted by hand, will fall apart again on release.

- **Wet snow.** Snow which, if compacted by hand, will stick together and tend to form a snowball.

- **Compacted snow.** Snow which has been compressed into a solid mass that resists further compression and will hold together or break into lumps if picked up.

Special VFR flight

A VFR flight cleared by air traffic control to operate within a control zone in meteorological conditions below VMC.

State of Design

The State that has jurisdiction over the organisation responsible for the design of a particular aircraft type.

State of Manufacture

The State that has jurisdiction over the organisation responsible for final assembly of an aircraft.

State of Occurrence

The State in which an aircraft accident or incident occurs.

State of the Operator

The State in which the operator's principal place of business is located, or if there is no such place, the operator's permanent residence.

State of Registry

The State (nation) in which an aircraft is registered.

Stopway

A defined rectangular area on the ground at the end of the take-off end of a runway, prepared as a suitable area in which an aeroplane can stop in the case of an abandoned take-off.

Surveillance radar

Radar equipment used to determine the range and position of aircraft in azimuth.

Take-off runway

A runway intended for take-off only.

Taxi-holding position

A designated position at an aerodrome where taxiing aircraft may be required to hold before entering or crossing a runway.

Taxiing

Movement on the surface of an aerodrome of an aircraft under its own power, excluding take-off and landing.

Taxiway

A defined path on an aerodrome for the taxiing of aircraft.

Terminal control area

A control area normally established around a major aerodrome.

Threshold

The beginning of the usable portion of a runway (normally indicated by 'piano key' markings).

ICAO ANNEX TERMINOLOGY

Touchdown zone

The portion of a runway, beyond the threshold, where it is intended that landing aeroplanes first contact the runway.

Track

The path of an aircraft in flight over the earth's surface.

Traffic avoidance advice

Advice given by air traffic control to pilots to assist in collision avoidance.

Traffic information

Information given by air traffic control to pilots regarding other known traffic near or on the flight-planned route.

Transition altitude

The altitude at or below which the vertical position of aircraft is controlled by reference to altitudes (i.e. with Regional Pressure Setting). Transition altitudes vary considerably between countries: 3,000 ft in the UK, 18,000 ft in the USA.

Transition layer

Airspace between the transition altitude and transition level.

Transition level

The lowest flight level available for use above the transition altitude.

Uncertainty phase

When the safety of an aircraft and its occupants is uncertain.

VFR flight

Flight conducted under the Visual Flight Rules.

Visibility

The distance over which prominent unlighted objects by day and prominent lighted objects by night can be seen.

Visual approach

An approach to land by an IFR flight where part or all of an instrument approach procedure is not completed and the approach is conducted by visual reference to terrain.

Visual meteorological conditions

Meteorological conditions expressed in terms of visibility, distance from cloud, and ceiling, equal or better than specified minima.

VMC

Visual meteorological conditions.

Waypoint

A specific geographical location used by an area navigation system.

Applicability

The Standards and Recommended Practices contained in Annex 6, Part II, sections 2 and 3, shall be applicable to international general aviation operations in aeroplanes.

Note. — *1 Standards and Recommended Practices applicable to the operation of aeroplanes by operators authorised to conduct international commercial air transport operations are to be found in Annex 6, Part I.*

Note. — *2 Standards and Recommended Practices applicable to international commercial air transport operations or international general aviation operations with helicopters are to be found in Annex 6, Part III.*

Note. — *3 Section 2 of Annex 6, Part II, applies to all international general aviation aeroplane operations, including those covered in Section 3. Section 3 adds additional requirements for large aeroplanes, turbojet aeroplanes and corporate aviation operations.*

ICAO Annex 6, General Requirements

International Flights (ICAO Annex 6)

The following extracts from Annex 6 cover matters particularly relevant to PPL holders making international flights.

GENERAL

3.1. The pilot-in-command shall comply with the relevant laws, regulations and procedures of the States in which the aircraft is operated.

3.2. The pilot-in-command shall be responsible for the operation and safety of the aeroplane and for the safety of all persons on board, during the flight.

3.3. Should an emergency situation occur which endangers the safety of the aeroplane or people, and requires the pilot to take action which violates local regulations or procedures, the pilot shall notify the appropriate authority as soon as possible. Some States may require the pilot to submit a report on the violation, normally within ten days.

3.4. In the event of an accident involving the aeroplane which results in serious injury or death or substantial damage to the aeroplane or property the pilot-in-command shall be responsible for notifying the appropriate authority as quickly as possible.

3.5. ICAO recommends that the pilot-in-command should carry on board the aeroplane essential information on search and rescue services in the areas over which the aeroplane will be flown.

ADEQUACY OF OPERATING FACILITIES

4.1. The pilot-in-command shall not begin a flight unless he has ascertained that the aerodrome facilities, communication facilities and navigation aids required are adequate for the safe operation of the aeroplane.

AERODROME OPERATING MINIMA

4.2. The pilot-in-command shall not fly below the operating minima specified for an aerodrome, except with State approval.

BRIEFING

4.3.1   The pilot-in-command shall ensure that crew members and passengers are briefed on the location and use of:

- seat belts;
- emergency exits;
- life jackets;
- oxygen equipment;
- any other emergency equipment, including passenger briefing cards.

4.3.2   The pilot-in-command shall ensure that everyone on board is familiar with the location and use of emergency equipment carried for collective use, such as life rafts.

AEROPLANE AIRWORTHINESS AND SAFETY PRECAUTIONS

4.4.1   The pilot-in-command shall not begin a flight unless he is satisfied that:

- the aeroplane is airworthy, registered and has the appropriate certificates on board;
- the instruments and equipment in the aircraft are appropriate to the expected flight conditions;
- necessary maintenance has been completed;
- the aeroplane's weight and balance will be within safe limits for the flight;
- cargo is correctly stowed and secured;
- the aeroplane's operating limitations, as described in the Flight Manual, will not be exceeded.

NOTE: ICAO recommends that the pilot-in-command should have sufficient information on climb performance to be able to determine the climb gradient that can be achieved during the departure phase in the prevailing conditions.

LIMITATIONS IMPOSED BY WEATHER CONDITIONS

4.6.1   Flights to be conducted under the visual flight rules shall not be commenced unless current weather reports and forecasts indicate that visual meteorological conditions exist along the flight-planned route.

4.6.3   Flights shall not be continued towards the planned destination aerodrome unless current weather reports indicate conditions at that aerodrome, or at least one alternate destination aerodrome, are at or above specified minima.

4.6.4 Aeroplanes on approach to land shall not exceed aerodrome operating minima, except in emergency situations.

4.6.5 A flight may not be conducted in known or expected icing conditions unless the aeroplane is equipped to cope with such conditions.

FUEL AND OIL SUPPLY

4.8.1 A flight may not be commenced unless the aeroplane carries sufficient fuel and oil to complete the flight safely, considering the weather conditions and any expected delays.

IN-FLIGHT EMERGENCY INSTRUCTION

4.11 In an in-flight emergency, the pilot-in-command shall ensure that passengers and crew are instructed in appropriate emergency action.

WEATHER REPORTING BY PILOTS

4.12 If weather conditions are encountered that are likely to affect the safety of other flights, they should be reported as soon as possible.

HAZARDOUS FLIGHT CONDITIONS

4.13 Hazardous flight conditions encountered in-flight such as volcanic ash and dust-storms, other than those associated with weather conditions, should be reported as soon as possible.

INSTRUCTION – GENERAL

4.17. An aeroplane may be taxied on the movement area of an aerodrome only if the person at the controls:

- has been authorised by the owner, lessee or agent to do so;
- is fully competent to taxy the aeroplane;
- is qualified to use the radio if radio communications are required;
- has received instruction from a competent person in aerodrome layout, routes, signs, marking, lights, ATC signals and instructions, phraseology and procedures and is able to conform safely to the operational standards required for the safe movement of aeroplanes at the aerodrome.

REFUELLING WITH PASSENGERS ON BOARD

4.18.1   ICAO recommends that aircraft should not be refuelled while passengers are boarding, on board, or leaving the aircraft, unless it is attended by the pilot-in-command or another qualified person who is able to organise an evacuation of the aircraft should it be necessary.

AEROPLANE PERFORMANCE AND OPERATING LIMITATIONS

5.1   An aeroplane shall be operated:
- in compliance with its airworthiness certificate;
- within the operating limitations prescribed by the certificating authority of the State of registry.

5.2   Placards, listings and instrument markings containing operating limitations prescribed by the State of registry shall be displayed in the aeroplane.

AEROPLANE INSTRUMENTS AND EQUIPMENT

6.1   In addition to the minimum equipment necessary to satisfy the Certificate of Airworthiness, an aeroplane shall carry the instruments, equipment and documents appropriate to the planned flight.

6.2   An aeroplane shall be equipped with instruments that will enable the flight crew to control the flightpath of the aeroplane, carry out any required procedural manoeuvre, and observe the operating limitations of the aeroplane in the expected flight conditions.

6.1.3   Aeroplanes shall be equipped with:
- an accessible first-aid kit;
- a safe portable fire extinguisher in the cockpit and in each passenger compartment if separate from the cockpit;
- a seat or berth for each person on board over a minimum age determined by the State of registry;
- a seat belt for each seat and restraining belts for each berth;
- the following manuals, charts and information:
  - the Flight Manual and other necessary related documents;
  - suitable aeronautical charts for the planned route and any diversions that could reasonably be anticipated;
  - procedures and visual signals for pilots-in-command of intercepted aircraft (for UK pilots, this is the CAA's General Aviation Safety Sense Leaflet No. 11);
- spare fuses for replacement of those accessible in flight.

VFR FLIGHTS

6.2   Aeroplanes operating on VFR flights shall be equipped with:
  * a magnetic compass;
  * an accurate timepiece that indicates the time in hours, minutes and seconds;
  * an altimeter;
  * an airspeed indicator;
  * additional instruments or equipment that may be prescribed by the appropriate authority.

FLIGHTS OVER WATER

6.3.2   All single-engined landplanes when flying over water beyond gliding distance from land should carry one life-jacket or equivalent flotation device for each person on board, stowed in an easily accessible position for its intended user.

NOTE : Landplanes above includes amphibious aircraft operated as landplanes.

6.3.3   All aeroplanes on extended flights over water shall be equipped as follows:
  * When over water and more than 50 nautical miles from land suitable for an emergency landing:
    – one life-jacket or equivalent flotation device for each person on board, stowed in an easily accessible position for its intended user.
  * When over water and more than 100 nautical miles from land suitable for an emergency landing in the case of single-engined aeroplanes, and more than 200 nautical miles in the case of multi- engined aeroplanes capable of continuing flight with one engine inoperative:
    – live-saving rafts capable of carrying all persons on board, stowed for ready access in an emergency, provided with appropriate life- saving equipment;
    – equipment for making pyrotechnic distress signals.

FLIGHTS OVER DESIGNATED LAND AREAS

6.4   Aeroplanes flying over land areas designated by the State as being areas in which search and rescue would be especially difficult, shall be equipped with appropriate signalling devices and life-saving equipment.

Compliance with Laws, Regulations & Procedures

The pilot-in-command (PIC) shall have responsibility for operational control.

PASSENGERS

The pilot-in-command (PIC) shall ensure that, during take-off and landing and whenever considered necessary by reason of turbulence or any emergency occurring during flight, all passengers on board an aeroplane shall be secured in their seats by means of the seat belts or harnesses provided.

FLIGHT PLANNING

A flight shall not be commenced unless, taking into account both the meteorological conditions and any delays that are expected in flight, the aeroplane carries sufficient fuel and oil to ensure that it can safely complete the flight. The amount of fuel to be carried must permit:

a.   When the flight is conducted in accordance with the visual flight rules by day, flight to the aerodrome of intended landing, and after that, for at least 30 minutes at normal cruising altitude; or

b.   When the flight is conducted in accordance with the visual flight rules by night, flight to the aerodrome of intended landing and thereafter for at least 45 minutes at normal cruising altitude.

Note. — Nothing precludes amendment of a flight plan in flight in order to replan the flight to another aerodrome, provided that the requirements above can be complied with from the point where the flight is replanned.

FLIGHT CREW MEMBERS AT DUTY STATIONS

When operating an aircraft flight crew members should be at the following positions during the flight:

Take-off & Landing. All flight crew members required to be on flight deck duty shall be at their stations.

En route. All flight crew members required to be on flight deck duty shall remain at their stations except when their absence is necessary for the performance of duties in connection with the operation of the aeroplane or for physiological needs.

Seat Belts. All flight crew members shall keep their seat belts fastened when at their stations.

Safety Harness. When safety harnesses are provided, any flight crew member occupying a pilot's seat shall keep the safety harness fastened during the take-off and landing phases; all other flight crew members shall keep their safety harnesses fastened during the take-off and landing phases unless the shoulder straps interfere with the performance of their duties, in which case the shoulder straps may be unfastened but the seat belt must remain fastened.

Note. — *Safety harness includes shoulder strap(s) and a seat belt which may be used independently.*

AEROPLANE COMMUNICATION AND NAVIGATION EQUIPMENT

An aeroplane to be operated in accordance with the instrument flight rules or at night shall be provided with radio communication equipment. Such equipment shall be capable of conducting two-way communication with those aeronautical stations and on those frequencies prescribed by the appropriate authority. The units should be independent of each other, so that in the event of failure, the remaining unit is still operational.

VFR flights operating within controlled airspace require a radio unless exempt by the appropriate authority.

The radio communication equipment shall provide for communication on the aeronautical emergency frequency 121.5 MHz.

INTENTIONALLY BLANK

Operation of Aircraft

1. What is the definition of a large aeroplane?

   a. An aeroplane of a maximum certificated take-off mass of over 5700 kg.

   b. A jet aeroplane with more than 9 seats.

   c. Any aeroplane with more than 9 seats.

   d. Any aircraft with more than 1 engine.

2. What is the definition of the pilot-in-command?

   a. The pilot who has the most flying experience on board the aircraft

   b. The pilot who sits in the left hand seat.

   c. The pilot designated by the operator or the owner as being in command and charged with the safe conduct of a flight.

   d. The pilot designated by the operator, or the owner as being the person who makes all the critical decisions in flight.

3. What is the definition of night?

   a. Any time that Air Traffic Control put the runway lights on.

   b. The hours between the end of evening civil twilight and the beginning of morning civil twilight, or such other period between sunset and sunrise, as may be prescribed by the appropriate authority.

   c. The hours between evening civil twilight and the morning civil twilight or such other period between sunset and sunrise, as may be prescribed by the appropriate authority.

   d. Any time the pilot-in-command cannot see sunlight.

4. What is the definition of the Operator?

   a. The person charged by the CAA to operate the aircraft.

   b. The pilot-in-command.

   c. The person or organisation that pays the bills.

   d. A person, organisation, or enterprise engaged in, or offering to engage in, an aircraft operation.

5. What is the definition of Flight Time — aeroplanes?

   a. The total time from the moment an aeroplane first moves for the purpose of taking off until the moment it finally comes to rest at the end of the flight.
   b. The total time from the moment an aeroplane first gets airborne until the moment it finally touches down.
   c. The moment you 'book out' with operations to moment you 'book in'.
   d. The total time the engine is running.

6. What is the ICAO definition of Aerial Work?

   a. Any aircraft operation in which an aircraft is being funded from a commercial venture.
   b. An aircraft operation in which an aircraft is used for specialised services such as agriculture, construction, photography, surveying, observation and patrol, search and rescue, aerial advertisement, etc.
   c. Any aircraft operation in which the pilot-in-command is required to hold a Commercial Pilot's Licence.
   d. An aircraft operation in which an aircraft is used for specialised services such as agriculture, construction, photography, surveying, observation and patrol, search and rescue, private hire and scheduled travel, etc.

7. What is a Flight Manual?

   a. A manual which describes the national aviation authorities' Rules of the Air and associated ICAO differences.
   b. A manual or book which describes how to operate the aircraft.
   c. A manual, associated with the certificate of airworthiness, containing limitations within which the aircraft is to be considered airworthy, and instructions and information necessary to the flight crew members for the safe operation of the aircraft.
   d. A manual containing limitations within which the aircraft is to be considered airworthy, and instructions and information necessary to the flight crew members for the safe operation of the aircraft.

8. What is the definition of a General Aviation Operation?

   a. An aircraft operation other than a commercial air transport operation or an aerial work operation.
   b. An aircraft operation that is general in nature.
   c. An aircraft operation other than a commercial air transport operation or an aerial work operation that uses light aircraft.
   d. An aircraft operation other than a commercial air transport operation or an aerial work operation that uses single engine piston aircraft.

9. What is an Operations Manual?

    a. A manual containing procedures, instructions and guidance for use by operational personnel in the execution of their duties.

    b. A manual or book containing procedures, instructions, and guidance for use by operational personnel in the execution of their duties.

    c. A manual containing procedures, instructions and guidance for use by Operations personnel only.

    d. A manual, associated with the certificate of airworthiness, containing limitations within which the aircraft is to be considered airworthy, and instructions and information necessary to the flight crew members for the safe operation of the aircraft.

10. What is the State of Registry?

    a. The State whose monarchy owns the aircraft.

    b. The State on whose register the aircraft is entered.

    c. The country where the insurance company is registered.

    d. The state where the aircraft is based.

11. What is a Safety Management System?

    a. A systematic approach to managing safety, including the necessary organisational structures, accountabilities, policies, and procedures.

    b. A systematic approach to managing the owners of flying schools, including the necessary organisational structures, accountabilities, policies, and procedures.

    c. A system devised by the Health and Safety Executive to monitor managers of flying schools and other aviation businesses.

    d. A manual containing procedures, instructions and guidance for use by operational personnel in the execution of their duties.

Noise Abatement Procedures

Noise Abatement Procedures (NAPs) were implemented to reduce the noise footprint of aircraft on the surrounding areas of airfields. Reduction of noise is very important, as the success of an airport is, in part, down to how it integrates with the local community.

Aviation legislation dictates how low above people, vessels and objects an aircraft may fly and if the Commander is found guilty of breaking the Air Navigation Order and Rules of the Air, then the CAA's Regulation Enforcement and Legal departments may seek a prosecution through the Magistrates and Crown Courts.

Although national aviation authorities, government agencies, and the aviation community as a whole recognise the impact that aircraft noise has on the local community living near an airfield, it is not covered by either the Environmental Protection Act 1990, or the Noise Act 1996. This means that local authorities do not have any right to legal action with respect to aircraft noise. If however, a new airport was built, or an existing airport operator wanted to develop their airport (such as building another runway), the local authority could impose operating conditions as part of the planning application and approval process.

The CAA must also consider the environmental noise impact before approving an airspace expansion, however, it can only prosecute if an aircraft has broken one of the low flying rules and it must have sufficient evidence before doing so.

When an airport receives a noise complaint an investigation will be carried out and the circumstances examined. At small airfields it is very difficult to gain sufficient evidence to confirm whether an aircraft did indeed break NAPs. It is often a case of one person's word against another's. If it is concluded that under normal operations a pilot did not comply with an airfield's NAPs then the operator may take action. Although the CAA cannot prosecute for noise impact, airport operators can impose their own penalties to persistent pilots and commercial operators who break Noise

Abatement Procedures, examples of which are detailed below:

i.   Verbal briefing from the tower.
ii.   Re-training with a local instructor.
iii. Restrictions on operating times.
iv.   Monetary fine.
v.   In extreme cases, temporary or permanent ban from operating
      at the airfield.

To avoid these sanctions and friction between the community and the airfield, review the airfield's Noise Preferential Routings and Noise Abatement Procedures at the pre-flight planning stage. Once airborne, contact the destination ATSU early, obtain the airfield information, plan the arrival and approach with reference to NAPs. If you are still in doubt regarding the procedures contact the destination ATSU.

EASA produces a Type-Certificate Data Sheet for Noise (TCDSN) for all aircraft built today and these have to meet noise requirements specified by ICAO. The CAA certifies light aircraft and helicopters through the Aeroplane Noise Regulations 1999, the Aeroplane Noise (Amendment) Regulations 1999 and the Air Navigation (Environmental Standards for Non-EASA Aircraft) Order 2008. Each aircraft is given a Noise Certificate, which remains valid unless the engine or airframe is modified. The Noise Certificate is usually kept in the 'Essential Documents' folder together with the Certificate of Insurance, Certificate of Airworthiness, etc.

In summary:

1.   Legal action cannot be taken against an aircraft for noise emissions, only
      for breaking the Rules of the Air.
2.   The flying community take their responsibilities towards being good
      neighbours very seriously.
3.   All aircraft have a noise certificate, which remains valid, unless engine or
      airframe modifications take place.
4.   Airfield operators can impose their own penalties for NAP offenders.

■ *Figure 2-1* **Noise Certificate**

	1. State of registry	3. Document Number:
Civil Aviation Authority	UNITED KINGDOM	019537
	2. NOISE CERTIFICATE	

4. Registration Marks:	5. Manufacturer and Manufacturer's Designation of Aircraft:	6. Aircraft Serial Number:
G-JDBC	PIPER AIRCRAFT CORPORATION PIPER PA-34-200T	34-7570150

7. Engine:	8. Propeller:
CONTINENTAL MOTORS CORP TSIO-360-E	HARTZELL BHC-C2YF-2CKUF/FC8459-8R

9. Maximum Take-Off Mass (kg)	10. Maximum Landing Mass (kg)	11. Noise Certification Standard:
1999	Not Applicable	Chapter 6

12. Additional modifications incorporated for the purpose of compliance with the applicable noise certification standards:

None

13. Lateral/Full-Power Noise Level:	14. Approach Noise Level:	15. Flyover Noise Level:	16. Overflight Noise Level:	17. Take-Off Noise Level:
N/A	N/A	N/A	71.7 dB(A)	N/A

Remarks:

None

18. This Noise Certificate is issued pursuant to Annex 16, Volume I to the Convention on International Civil Aviation dated 7 December 1944 and Regulation (EC) No. 216/2008, Article 6 in respect of the above-mentioned aircraft, which is considered to comply with the indicated noise standard when maintained and operated in accordance with the relevant requirements and operating limitations.

19. Date of Issue...... **10 December 2008** ......   20. Signature..............

EASA Form 45 18042008

Influence of the Flight Procedure (Departure, Cruise and Approach)

Noise Abatement Procedures (NAPs) for large turboprop or turbojet aircraft combine a reduction in thrust with a departure route, which reduces noise ground pattern to a minimum. Noise sensors are positioned on the departure route and operators who do not reduce thrust or follow the tracks accurately are fined. ICAO PANS-OPS defines two types of Noise Abatement Departure Procedures (NADPS) often referred to as NADP1 and NADP2, which you may read in the Noise Abatement Procedures section of applicable aerodrome entry in the AIP.

Licensed to Admin. Printed on 23 Sep 2010.
Notice: After 8 Oct 2010 0901Z, this chart may no longer be valid. Disc 19-2010

JEPPESEN
JeppView 3.7.2.1

■ *Figure 2-2* Noise Abatement Sensor Locations, which monitor compliance with NAPs.

EGSS/STN
STANSTED

◣ **JEPPESEN**

23 APR 10 (30-4) **Eff 6 May**

LONDON, UK

NOISE

Apt Elev 348'

NOISE ABATEMENT

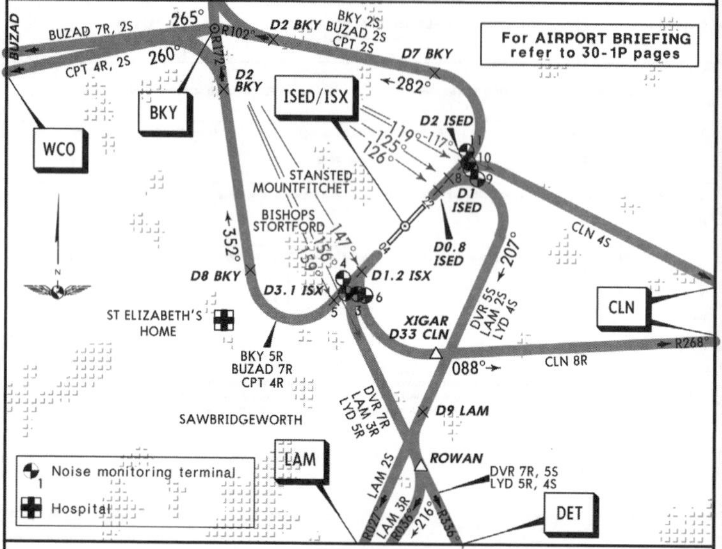

BUZAD 7R, 2S 265°
CPT 4R, 2S 260°
R102°

BKY 2S
D2 BKY BUZAD 2S
CPT 2S
D7 BKY

D2 BKY ←282°

BKY ISED/ISX

D2 ISED
119° 117°
125°
126°
B10

WCO

STANSTED MOUNTFITCHET
D1 ISED

BISHOPS STORTFORD 352°
D0.8 ISED

CLN 4S

D8 BKY D3.1 ISX D1.2 ISX

ST ELIZABETH'S HOME

XIGAR
D33 CLN

DVR 5S
LAM 2S
LYD 4S

CLN

R268°

BKY 5R
BUZAD 7R
CPT 4R

088°→

CLN 8R

SAWBRIDGEWORTH

DVR 7R
LAM 3R
LYD 5R

D9 LAM

Noise monitoring terminal. LAM ROWAN
DVR 7R, 5S
LYD 5R, 4S

Hospital

LAM 25
LAM 3R

216°

DET

For AIRPORT BRIEFING refer to 30-1P pages

The operation limits as specified in para 3.1.1. (refer to Airport Briefing Page 30-1P5) shall be adjusted in respect of any noise monitoring terminal to take account of the location and its ground elevation relative to the aerodrome elevation as follows:

NOISE MONITORING TERMINAL/NAME/LOCATION			ELEVATION ABOVE AERODROME	ADJUSTMENT db(A)
⊕3	Howe Green School, Great Hallingbury	N51 50.8 E000 11.5	- 21m	- 1.0
⊕4	Thames Water, Bishop's Stortford	N51 51.3 E000 10.7	- 36m	- 1.4
⊕5	Woolcott Restaurant, Great Hallingbury	N51 50.9 E000 10.9	- 26m	- 1.4
⊕6	Morley, Woodside Green	N51 50.8 E000 11.9	- 26m	- 1.1
⊕8	Anglian Water, Broxted	N51 54.9 E000 17.5	- 16m	- 0.6
⊕9	Moor End Farm, Broxted	N51 54.6 E000 17.9	- 16m	- 0.8
⊕10	Goodacres, Broxted	N51 55.1 E000 17.4	9m	+ 0.2
⊕11	Chickney Hall Villas, Broxted	N51 55.5 E000 17.3	-15m	- 1.3

If the aircraft was required to take-off with a tailwind an amount of the noise recorded at the noise monitor should be disregarded.

Tailwind component	≤1 KT	≤2 KT	≤3 KT	≤4 KT	>4 KT
Amount to be disregarded	0.4 dB	0.8 dB	1.2 dB	1.6 dB	2.0 dB

CHANGES: SIDs renumbered.

Most piston engine aircraft do not have sufficient climb performance to enable them to reduce power after departure, and as most light aircraft operate VFR they will not follow the instrument departure routings. Therefore any noise abatement procedure will only affect the lateral profile flown. The following lists the most common noise complaints associated with the operation of light aircraft:

i.   Circuit training
ii. Parachute dropping/Glider tug towing
iii. General noise pattern of a piston engine aircraft
iv. Aerobatics
v.   Low level flying
vi. Ground running of engines

It is in the interests of all airfield operators to be good neighbours and to integrate the operations of the airfield into the local community. Therefore, most airfields will voluntarily create NAPs and noise limiting procedures to minimise noise levels. All licensed airfields' NAPs will be listed in the appropriate entry in the AIP, and those for non-licensed airfields are listed in a suitable commercial publication such as 'Pooley's Flight Guide'.

■ *Figure 2-3*
An extract from the UK AIP describing Denham's Noise Abatement Procedures (NOT FOR OPERATIONAL USE)

EGLD AD 2.21 NOISE ABATEMENT PROCEDURES

(a) Circuits should be flown as small as practicable without reducing flight safety.

(b) Runway 24 Departures: After take-off continue straight ahead until past the houses on the right, then turn right before the A413 road to avoid overflying Gerrards Cross.

(c) Runway 06 Departures: Turn left over the lakes to avoid Harefield.

(d) Runway 24 Arrivals: From Maple Cross, fly the base leg over the lakes to avoid Harefield.

(e) Runway 06 Arrivals: From Chalfont St Giles, the base leg should be flown to the east of the A413 road to avoid Gerrards Cross.

(f) Circuit Traffic: Circuit traffic should stay south of Hogtrough Wood to avoid a noise sensitive area in Chalfont St Peter. Additional restrictions apply to twin-engined aircraft and helicopters at weekends.

(g) North of the London CTR aircraft should fly as high as permitted. ATSOCAS may be obtained from Northolt Approach on 126.450 MHz.

CHICHESTER (Goodwood)
Noise Abatement Procedures

■ *Figure 2-4*
An extract from Pooley's Flight Guide describing Chichester Goodwood's Noise Abatement Procedures (NOT FOR OPERATIONAL USE)

Fixed Wing:

Standard join is overhead at 2000 ft. 'Straight-in' and 'base' joins are strongly discouraged when circuit is active. Outside ATS hours and after sunset, overhead join is mandatory.

Circuit height: 1200 ft QFE. No fixed-wing circuits after 1400 on Sundays.

Circuit directions: Rwys 06,10 and 14L/14R – Left Hand.
                  Rwys 24, 28 and 32L/32R – Right Hand.
                  Note: Rwy 14L/32R **in use** 1 Nov to 31 Mar only.

Runway 06
Take-off: No restrictions.
Landing: No low approaches over the built up-areas in the undershoot.

Runway 24
Take-off: As soon as practicable after departure, turn right to avoid built up area. Maintain track until reaching or passing circuit height. No practice engine failures after take-off until west of A286 road.
Landing: No restrictions.

Runway 14L/14R
Take-off: Turn left as soon as practicable after departure to avoid overflying the school and houses under the climb out path. No practice engine failures after take-off until well clear of the school and houses.
Landing: No low approaches over East Lavant village. Light aircraft should aim to touch down beyond the intersection of runways 10 and 14.

Runway 32L/32R
Take-oft: Turn right 20° as soon as practicable after departure to avoid East Lavant village. Maintain that heading until well beyond the village. No practice engine failures after take-off until well beyond the village.
Landing: No restrictions.

Runway 10
Take-off: No restrictions.
Landing: No restrictions.

Runway 28
Take-off: Maintain runway heading until clear of Lavant village.
Landing: No restrictions.

Helicopters:

Circuit height: 900 ft QFE or as directed by ATS. No helicopter circuits on Sun.

Circuit directions: When Rwys 14 or 32 are in use, circuits are flown from the 'triangle' and are flown inside and below the fixed wing circuit.

When Rwys 06,10, 24 or 28 are in use, circuits are flown from Rwy 32 threshold parallel to, but in opposite direction to the fixed wing circuit, i.e to the south of aerodrome.

Helicopters are to avoid routeing over Chichester, Westerton and Summersdale. Helicopters are not permitted to join the circuit below 700 ft QFE unless weather dictates a lower height.

Noise Abatement and Circuits – see pages 182 & 183.

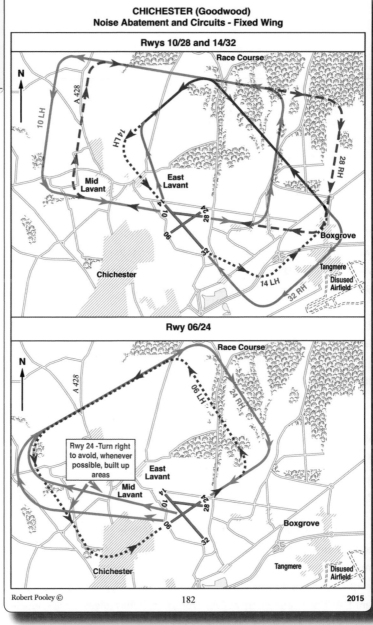

■ Figure 2-5
An extract from Pooley's
Flight Guide describing
Chichester Goodwood's
Noise Abatement
Procedures (NOT FOR
OPERATIONAL USE)

CHICHESTER (Goodwood)
Noise Abatement and Circuits - Fixed Wing

Rwys 10/28 and 14/32

Rwy 06/24

Rwy 24 -Turn right
to avoid, whenever
possible, built up
areas

Robert Pooley ©   182   2015

The complexity of the NAP depends on the surrounding neighbourhood, terrain, runway layout, and type of aircraft using the airfield. Noise Preferential Routings are created to stop aircraft flying over certain areas and certain airfields have a variable circuit pattern to avoid aircraft repeatedly flying over the same houses.

Examples of simple NAPs are as follows:

i.   After departure avoid flying over the village of Cranfield.
ii. Pilots should route to the East of Whitstable.
iii. After departure pilots should set course from overhead or abeam Congleton VRP.
iv. Power checks should be conducted on the Alpha taxiway.
v.   Pilots are encouraged not to complete repetitive Practice Forced Landings over the area surrounding Deal.

Airfields that have very noise sensitive surrounding areas and have different types of aircraft using the airfield may have more complex NAPs. ICAO provides two Noise Abatement Departure Procedures (NADPs) which are designed for large aircraft, however, these do not apply to light aircraft. Examples of more complex NAPs applicable to light aircraft which you may find at smaller airfields are shown below:

i.   All turbojet aircraft shall apply ICAO NADP 1.
ii. After departure all aircraft must turn at 500ft onto a track of 030° until reaching 1500ft before setting course.
iii. Pilots must leave the VRP of Mars on a track of 140°, upon crossing the railway line fly towards the 'tall tower' and intercept the final approach course.
iv. All aircraft must follow the M25 motorway and join on an extended final reporting at approximately 4 miles (overhead the 'Golf course') and 2 miles (the 'Tall Tower').
v.   All pilots must obtain a briefing from ATC before departure.

Before visiting an airfield, review the NAPs in the AIP for a licensed airfield and a commercial flight guide in the case of an unlicensed one. After reading the procedures, if you are still in doubt about what to do, contact the airfield and obtain a briefing. The CAA produce a document entitled 'Noise Abatement at GA Aerodromes' which gives a more detailed description about NAPs. One final point:

NOISE ABATEMENT PROCEDURES DO NOT APPLY IN THE EVENT OF AN EMERGENCY.

Runway Incursion Awareness (meaning of surface markings and signals)

A runway incursion is defined as the following:

A Runway Incursion is any occurrence at an airport involving the unauthorised or unplanned presence of an aircraft, vehicle, or person on the protected area of a surface designated for aircraft take-offs and landings.

They are caused by a variety of reasons but pilot/air traffic controller workload, distraction and incorrect radio phraseology are often cited as primary causes.

Whilst rare, runway infringements can have catastrophic results; below are a selection of accidents caused by an aircraft manoeuvring on a runway without clearance (credit to www.SKYbrary.com):

i.   On 2 July 2008, an Air Tran Airways B737-700 which had just landed at night on runway 34C at Seattle-Tacoma, failed to hold clear of runway 34R during taxi as instructed and passed almost directly underneath a North West Airlines A330-200 which had just become airborne from Runway 32R. The Investigation found that the 737 crew had been unaware of their incursion and that the alert provided by the airport surface detection equipment had not provided an opportunity for ATC usefully to intervene to prevent the potential conflict.

ii. On 12 January 2006, an Air China Boeing 747-200, which had just landed at Frankfurt failed correctly to understand and read back its taxi-in clearance and the incorrect read back was not detected by the controller. The 747 then crossed another runway at night and in normal visibility whilst an A320 was landing on it. The A320 responded by increased braking and there was consequently no actual risk of collision. The controller had not noticed the incursion and, in accordance with instructions, all stop bars were unlit and the RIMCAS had been officially disabled as a result of too many nuisance activations.

iii. A Boeing 737 (B737), operating a scheduled service from Aberdeen to London Gatwick, at a speed of 100kt was obliged to abort its take-off run to avoid a possible collision with a Super Puma (AS332L) helicopter. The helicopter had been hovering at a holding point close to the upwind end of the runway when, because of the crew's misinterpretation of their clearance, it manoeuvred to hover above the runway into the path of the departing B737.

iv. On 30 October 2009, a Bombardier DHC8-400 being operated by Flybe on a scheduled passenger flight from Exeter to Edinburgh failed to follow its acknowledged ATC taxi out clearance to the runway holding point 08 and entered and lined up on the active runway at night in normal visibility at the same time as a Boeing 737-500 being operated by Astraeus Airlines on a non revenue positioning flight to Exeter, was landing on the opposite (26) direction of the same runway. The landing B737 was able to stop before reaching the other aircraft and clear the runway.

v. On 8th October 2001, a Boeing MD-87 being operated by SAS and departing Milan Linate on a scheduled passenger flight to Copenhagen in thick fog in daylight collided at high speed with a German-operated Cessna Citation taxiing for departure on a non scheduled passenger flight from Paris Le Bourget. The MD-87 failed to get airborne and continued along the ground until it impacted, still at high speed, a ground handling building. Both aircraft caught fire and were destroyed. All 114 occupants of both aircraft and 4 personnel on the ground were killed. The Italian ANSV carried out an Investigation. It was found that, unknown to ATC because of the prevailing thick fog, the Cessna had failed to follow the taxi clearance issued and correctly acknowledged and had eventually entered the active runway after crossing a lit red stop bar just as the departing MD-87 was reaching V_R at the same point. The Investigation was unable to find any evidence that either of the Cessna pilots was trained or authorised to operate a public transport flight departure in the prevailing low visibility. The majority of the investigation concentrated on documenting the widespread organisational failings which, although they had not been the direct cause of the accident and its aftermath, it was concluded had facilitated the accident scenario.

Depending on the complexity of the airfield, taxiing can often be one of the hardest parts of operating a light aircraft. If you are learning to fly at a large international airport such as Newcastle or Edinburgh, you have probably already found that it can be quite confusing which way to go in order to get to, or from, the runway. Not to mention having larger aircraft moving around you!

■ *Figure 2-6*
Having large aircraft
moving around you
can be daunting!

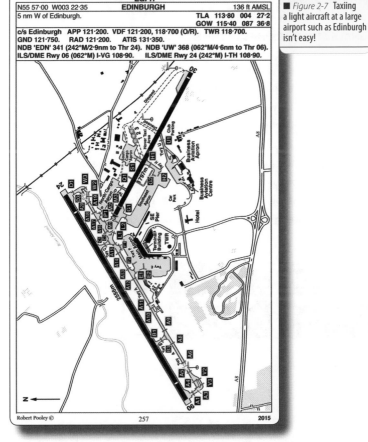

■ *Figure 2-7* Taxiing
a light aircraft at a large
airport such as Edinburgh
isn't easy!

Because airport taxiways and runways layouts can be confusing ICAO defines visual aids in order to standardise airport markings around the world. This enables pilots to recognise the difference between runway markings and taxiways whether they are operating at a small grass airport or a large international one. The CAA produce CAP 637 'Visual Aids Handbook' which is a compendium of Visual Aids intended for the guidance of Pilots and Personnel engaged in the handling of aircraft.

Aerodrome Signals & Markings
(SERA Appendix 1 (EU Reg 923/2012))

A signals area is positioned near the control tower at some aerodromes to allow messages to be passed to a pilot without the use of radio:

- **in flight,** by signals laid out on the ground; and
- **on the ground,** by signals hoisted up a mast located in the signals area.

SIGNALS AND MARKINGS IN THE SIGNALS AREA

Direction of Take-Off and Landing

A **white 'T'** signifies that aeroplanes and gliders taking off or landing shall do so parallel with the shaft of the 'T' and towards the cross arm, unless otherwise authorised by the appropriate ATC unit.

A **white disc** at the head of the 'T' means that the direction of landing and the direction of take-off do not necessarily coincide. This latter situation may also be indicated by a **black ball** suspended from a mast. A rectangular **green flag** flown from a mast indicates that a right-hand circuit is in force.

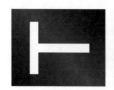  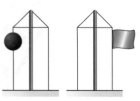

■ *Figure 2-8* **Direction of take-off and landing**

Use Hard Surfaces Only

A **white dumb-bell** signifies that movements of aeroplanes and gliders on the ground shall be confined to paved, metalled or similar hard surfaces. The addition of black strips in each circular portion of the dumb-bell, at right angles to the shaft, signifies that aeroplanes and gliders taking off or landing must do so on a runway, but that movement on the ground is not confined to hard surfaces.

■ *Figure 2-9* Use of hard surfaces signals

■ *Figure 2-10* Right-hand circuit indicator

Right-Hand Circuit

A red-and-yellow striped arrow bent through 90 degrees around the edge of the signals area and pointing in a clock- wise direction means that a right-hand circuit is in force.

Where the circuit direction at an aerodrome is variable (left-hand or right-hand) a rectangular **red flag** on the signals mast indicates that a **left-hand** circuit is in operation. A rectangular **green flag** signifies that the circuit is **right-hand**.

■ *Figure 2-11* Special precautions signal

Special Precautions

A red square panel with a single yellow diagonal stripe means that the state of the manoeuvring area is poor and that pilots must exercise special care when landing.

■ *Figure 2-12* Landing prohibited signal

Landing Prohibited

A red square panel with a diagonal yellow cross signifies that the aerodrome is unsafe for the movement of aircraft and that landing is prohibited.

Helicopter Operations

A **white 'H'** in the signals area means that helicopters must take off and land only within a designated area (that area itself being marked by a much larger white 'H').

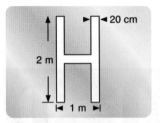 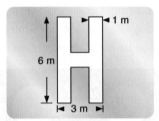

(a) A white letter H is displayed in the signals area

(b) A white letter H indicates the area to be used only by helicopters for take-off and landing

■ *Figure 2-13*
Helicopter operations markers

Gliding

A double white cross and/or two red balls suspended from a mast, one above the other, signifies that glider-flying is taking place at the aerodrome. (A similar but much larger signal is used to mark an area on the aerodrome which is to be used only by gliders).

A **yellow cross** indicates the tow-rope dropping area.

Tow-ropes, banners, etc. can only be picked up or dropped at an aerodrome, and then only as directed by the aerodrome authority, or in the designated area (yellow cross) with the aircraft flying in the direction appropriate for landing (ANO Article 87 and Rule of the Air 7).

 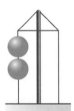 

■ *Figure 2-14*
Gliding in progress

SIGNALS ON PAVED RUNWAYS AND TAXIWAYS

Unserviceable Portion of Runway or Taxiway

Two or more white crosses along a section of runway or taxiway, with the arms of the crosses at an angle of 45 degrees to the centreline of the runway or taxiway at intervals of not more than 300 metres, signify that the section of the runway or taxiway marked by them is unfit for the movement of aircraft.

Figure 2-15
Unfit section of
runway or taxiway

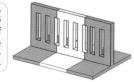
Figure 2-16
Boundary of
unserviceable
area marker

Orange and white markers as illustrated, spaced not more than 15 metres apart, signify the boundary of that part of a paved runway, taxiway or apron which is unfit for the movement of aircraft. Each marker comprises a base board supporting a slatted vertical board, both of which are striped orange–white–orange.

Holding Point on Paved Taxiway

Parallel yellow lines – usually marked as a set of double continuous and double broken lines – across a taxiway signify a holding point, beyond which no part of an aircraft or vehicle may proceed in the direction of the runway, without ATC permission.

Of the two sets of lines, the **broken yellow lines** are located on the runway side, enabling the pilot to determine if the holding point affects him. Moving in the reverse direction towards a holding point, with the broken yellow lines encountered first (for example, having turned off the runway after landing), the holding point does not require a clearance to cross it.

Figure 2-17 Typical
taxiway markings and
holding position sign

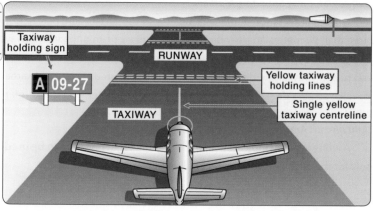

Note. – Older holding points may be marked with white lines, but most are now yellow. Also, older holding points may still be marked with a single continuous line and a single broken line.

MARKERS ON UNPAVED MANOEUVRING AREAS

Aerodrome Boundary Markers

Orange/white striped wedge-shaped markers (like elongated wheel-chocks in shape), placed not more than 45 metres apart, indicate the boundary of an aerodrome. These are supplemented by flat orange/white markers, also placed 45 metres apart, on any structures which lie on the

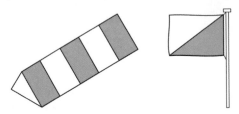

■ *Figure 2-18*
Boundary marker

boundary.

Unserviceable Portion

The orange/white striped wedge-shaped markers shown above are also used to mark the boundary of an unpaved area which is unserviceable for aircraft movement. These alternate with square flags showing equal orange and white triangular areas. Within this marked area the bad ground is itself marked with one or more white crosses (as described above).

Runway/Stopway Boundary Markers

White, flat rectangular markers, flush with the surface and placed not more than 90 metres apart, indicate the boundary of an unpaved runway or of a stopway. (A stopway is a prepared rectangular area of ground at the end of a runway, in the direction of take-off, designated as a suitable area in which an aircraft can be stopped in the case of an interrupted take-off.)

Light Aircraft Area

A white letter 'L' indicates a part of the manoeuvring area to be used only for the taking off and landing of light aircraft.

■ *Figure 2-19*
Light aircraft areas

If a dumb-bell displayed in the aerodrome signals area has a red 'L' superimposed, it means that light aircraft are allowed to take off and land either on a runway or on the area designated by the white 'L'.

■ *Figure 2-20*
Runway to be used

Runway to be Used

A white 'T' (placed on the left side of a runway when viewed from the landing direction) indicates that it is the runway to be used. Where there is no runway it indicates the direction for take-off and landing.

■ *Figure 2-21*
Landing dangerous

Landing Dangerous

A white cross displayed at each end of a runway indicates that landing is dangerous and that the aerodrome is used for storage purposes only.

■ *Figure 2-22*
Emergency use only

Emergency Use Only

A white cross and a single white bar displayed at each end of the runway at a disused aerodrome indicates that the runway is fit for emergency use only. Runways so marked are not safe-guarded and may be temporarily obstructed.

■ *Figure 2-23*
Land in emergency only

Land in Emergency Only

Two vertical yellow bars on a red square on the signals area indicate that the landing areas are serviceable but the normal safety facilities are not available. Aircraft should land in emergency only.

DISPLACED THRESHOLD MARKINGS

The threshold marking on a runway delineates the beginning of the usable portion of that runway (at the downwind end). Sometimes the threshold marking is moved, or displaced, some distance up the runway from the end of the paved area. Such a displaced threshold may be either temporary, to allow for maintenance, for instance, or permanent.

There are various displaced threshold markings, depending on the type (if any) of aircraft movement permitted in the first portion of the runway, and whether the displacement is temporary or permanent. Some pre-threshold areas may be usable for take-off, but not for landing; some may be unfit for any kind of aircraft movement.

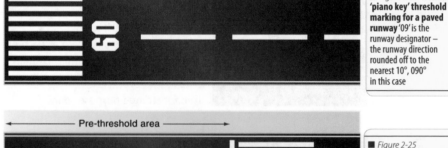

■ *Figure 2-24* **Normal 'piano key' threshold marking for a paved runway** '09' is the runway designator – the runway direction rounded off to the nearest 10°, 090° in this case

Pre-threshold area

New threshold

■ *Figure 2-25* **Permanently displaced threshold** White arrows indicate that the pre-threshold area is available for taxi and take-off, but not for landing

White crosses, not more than 300 metres apart, arms at 45° to runway centreline

■ *Figure 2-26* **Permanently displaced threshold** White crosses indicate that the pre-threshold area is unfit for movement of aircraft and unsuitable as a stopway

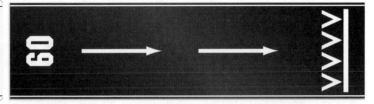

■ Figure 2-27
Temporarily displaced threshold
Pre-threshold area is available for taxi and take-off, but not for landing

■ Figure 2-28
Temporarily displaced threshold
Pre-threshold area is unfit for movement of aircraft and unsuitable as a stopway

NORMAL THRESHOLD MARKING (TOP) AND DISPLACED THRESHOLD MARKINGS

SUMMARY OF AERODROME SIGNALS VISIBLE ONLY WHEN ON THE GROUND

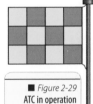

In the Signals Area

1. A black ball on a mast signifies that the directions of take-off and landing are not necessarily the same.

2. Two red balls on a mast signify that gliding is taking place.

■ Figure 2-29
ATC in operation

3. A rectangular red/yellow chequered flag or board means that aircraft may move on the manoeuvring area and apron only with the permission of ATC.

4. If the circuit direction at the aerodrome is variable, and a left- hand circuit is in operation, a red flag will be flown from the mast. A green flag on the mast signifies that a right-hand circuit is in force at the aerodrome. (Note that the colours of the flags for left and right circuits are the same as for aircraft navigation lights.)

■ Figure 2-30 Location of aerodrome authority

Away from the Signals Area

5. A square yellow board bearing a black 'C' indicates the position at which a pilot can report to ATC or other aerodrome authority.

■ Figure 2-31 Signals area at Wycombe (WP); clockwise from bottom left corner – special precautions; gliding in progress; (white dash symbol is part of dumb-bell not in use); right-hand circuits; and in centre: take-off and landing direction (towards the cross-arm)

Light Signals (SERA Appendix 1 (EU Reg. 923/2012))

You should be aware of standard light signals that ATSU personnel may beam to aircraft. The light signals differ in meaning according to whether you are in flight or on the ground. Green flashes, for instance, when beamed at an aircraft in flight mean "Return for a landing", whereas when beamed to an aircraft on the ground they mean "Authorised to taxi".

FROM ATSU TO AIRCRAFT

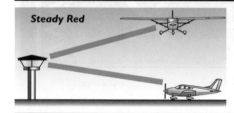

Steady Red

Do not land. Give way to other aircraft and continue circling.

Stop.

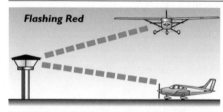

Flashing Red

Do not land. Aerodrome closed (go to another aerodrome).

Move clear of landing area.

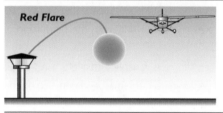

Red Flare

Do not land; wait for permission.

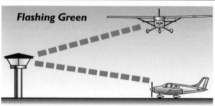

Flashing Green

Return to this aerodrome and wait for permission to land.

Cleared to taxi on the manoeuvring area if pilot satisfied no collision risk exists.

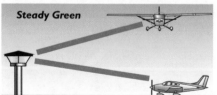

Steady Green

Cleared to land if pilot satisfied no collision risk exists.

Cleared to take-off if pilot satisfied no collision risk exists.

FROM ATSU TO AIRCRAFT

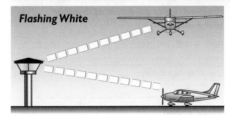

Flashing White — Land at this aerodrome after receiving a steady green light

Return to starting point on aerodrome.

Light signals can also be sent from an aircraft, but the equipment (such as flares) is rarely available for a pilot to use. The one signal that can be used in almost any aircraft, however, is flashing the landing lights or position navigation lights on and off (usually visible from the ground only at night) to indicate "I am compelled to land".

FROM AIRCRAFT TO ATSU

Flashing landing and/or navigation lights

I am compelled to land.

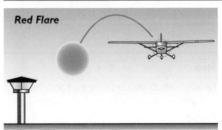

Red Flare

Immediate assistance required.

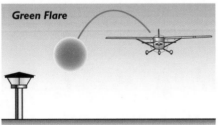

Green Flare

By night
May I land?

By day
May I land in a different direction from that indicated by the landing T?

FROM MARSHALLER TO PILOT

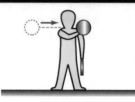

Proceed under guidance of another marshaller

Right or left arm down, the other arm moved across body and extended to indicate position of the other marshaller.

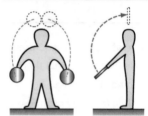

Move ahead

Arms repeatedly moved upward and backward, beckoning onward.

Open up starboard engine(s) or turn to port

Right arm down, left arm repeatedly moved upward and backward. The speed of arm movement indicates the rate of turn.

Open up port engine(s) or turn to starboard

Left arm down, the right arm repeatedly moved upward and backward. The speed of arm movement indicates the rate of turn.

Stop

Arms repeatedly crossed above the head. The speed of arm movement indicates the urgency of the stop.

FROM MARSHALLER TO PILOT

Start engine

A circular motion of the right hand at head level, with the left arm pointing to the appropriate engine.

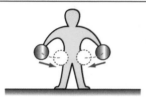

Chocks inserted

Arms extended, the palms facing inwards, then swung from the extended position inwards.

Chocks away

Arms down, the palms facing outwards, then swung outwards.

Cut engines

Either arm and hand placed level with the chest, then moved laterally with the palm facing downwards.

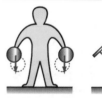

Slow down

Arms placed down, with the palms towards the ground, then moved up and down several times.

Slow down engine(s) on indicated side

Arms placed down, with the palms towards the ground, then either the right or left arm moved up and down indicating that the motors on the left or right side, as the case may be, should be slowed down.

FROM MARSHALLER TO PILOT

This bay

Arms placed above the head in a vertical position.

Release brakes

Raise arm, with fist clenched, horizontally in front of the body, then extend fingers.

Engage brakes

Raise arm and hand, with fingers extended, horizontally in front of body, then clench fist.

All clear – marshalling finished

The right arm raised at the elbow with the palm facing forwards.

Start engine(s)

Left hand overhead with the number of fingers extended, to indicate the number of the engine to be started, and circular motion of right hand at head level.

Back aircraft tail to starboard

Point left arm down, move right arm down from overhead, vertical position to horizontal forward position, repeating right arm movement.

FROM MARSHALLER TO PILOT

Back aircraft tail to port

Point right arm down, move left arm down from overhead, vertical position to horizontal forward position, repeating left arm movement.

 indicates that the signal is applicable only to helicopter operations.

 Hover

Arms placed horizontally sideways.

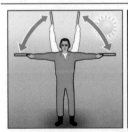

 Land

Arms placed down and crossed in front of the body.

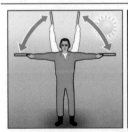

ARMS PLACED HORIZONTALLY SIDEWAYS, WITH THE PALMS UP, BECKONING UPWARDS. THE SPEED OF ARM MOVEMENT INDICATES THE RATE OF ASCENT.

MEANING: **MOVE UPWARDS.**

ARMS PLACED HORIZONTALLY SIDEWAYS, WITH THE PALMS TOWARDS THE GROUND, BECKONING DOWNWARDS. THE SPEED OF ARM MOVEMENT INDICATES THE RATE OF DESCENT.

MEANING: **MOVE DOWNWARDS.**

FROM MARSHALLER TO PILOT

EITHER ARM PLACED HORIZONTALLY SIDEWAYS, THEN THE OTHER ARM MOVED IN FRONT OF THE BODY TO THAT SIDE, IN THE DIRECTION OF THE REQUIRED MOVEMENT; REPEATED SEVERAL TIMES.

MEANING: **MOVE HORIZONTALLY IN THE DIRECTION INDICATED.**

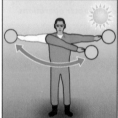 

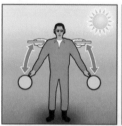 

ARMS PLACED DOWN, THE PALMS FACING FORWARD, THEN REPEATEDLY SWEPT UP TO SHOULDER LEVEL AND BACK DOWN.

MEANING: **MOVE BACK.**

  Release load

Left arm extended horizontally forward, then right arm making a horizontal slicing movement below left arm.

FROM PILOT TO MARSHALLER

Brakes engaged

Raise arm and hand with fingers extended horizontally in front of face, then clench fist:

Brakes released

Raise arm with fist clenched horizontally in front of face, then extend fingers:

Insert chocks

Arms extended palms facing outwards, move hands inwards to cross in front of face:

Remove chocks

Hands crossed in front of face, palms facing outwards, move arms outwards:

Ready to start engines

Raise the number of fingers on one hand indicating the number of the engine to be started. For this purpose the aircraft engines shall be numbered in relation to the marshaller facing the aircraft, from his right to his left.

For example, No. 1 engine shall be the port outer engine, No. 2 shall be the port inner, No. 3 shall be the starboard inner, and No. 4 shall be the starboard outer.

In order to highlight where a runway incursion risk is more likely 'runway incursion hotspots' are marked on airport taxiway charts. A 'runway hotspot' is an area, which has the potential of having, or has had, a higher number of runway incursions because of the complexity of the taxiways, number of runways, traffic flow, etc. At the planning stage, it is good airmanship to review these areas, and the route you may take to get to the departure runway. If you are flying with another pilot, ask them to monitor the taxi routing to ensure that you are adhering to your ATC clearance.

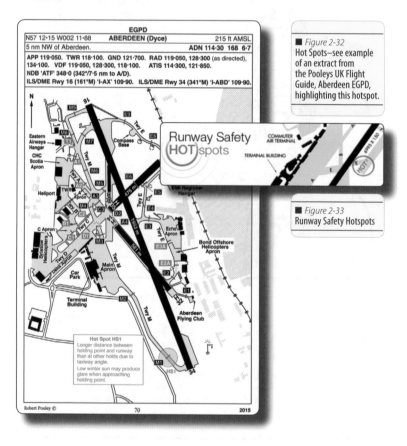

■ *Figure 2-32*
Hot Spots–see example of an extract from the Pooleys UK Flight Guide, Aberdeen EGPD, highlighting this hotspot.

■ *Figure 2-33*
Runway Safety Hotspots

Airports have a variety of methods to warn the pilot that they are approaching a runway holding point, the position of which ensures that a safe clearance exists between the aircraft holding and any aircraft passing in front of it. The diagram below is an extract from CAP 637 showing taxiway markings:

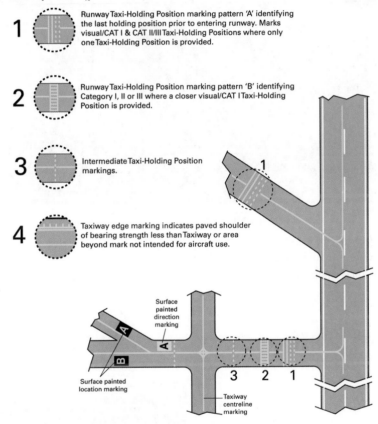

1 Runway Taxi-Holding Position marking pattern 'A' identifying the last holding position prior to entering runway. Marks visual/CAT I & CAT II/III Taxi-Holding Positions where only one Taxi-Holding Position is provided.

2 Runway Taxi-Holding Position marking pattern 'B' identifying Category I, II or III where a closer visual/CAT I Taxi-Holding Position is provided.

3 Intermediate Taxi-Holding Position markings.

4 Taxiway edge marking indicates paved shoulder of bearing strength less than Taxiway or area beyond mark not intended for aircraft use.

Surface painted direction marking

Surface painted location marking

Taxiway centreline marking

The last holding position marking is an important sign to remember (item 1 in the CAP 637 extract). You must not cross this without a specific clearance to do so, however, when vacating the runway after landing, you do not need to gain permission to cross it.

■ *Figure 2-34* Runway holding point – do not cross without a clearance

To provide a further warning of the close proximity of a runway, guard lights may be fitted. These are one pair of alternating flashing yellow lights, situated on either side of the runway, (wider taxiways may have them stretched over the full width) often referred to as 'Wig Wags'.

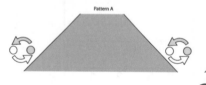
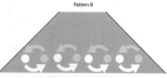

■ *Figure 2-36*
Runway wigwags are fitted to provide a warning

■ *Figure 2-37*
Runway guard lights (picture A) and 'Wig Wag lights (picture B)

Airfields certified for Low Visibility Procedures (LVPs) will have red Stop Bars at certain holding points. Stop Bars consist of a group of red lights situated at 90° to the taxiway and face the oncoming traffic. Put simply, they act like traffic lights, therefore you must **NOT** cross a lit stop bar. When ATC issues a line-up or take-off clearance they switch off the Stop Bars. They are on a timing circuit, so if you delay lining up they may come on again before you have passed them.

■ *Figure 2-38*
Never Cross-
illuminated Stop Bars

Of course a smaller grass strip also presents its challenges with regard to runway infringement, as it can sometimes be difficult to distinguish the taxiway from the runway. All licensed airfields, however, will have signage delineating the runway.

On page 322 is an extract from CAP 637 showing taxiway holding positions.

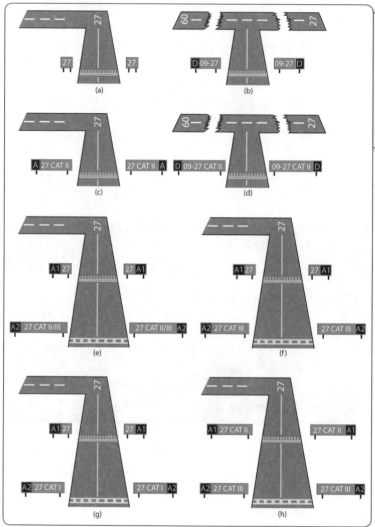

■ *Figure 2-39*
These diagrams illustrate typical signs associated with various Runway and Taxi-holding positions on Taxiway 'A' leading to the threshold of Runway 27 and on Taxiway 'D' leading to an intermediate taxiway entrance to Runway 09-27.

Note. – The signs at intermediate taxiway entrances as shown at (b) and (d) show the runway designation in both directions; a left turn is required to reach the threshold of Runway 09 and a right turn to reach the threshold of Runway 27.

CAT I, II and III relate to a category of Instrument Landing System which aircraft use in bad weather; the worse the weather, the more the radio signal has to be protected, hence why the holding points move further away from the runway.

■ *Figure 2-40*
Runway holding position sign at the take-off end of Runway 14 with co-located Taxiway Alpha location sign.

The marker boards used at smaller airfields are often portable and these can be blown over by the preceding aircraft, or the board itself might be obscured by grass. Runway markings are sometimes not as easy to see from the ground as they are from the air. Non-radio aircraft may also operate from the airfield increasing the likelihood of a runway incursion if a light signal was misunderstood.

■ *Figure 2-41*
Well-kept runway markings on a grass runway

The airport operator has an obligation to maintain the signage and runway markings, but do not be afraid to inform the operator either over the radio or in person about any signs/markings which may need attention.

The taxi-out, take-off, approach, landing, and taxi-in phases of the flight are all safety critical; therefore it is prudent to adopt a 'sterile cockpit' policy. A sterile cockpit is one where only tasks relating to the handling and safety of the aircraft for the related phase of flight are carried out. European rules governing commercial operators state the following with regard to sterile cockpit:

EU-OPS.1085 Rule 9 States:
The commander shall not permit any crew member to perform any activity during take-off, initial climb, final approach, and landing except those duties required for the safe operation of the aeroplane.

Whilst this rule is clearly aimed at commercial operators operating in a multi-pilot environment, when you obtain your PPL(A) you will undoubtedly take friends and relatives flying who will be sitting next to you. They will most likely be unfamiliar with the aviation environment and will naturally be inquisitive. It is good airmanship to explain to passengers that taxi, take-off, approach, landing and taxi-in are critical phases of flight, therefore it is best to ask questions once you are in the cruise. However, all passengers no matter where they are sitting, should be encouraged to mention anything that concerns them.

An essential part of taxiing safely and in accordance with the clearance (and flying in general) is Situational Awareness (SA). SA is about knowing where you are in relation to what is going on around you. SA is fluid, therefore it needs to be updated constantly, it is best described by the following cycle:

When applied to taxiing an aircraft, SA is about constantly asking yourself, 'Where am I in relation to my clearance limit, where is the runway and where are the other aircraft moving around me going?'

To help you answer these questions here are some tips:

- Have a taxi chart to hand and mark the clearance limit.
- Know where you are going **BEFORE** you start taxiing.
- Keep your eyes outside the cockpit.
- Listen to what ATC have told you to do-if in doubt stop.
- Don't rush.
- Taxi at an appropriate speed - CAA guidance is to taxi defensively
- Make sure that you have selected the correct radio frequency and have the next frequency in standby.
- Make sure that the volume level is correctly set.
- Keep on the yellow centreline.
- If you are following an aircraft, don't get too close to it.

- Anticipate the next turn and taxiway.
- Listen to ATC transmissions and build up a mental picture of where people are going, what's moving around you and how they may affect you.

Situational Awareness relies on having spare mental capacity. In the early stages of training you are unlikely to have much of this, because you will still be learning how to taxi the aircraft and understand what is being said on the radio. However, as you progress through the course, taxiing will become second nature, and you will be able to analyse what is going on around you.

Some light aircraft fitted with advanced avionics have the ability to display a taxi chart with the aircraft's current position superimposed on the display. This enables the pilot to update their Situational Awareness and confirm that the correct routing is being followed. It also allows the pilot to concentrate on taxiing the aircraft whilst not having to look inside the cockpit to find paper charts at a critical time. However, as with any cockpit instrumentation avoid being 'heads in' for a protected period of time.

■ *Figure 2-42*
The Avidyne Ex600 Multi Function Display has the ability to display the aircraft's current position on the taxi chart.

To increase SA and consequently reduce the risk of making a mistake whilst taxiing, consider adopting the following best practices (your instructor may well have additional advice):

- Review the airport diagram and check any NOTAMs that may affect a taxi route.
- Brief passengers regarding a sterile cockpit – but not to keep quiet if they see something that concerns them!
- Familiarise yourself with all possible taxi routes.
- Listen to the ATIS before taxiing to establish the runway in use.
- At smaller airfields look at the windsock or direction of departing/ landing aircraft to establish the runway in use.
- Have a taxi chart to hand.
- Monitor the taxi route on the moving map.
- Write down the clearance limit and identify it on the taxi chart.
- Put the transponder to ground mode to enable ATC to monitor your position.
- **NEVER** cross-illuminated red Stop Bars.
- Avoid completing checks whilst approaching and/or crossing runways.
- If in doubt, **STOP** and ask ATC for clarification, or help if needed.

The use of correct radio phraseology is an important part of avoiding runway incursions. CAP 413 Radiotelephony Manual and Air Pilot's Manual Volume 7 describe all aviation phraseology in detail. The following text regarding clearances is applicable at controlled airports. For communications at non-controlled airports refer to CAP 413 or APM 7.

Callsigns for Aircraft

PILOT: Oxford Tower, G-ABCD, request Basic Service.

ATC: G-ABCD, Oxford Tower, pass your message.

After satisfactory communication has been established and provided that no confusion is likely to occur, the ground station may abbreviate callsigns (see table below). A pilot may only abbreviate the callsign of his aircraft if the aeronautical station has first abbreviated it. For example:

FULL CALLSIGN	ABBREVIATION
GABCD	G-CD
Jetset GABCD	Jetset CD
N31029	N029
Thomson 12A*	No abbreviation
Cessna GABCD **	Cessna G-CD
Helicopter GABCD **	Helicopter G-CD

* Represents a Type C callsign.

** The name of either the aircraft manufacturer, or name of aircraft model, or name of the aircraft category (e.g. helicopter or gyrocopter) may be used as a prefix to the callsign.

Taxi Clearances

Taxi instructions issued by a controller will always contain a clearance limit, which is the point at which the aircraft must stop, unless further permission to proceed is given. For departing aircraft, the clearance limit will normally be the holding point of the runway in use, but it may be any other position on the aerodrome depending on the prevailing traffic. Pilots should, wherever possible, note taxi clearances down. For example:

PILOT: Shoreham Tower, G-ABCD, DA-40 by the south side hangars
request taxi for VFR flight to Calais, 2 POB.

ATC: G-ABCD, squawk 3763 taxi holding point K1 runway 20 via taxiway Kilo, QNH 967 hectopascals.

If the instructions given to surface traffic involve crossing a runway in use, clearance to cross should normally be withheld until no confliction exists. However, to achieve greater efficiency of operation, clearance to cross may be given subject to aircraft which are landing or taking off. The conditional clearance shall contain sufficient information to enable the pilot of the taxiing aircraft or vehicle driver to identify the other traffic and should be related to one movement only. For example:

A T C : JETSET 007, behind the landing A320, via Bravo 1 cross runway 26, report vacated.

P I L O T : Behind the landing A320, via Bravo 1 cross runway 26, wilco, JETSET 007.

Conditional clearances, in which an ATC issues an instruction that becomes valid after another event has occurred, have been identified as a contributory factor in a significant number of incidents, particularly in relation to clearances issued to aircraft in the vicinity of a runway.

■ *Figure 2-43*
Always write down the taxi clearance limit

Conditional clearances are only to be provided subject to conditions specified by the relevant authority. Conditional phrases will not be used for movements affecting the active runway(s), except when the aircraft or vehicles concerned are seen by the controller and pilot. Conditional clearances are to relate to one movement only and, in the case of landing traffic; this must be the first aircraft on approach. A conditional instruction shall be given as follows:

1. Call sign;
2. The condition;
3. Identification of subject of the condition;
4. The instruction.

FOR EXAMPLE:

ATC: JETSET 007, behind the landing PA-28, line up, behind.

PILOT: Behind the landing PA-28 line up, behind, JETSET 007

Take-off Clearance

Except in cases of emergency, messages will not be transmitted to an aircraft in the process of taking off or in the final stages of an approach and landing. Controllers will use the following phraseology for take-off.

ATC: G-CD, cleared for take-off

PILOT: Cleared for take-off, G-CD

BEFORE LINING UP SUMMARY:

- Look left and right and check the approaches and runway are clear.
- Position the aircraft at 90° to the runway to ensure maximum field of vision.
- Turn aircraft lights on.
- Identify the correct runway.
- Check that runway Stop Bars have been extinguished.
- Avoid completing non-essential tasks whilst lining up.
- Ensure transponder is selected on.
- Do not stop on a runway unless told to do so, or if it's an emergency.
- Do not enter without a specific clearance from ATC.
- Use correct radio phraseology.

FURTHER READING

The following documents give more guidance on avoiding runway incursions and you may find them useful in preparing for your exam:

- FAA RUNWAY INCURSION AVOIDANCE.
- CAP 413.
- CAP 637 VISUAL AIDS HANDBOOK.

INTENTIONALLY BLANK

Noise Abatement

1. Can the CAA prosecute a pilot for breaking an airfield's Noise Abatement Procedures?

   a. Yes, the CAA can prosecute a pilot for anything they wish.
   b. No, the CAA can only prosecute a pilot for breaking the ANO and Rules of the Air.
   c. It depends on the size and location of the airfield.
   d. The CAA will prosecute a pilot when asked to do so by an airfield operator.

2. Where would you find Noise Abatement Procedures for a licensed airfield?

   a. In the applicable airfield entry in the AIP.
   b. In the ANO.
   c. Each airfield's Noise Abatement Procedures are published in an AIC.
   d. You MUST ring the ATSU for a verbal briefing.

3. Where would you find Noise Abatement Procedures for an unlicensed airfield?

   a. In the applicable airfield entry in the AIP.
   b. In the ANO.
   c. Each airfield's Noise Abatement Procedures are published in an AIC.
   d. In a commercial flight guide such as 'Pooley's Flight Guide'.

4. Should you cross Stop Bars at a runway holding point?

   a. Yes, these are only for large aeroplanes.
   b. Yes, they might be faulty.
   c. No, wait until they have been extinguished by ATC.
   d. Only if you see them.

5. Before entering a runway what should you do regarding lookout?

   a. Look both left and right to check the approach and runway are clear.
   b. Turn off all aircraft lights in order not to dazzle other pilots.
   c. Do nothing; it is ATC responsibility to check that the runway is clear.
   d. Taxi onto the runway very slowly, stop and apply the parking brake, complete the before take-off checklist.

6.   Do Noise Abatement Procedures apply to PPL holders?

    a.   No, only to Commercial Pilots

    b.   No, PPL holders generally do not operate at larger airfields, which are the only types
that have Noise Abatement Procedures.

    c.   No, PPL holders are immune from any penalty that the airfield operator may impose
on them for disregarding their Noise Abatement Procedures.

    d.   Yes, as most airfields now have Noise Abatement Procedures, PPL holders should
follow them.

7.   The position of runway holding points ensures:

    a.   That a safe gap exists between the aircraft holding and any aircraft that may pass in
front of it.

    b.   That a safe gap exists between the aircraft holding and any aircraft that may pass in
front of, or behind it.

    c.   Nothing is assured-it is the pilot-in-command's responsibility.

    d.   That a safe gap exists to protect the radio signals for the applicable instrument
approach only.

8.   If in doubt about the correct route to follow whilst taxiing the pilot should:

    a.   Bring the aircraft to a stop, inform ATC, and ask for clarification.

    b.   Bring the aircraft to a stop, shutdown the engine and call ATC using a mobile phone.

    c.   Bring the aircraft to a stop, inform ATC, and call the flying school.

    d.   Keep moving at all times; ATC need to ensure that an efficient flow of traffic exists at
all times.

9.   What is the correct phraseology for the issue of a take-off clearance?

    a.   ATC: G-CD, cleared for take-off. Pilot: Cleared for take-off, G-CD.

    b.   ATC: G-CD, cleared for departure. Pilot: Cleared for departure, G-CD.

    c.   ATC: G-CD, cleared to go. Pilot: Cleared to go, G-CD.

    d.   ATC: G-CD, cleared to light the fires. Pilot: Cleared to light the fires, G-CD.

10.   Should a clearance limit be written down?

    a.   Yes.

    b.   No.

    c.   Depends on the pilot's mental capacity.

    d.   Only if the pilot is not familiar with the airport.

11.   What is the colour of runway Stop Bars and Guard Lights respectively?

    a.   Red and Yellow.

    b.   Yellow and Blue.

    c.   Blue and Green.

    d.   Red and White.

ANSWERS: 1b, 2a, 3d, 4c, 5a, 6d, 7a, 8a, 9a, 10a, 11a.

Fire or Smoke

Cause

All fires must have 3 components to sustain combustion, as shown in the triangle below:

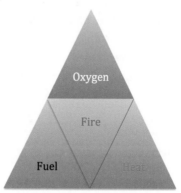

If any one component is removed from the triangle then the fire will extinguish. The types of components found in aircraft are as follows:

Oxygen =   Atmosphere, portable breathing equipment for high altitude flight, oxygen generators used in pressurised cabins, chemical reactions between components.

Fuel =   Fuel, hydraulic fluid, oil, or any combustible material.

Ignition =   Engine ignition system, hot pipes, internal combustion chamber, cigarettes, electrical system, lightning strikes, static charges, arcing.

A fire in an aircraft is a rare event and it is most likely to occur due to poor maintenance, failing components, or incorrect adherence to manufacturers' procedures. Although rare, a fire in any aircraft is about the most serious situation a pilot can face. Actions must be immediate, accurate and effective. **DO NOT DELAY**: investigations have revealed that an aircraft's structural integrity is affected within minutes of a major fire taking hold. There are four causes of fire in an aircraft:

1. Engine start.
2. Inflight.
3. Electrical.
4. Post-crash.

In all cases, the pilot must fly the aircraft first, get the aircraft on the ground as quickly as possible, declare a '**MAYDAY**' and action the appropriate checklist or drill. Any drill, procedure or checklist associated with fire or smoke should be memorised. Commercial operators call these checks 'Memory Items'. The objective of an engine fire or smoke checklist is threefold:

1. Extinguish the fire &/or smoke.
2. Get the aircraft on the ground as quickly as possible.
3. Minimise damage to other critical components.

Smoke is just as much of a threat if not a greater one, because of physiological effects that smoke inhalation and impaired vision have on the pilot and his ability to fly the aircraft.

WARNING:
The following text is general in nature and in all cases the instructions in appropriate AFM/POH/Checklist must be followed.

Carburettor Fire

Over priming the engine can cause excess fuel to enter the air intake; if the engine backfires during start the excess fuel may ignite. This can be quite difficult to detect because the fire may be contained within the carburettor; or the fire may have extinguished itself before detection. It is only when maintenance is being carried out that evidence of a fire is noticed.

The first actions after suspecting, or detecting a carburettor fire, are to continue turning the engine over and draw excess fuel back into the induction system. If the fire is present before the engine has started running, or the fire persists for more than a few seconds, then the engine must be shut down and aircraft evacuated.

Generic actions for a carburettor fire are as follows:

1. Starter .... Crank engine
2. Mixture .... Idle Cut-Off
3. Throttle .... Open
4. Electric fuel pump (if fitted) .... Off
5. Fuel selector...................................... Off

Subsequent actions:

6. Ignition .... Off
7. ATC (if able) .... Inform
8. Electric Master.................................... Off
9. Locate fire extinguisher and evacuate upwind of the aircraft.

Engine Fire

An engine fire in flight is often preceded by another indication other than visible flames around the coaming. A fuel check, or pressure drop, may indicate a leak, which may cause a fire; a rough running may indicate a damaged cylinder causing fuel or oil to spill into the engine component.

Any one of the following may also be evidence of an engine fire:

1. Flames &/or smoke around the engine.
2. Increased cabin temperature especially in the foot-well.
3. Fuel smell.
4. Rough running or engine failure.
5. Fire warning system (if fitted).
6. ATC may try to contact you.
7. Other aircraft.
8. Passengers.

The colours of the flames indicate the fuel source of the fire. Black coloured flames indicate oil based and orange fuel based.

■ *Figure 3-1*
Oil based fire

■ *Figure 3-2*
Fuel based fire

Once you have confirmed the engine fire, your actions need to be carried out immediately.

Generic actions for an engine fire are as follows:

1. Fuel Selector...Off
2. Throttle..Closed
3. Mixture..ICO
4. Electric fuel pump (if fitted).....................Off
5. Heater...Off
6. Defroster...Off
7. Execute power-off landing

Once the checklist has been completed in a single engine aircraft you have no choice but to execute a forced landing. This may also be appropriate in a multi-engine aircraft if the fire is not extinguished. The type of descent flown is dependent on whether fire or smoke is still present. If either fire or smoke still exists then an emergency descent might be the appropriate course of action. Be aware that fire can damage the aircraft's wing spar very quickly. The wing spar carries the major structural load in an aircraft, so descending rapidly may exert extra strain on the aircraft. Of course there is a balance between getting the aircraft on the ground ASAP, and the potential of structural damage; this is a decision that can only be made on the day.

There are two accepted techniques of emergency descent, unless prohibited by the aircraft manufacturer:

1. Initially roll 30° AOB to maintain a positive load factor, lower the nose and once established in the descent return to wings level. Descend at a high speed-not above VNE; or
2. Reduce speed to below VFE and VLE and lower the flaps and landing gear (if applicable) then descend at the most limiting manoeuvre speed.

In both cases, at a suitable altitude, execute the applicable emergency descent profile and adjust speed for a forced landing in a suitable field.

Technique 1 requires a high-speed descent: as such, consideration to V_A must be given in turbulent air. In an aircraft fitted with a variable pitch propeller, positioning the RPM lever to 'high' will allow the aircraft to act as an aerodynamic brake and prevent excessive airspeed building up. If a fire still exists after the checklist is completed, the high airflow generated by the high speed may extinguish the fire during the descent.

Technique 2 increases the drag on the aircraft by extending the flap and landing gear and thus increasing the rate of descent. The applicable flap and landing gear extension speed limitations must be observed in the descent. This imposes less strain on the airframe and puts the aircraft in a configuration for landing sooner.

Transmit a '**MAYDAY**' call to ATC as high as possible, as the radio range increases with altitude. Whichever technique is used, check every 500-1000ft during the descent, to assess whether the fire still exists and manoeuvre the aircraft over a suitable landing area.

Before practising this manoeuvre during training, you MUST conduct an excellent lookout in the airspace immediately below the aircraft and it is good airmanship to inform ATC.

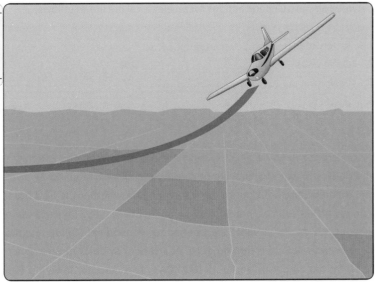

■ *Figure 3-3*
Emergency descent-check every 500-1000ft whether the fire still exists

Fire in the Cabin and Cockpit (choice of extinguishing agents according to fire classification and use of the extinguisher)

A fire in the cabin may occur for any one of the following reasons:

1. Faulty wiring in the avionic components.
2. Smoking.
3. Cigarette lighter igniting a material.
4. Flammable cargo.
5. Fuel line puncture.
6. Thermal runaway in a battery in a personal tablet/laptop.

The most common cause is an electrical fire caused through arcing within the wiring circuitry or a faulty avionic component. Electrical fires are identified by an acrid smell and fine, light grey/white smoke coming from the instrument panel. If the faulty component is easily identified, then the first course of action is to turn it off and locate the fire extinguisher. If you have a passenger, then it may be appropriate for them to fight the fire whilst you fly the aircraft and action the checklist. Always follow the actions described in the aircraft AFM/POH as procedures differ greatly between aircraft. Generic actions for an electrical fire are as follows:

1. Battery master.................................... Off
2. Cabin vents....................................... Open
3. Cabin heat .... OFF
4. Locate BCF fire extinguisher
5. Land as soon as practicable

In a piston-engine aircraft using AVGAS, turning off the Alternator and Battery Master switch will not cause the engine to stop, however, in diesel engine aircraft it might do, depending on whether the ECU has a standby power source. Therefore be prepared to execute a forced landing without power. Cabin vents are opened to increase ventilation and aid smoke removal. Before turning off the battery or avionics master switch (if fitted) remember to declare a '**MAYDAY**', and consider lowering flap and/or landing gear if they require electric power.

Fires are classified into four types:

Class A – Solids.
Class B – Flammable liquids.
Class C – Electrical.
Class D – Metals.

FIRE CLASS	MATERIAL	EXTINGUISHING AGENT	AGGRAVATED BY	SMOKE COLOUR & CHARACTERISTICS
A	Wood, paper, cloth or plastic	Requires a cooling agent, e.g. water, tea, coffee, etc. Water or Glycol is the best	Alcohol	Grey/brown Thick depending on quantity of fuel source
B	Flammable liquid, hydraulic fluid, oil, tar, or aircraft fuel	Foam or Halon, fire extinguisher	Water will not extinguish the fire	Black Very thick, with a distinct oil/ petrol-like odour
C	Electrical	Non-conducting mixture, in order to avoid electrocution and damage to electrical circuitry, e.g. Halon fire extinguisher	Water	Light grey or white, with a bluish tinge. Very fine and can disperse rapidly. Has a distinct acrid odour.
D	Metals, such as sodium, magnesium, lithium, and potassium	Special powder extinguishers are effective on class D fires, because of the possible chemical reaction between the burning and extinguishing agents	Halon fire extinguishers	-

Class A and C fires are the most common in aircraft cabins. Larger aircraft may have multiple types of portable fire extinguisher on board, however, on a light aircraft only one is fitted which must be within easy access for the pilot whilst in the seat position.

Halogenated hydrocarbons (Halons) have been practically the only fire-extinguishing agents used in civil aviation. Unfortunately, Halon is damaging to the environment and aids global warming, and its production has been banned by international agreement. However, because of its special properties and aviation's unique operational environment an exemption has been given for its use, although production of new extinguishers has been extremely limited. Halon is the generic name for the group of BromoChlorodiFluoromethane (BCF) extinguishers that can be used for class A, B, and C fires making them ideal for use in all aircraft. However, do not use Halons on a class D fire. Halon agents may react vigorously with the burning metal. For information only-other extinguishing agents used in aviation have the following properties:

1. CO_2, which smothers the fire as it is heavier than Oxygen and forces itself immediately around the material. The problem with using this in a confined space is that it can cause unconsciousness, and death by suffocation, if the victim is allowed to breathe CO_2 in fire extinguishing concentrations for 20 to 30 minutes. It is not effective as an extinguishing agent on fires involving chemicals containing their own oxygen supply, such as cellulose nitrate (used in some aircraft paints) and fires involving magnesium and titanium.

2. Dry chemical extinguishing agents can be used on Class A, B, and C fires. Dry chemical powder extinguishers contain mono- ammonium phosphate. All other dry chemical powders are restricted to Class B or C fires. Dry powder chemical extinguishers create a lot of residue, which is not ideal in the confines of an aircraft cockpit or cabin!

3. Water can be used on Class A type fires by cooling the material below its ignition temperature and soaking the material to prevent re-ignition. Water is not suitable for Class C fires, so generally water-based extinguishers are not used on board an aircraft.

The following hand-held extinguishers are unsuitable as cabin or cockpit equipment:

* CO_2.
*   Dry chemicals (because of the potential for corrosion damage to electronic equipment, potential for obscuring instrumentation, and the clean up problems from their use).
*   Specialised dry powder (suitable for ground operations).

■ *Figure 3-4*
A portable fire extinguisher-Halon gas is the most popular type in light aircraft.

Hand-held fire extinguishers discharge an extinguishing agent for 8 to 25 seconds, depending on their type and capacity. It is therefore essential that you select, and know how to use the fire extinguisher properly. It is good airmanship also to brief passengers on how to use the fire extinguisher. Using the mnemonic PASS can help when remembering how to use a fire extinguisher:

PULL the pin;
AIM the fire extinguisher at the base of the fire;
SQUEEZE the top handle or lever;
SWEEP the fire extinguisher nozzle from side to side in a sweeping motion.

WARNING: *Because of the chemical composition of HALON it is three times as effective as CO_2 extinguishers that contain the same amount of extinguishing agent. Airline crews are advised to use Portable Breathing Equipment (PBE) if using it in a confined space. Therefore it is advisable to increase ventilation in the cockpit and wear an O_2 mask if one is on board. If used on Class A fires the surrounding area should be cooled with a non-alcoholic liquid.*

FURTHER READING

The following articles are excellent and provide further reading if required:

- FAA ADVISORY CIRCULAR 120-80.
- AIRBUS FLIGHT OPERATIONS BRIEFING NOTES, CABIN OPERATIONS, MANAGING IN-FLIGHT FIRES.
- FAA AIRPLANE FLIGHT MANUAL, CHAPTER 17, FIRE PROTECTION SYSTEMS.

Smoke in the Cockpit and Cabin
(Effects and action to be taken)

The first priority when dealing with a fire is to extinguish it, the second is to remove the smoke/fumes created by burning material. Smoke inhalation is often the primary cause of death in a household fire and the same is true in an aircraft fire, large or small.

The gases contained within the smoke depend on the material being burnt. Aircraft are constructed of the following combustible materials:

- Synthetic Material.
- Wood.
- Petro Chemicals.
- Metal.
- Natural Cloths.
- Plastic.
- Wiring.

The two main toxic gases contained within smoke are:

- Carbon Monoxide.
- Hydrogen Cyanide.

Most materials contain Carbon; consequently they release both Carbon Monoxide and Dioxide when burnt. You may have seen a Carbon Monoxide detector fitted in the cockpit; this is because broken cabin heaters can leak Carbon Monoxide from engine exhaust gases into the cabin. Carbon Monoxide is an odourless, and colourless gas, so a detector which changes colour when it comes into contact with it is fitted to warn the pilot of its presence.

Carbon Monoxide affects people in different ways and the levels required to induce degradation of a pilot's performance vary greatly. The following are possible symptoms and effects of Carbon Monoxide poisoning:

■ *Figure 3-5*
A typical CO detector for a light aircraft

- Headache.
- Weakness.
- Nausea.
- Dizziness.
- Confusion.
- Dimness of Vision.
- Impaired Judgement.
- Unconsciousness leading to Death.

Synthetic materials found in the cabin will contain Hydrogen which, when burnt, produces Hydrogen Cyanide gas which is highly toxic. Symptoms of Hydrogen Cyanide poisoning are similar to those of Carbon Monoxide with the addition of possible convulsions and vomiting. The effects of Hydrogen Cyanide poisoning are rapid.

Smoke has numerous further effects on the occupants:

- Reduces Visibility.
- Disorientation.
- Eyes, Nose and Throat Irritation.
- Hypoxia.
- Increased Breathing Rate.

Because of the speed at which the smoke and fumes can reduce pilot performance, the removal checklist MUST be carried out without delay. Generic actions to be followed in the event of smoke in the cabin are as follows:

1. Source of fire .... Check

Electrical fire (smoke in cabin):
2. Master switch .... OFF
3. Vents .... OPEN
4. Cabin heat .... OFF
5. Locate fire extinguisher
6. Land as soon as practicable

If the smoke is still not clearing, consider cracking open one of the doors or ventilation windows. Transmit a '**MAYDAY**' call to ATC before turning off the master switch, because the radio will be turned off, as a consequence of actioning the smoke checklist.

Pressurised aircraft will be fitted with Oxygen masks for the pilots, which have the facility to provide 100% Oxygen delivered under a positive pressure, allowing the pilots to breathe uncontaminated air. Unfortunately, most light aircraft do not have them fitted, however, covering the nose and mouth with a damp cloth will provide protection from smoke particulates and will absorb most of the water-soluble gases (i.e. hydrogen cyanide and hydrogen chloride). This gives the pilot valuable time to get the aircraft on the ground, and provides (albeit limited) protection from the effects of smoke inhalation.

■ *Figure 3-6*
If you have an oxygen mask fit it when dealing with a smoke or fumes incident

FURTHER READING
The following article is excellent and provides further reading if required:

- MEDICAL FACTS FOR PILOTS - SMOKE TOXICITY. PUBLICATION AM-400-95/1 WRITTEN BY: ARVIND K. CHATURVEDI, PH.D. PREPARED BY: FAA CIVIL AEROSPACE MEDICAL INSTITUTE AEROSPACE MEDICAL EDUCATION DIVISION.

Fire or Smoke

1. How many components must a fire have?

   a. 2.
   b. 3.
   c. 4.
   d. 5.

2. What type of distress call should be made in the event of a fire?

   a. 'PAN' call.
   b. 'Help' call.
   c. 'We are declaring an emergency'.
   d. 'MAYDAY'.

3. Should fire drills be memorised?

   a. No.
   b. Yes.
   c. Yes – the 'Memory items' are stipulated in the aircraft checklist.
   d. It depends on what your instructor has taught you.

4. What is the authoritative document on handling emergencies?

   a. Approved Training Organisation's Training Manual.
   b. Approved Training Organisation's Safety Management Manual.
   c. Aircraft Flight Manual/Pilot's Operating Handbook.
   d. AIP.

5. What is the main cause of an engine fire upon start?

   a. Over priming.
   b. Setting the throttle/power lever too far open.
   c. Not setting the mixture control at the rich setting.
   d. A crack in the exhaust pipe.

6. What is the first action after suspecting or detecting a carburettor fire?

   a. Evacuate the aircraft immediately.
   b. Nothing, the engine is designed to cope with the event.
   c. Continue to turn the engine over, and then proceed with the checklist.
   d. Declare a 'MAYDAY' with ATC, and then continue to turn the engine over.

7.   Put the following initial generic actions in the correct order for a carburettor fire:

     1.   Starter .... Crank engine
     2.   Fuel selector .... Off
     3.   Throttle .... Open
     4.   Mixture .... Idle Cut-Off
     5.   Electric fuel pump (if fitted) .... Off

8.   Where will the emergency descent (if any) be described?

     a.   In the AFM/POH.
     b.   In the checklist.
     c.   Light aircraft are not authorised to conduct an emergency descent.
     d.   A spiral dive is the safest manoeuvre to descend rapidly.

9.   How many fire classifications are there?

     a.   3.
     b.   4.
     c.   5.
     d.   6.

10.   What is a Class A fire?

     a.   Flammable liquids.
     b.   Metals.
     c.   Electrical.
     d.   Solids.

11.   What is a Class B fire?

     a.   Flammable liquids.
     b.   Metals.
     c.   Electrical.
     d.   Solids.

12.   What is a Class C fire?

     a.   Flammable liquids.
     b.   Metals.
     c.   Electrical.
     d.   Solids.

13. What is a Class D fire?

   a. Flammable liquids.
   b. Metals.
   c. Electrical.
   d. Solids.

14. What is the most common extinguishing agent used in light aircraft?

   a. Halon.
   b. Water.
   c. CO2.
   d. Dry Chemical.

15. How long does a hand-held fire extinguisher last for?

   a. 60 to 75 seconds.
   b. 30 to 60 seconds.
   c. 8 to 25 seconds.
   d. 120 to 180 seconds.

16. What are the two main toxic gases within smoke?

   a. Oxygen and Chloride.
   b. Oxygen and Hydrogen.
   c. Carbon Monoxide and Hydrogen Cyanide.
   d. Carbon Monoxide and BromoChlorodiFluoromethane.

17. What is the purpose of a CO detector?

   a. To detect Carbon Monoxide in the cabin.
   b. To detect Carbon Dioxide in the cabin.
   c. To detect Hydrogen Cyanide in the cabin.
   d. To detect Oxygen in the cabin.

18. What could you do to limit the amount of toxic gases entering your lungs, if you don't have an Oxygen mask?

   a. Put your head out of the door.
   b. Put a sock in your mouth.
   c. Cover your nose and mouth with a damp cloth.
   d. Cover your nose only with a damp cloth.

ANSWERS: 1b, 2d, 3c, 4c, 5a, 6c, 7. 1, 4, 3, 5 & 2, 8a, 9b, 10d, 11a, 12c, 13b, 14a, 15c, 16c, 17a, 18c.

Windshear and Microburst

Effects and Recognition during Departure and Approach

The Effect of Windshear

Windshear is defined as a change in wind direction and/or speed in space. The term 'Windshear' simply describes a changing wind. This can result in a wind the speed of which alters as an aircraft climbs or descends or the direction of which changes from place to place. It can generate a downdraft through which an aircraft has to fly. Windshear is generally understood to mean a wind change within a short distance or a short time.

OVERSHOOT EFFECT. Flying into an updraft will increase the rate of climb and will increase the angle of climb relative to the ground. Flying into a downdraft will have the opposite effect.

Because of its own inertia (or resistance to change), an aeroplane flying into an increasing headwind will want to maintain its original speed relative to the ground. Thus the effect of flying into an increasing headwind will be to increase the airspeed temporarily.

Attempting to maintain the correct climbing speed by raising the nose will lead to increased climb performance (only transient as the shear is flown through).

In this way, the climb performance will increase when flying into an increasing headwind, a decreasing tailwind or into an updraft. The aeroplane has a tendency to overshoot, or go above, the original flightpath, or to gain airspeed temporarily – hence the term overshoot effect.

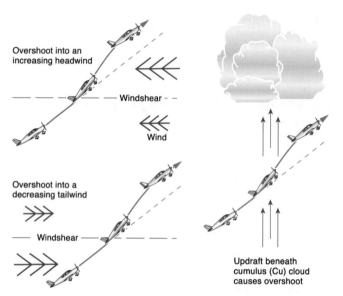

Overshoot into an increasing headwind

Windshear

Wind

Overshoot into a decreasing tailwind

Windshear

Updraft beneath cumulus (Cu) cloud causes overshoot

■ *Figure 4-1*
Overshoot effect is a (temporary) gain in performance

Again, the advantages of taking off into wind are clear. Wind strength usually increases as you climb away from the ground, so you would normally expect an aircraft taking off into the wind to climb into an increasing headwind. This leads to increased climb performance over the ground, i.e. a steeper climb-out gradient over ground obstacles.

UNDERSHOOT EFFECT.   Taking off downwind, the aeroplane would normally climb into an area of increasing tailwind. As a result of its inertia, the aeroplane would temporarily tend to maintain its original speed over the ground, leading to a decreased airspeed. To maintain the target climb speed, the pilot would have to lower the nose. Climb performance, both rate and gradient, would fall off.

Exactly the same effect of decreased climb performance will occur flying into an increasing tailwind, a decreasing headwind, or a downdraft. The aeroplane will tend to fall below the original flightpath, or to lose speed, hence the term undershoot effect.

An initial overshoot effect (for example, when flying into an increasing headwind coming out of the base of a cumulonimbus storm cloud) may be followed by a severe undershoot effect as you fly into the downdraft and then the rapidly increasing tailwind. Treat cumulonimbus clouds with great caution.

Avoid flying near cumulo-nimbus (Cb) clouds.

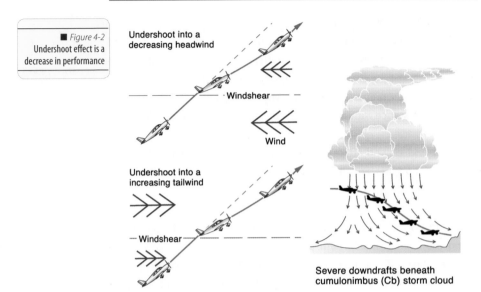

■ Figure 4-2
Undershoot effect is a
decrease in performance

Undershoot into a
decreasing headwind

Windshear

Wind

Undershoot into a
increasing tailwind

Windshear

Severe downdrafts beneath
cumulonimbus (Cb) storm cloud

Windshear

The study of windshear and its effect on aeroplanes and what
protective measures can be taken to avoid unpleasant results is still in
its infancy and much remains to be learned. What is certain is that every
aeroplane and every pilot will be affected by windshear – usually the light
windshears that occur in everyday flying, but occasionally a moderate
windshear that requires positive action from the pilot and, on rare
occasions, severe windshear that can put an aeroplane out of control.

Severe windshears have caused the loss of a number of aircraft, some of
them large passenger aircraft. A little knowledge will help you understand
how to handle windshear and how to avoid unnecessary problems with it.

WINDSHEAR TERMINOLOGY

A windshear is defined as a change in wind direction and/or wind speed, including updrafts and downdrafts, in space. Any change in the wind velocity (be it a change in speed or in direction) as you move from one point to another is a windshear. The stronger the change and the shorter the distance within which it occurs, the stronger the windshear.

> Windshear is a change in wind direction and/ or wind speed.

Updrafts and downdrafts are vertical components of wind. The most hazardous updrafts and downdrafts are usually those associated with thunderstorms.

The term low-level windshear is used to specify the windshear, if any, along the final approach path prior to landing, along the runway and along the take-off/initial climb-out flightpath. Windshear near the ground (i.e. below about 3,000 ft) is often the most critical in terms of safety for the aeroplane.

Turbulence is eddy motions in the atmosphere which vary with time and from place to place.

EFFECTS OF WINDSHEAR ON AIRCRAFT

Most of our studies have considered an aeroplane flying in a reasonably stable air mass which has a steady motion relative to the ground, i.e. in a steady wind situation. We have seen how an aeroplane climbing out in a steady headwind will have a better climb gradient over the ground compared to the tailwind situation, and how an aeroplane will glide further over the ground downwind compared to into wind.

In reality an air mass does not move in a totally steady manner – there will be gusts and updrafts and changes of wind speed and direction which the aeroplane will encounter as it flies through the air mass. In this chapter, we look at the transient effects that these windshears have on the flightpath of an aeroplane.

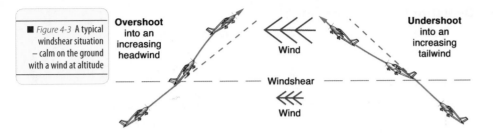

■ *Figure 4-3* **A typical windshear situation – calm on the ground with a wind at altitude**

A Typical Windshear Situation

Often when the wind is relatively calm on the ground, at several hundred feet above the ground the light and variable wind conditions change suddenly into a strong and steady wind. If we consider an aeroplane making an approach to land in these conditions, we can see the effect that the windshear has as the aeroplane passes through the shear.

An aeroplane flying through the air will have a certain inertia depending on its mass and its velocity relative to the ground. If the aeroplane has a true airspeed of 80 knots and the headwind component is 30 knots, then the inertial speed of the aeroplane over the ground is (80 − 30) = 50 knots.

When the aeroplane flies down into the calm air, the headwind component reduces quickly to say 5 knots. The inertial speed of the aeroplane over the ground is still 50 knots, but the new headwind of only 5 knots will mean that its true airspeed has suddenly reduced to 55 knots.

In gusty conditions, use a power-on approach and landing, and consider adding a few knots to the approach speed.

The pilot would observe a sudden reduction in indicated airspeed and a change in the performance of the aeroplane – at 55 knots airspeed the performance will be quite different from when it is at 80 knots airspeed. The normal reaction would be to add power or to lower the nose to regain airspeed, and to avoid undershooting the desired flightpath.

The pilot can accelerate the aeroplane and return it to the desired flight path by changes in attitude and power. The more the windshear, the more these changes in power and attitude will be required. Any fluctuations in wind will require adjustments by the pilot, which is why you have to work so hard sometimes, especially when approaching to land.

Overshoot and Undershoot Effect

The effects of windshear on an aeroplane's flightpath depend on the nature and location of the shear, as follows.

OVERSHOOT EFFECT

Overshoot effect is caused by a windshear which results in the aeroplane flying above the desired flightpath and/or an increase in indicated airspeed. The nose of the aircraft may also tend to rise. Overshoot effect may result from flying into an increasing headwind, a decreasing tailwind, from a tailwind into a headwind, or an updraft.

UNDERSHOOT EFFECT

Undershoot effect is caused by a windshear which results in an aircraft flying below the desired flightpath and/or a decrease in indicated airspeed. The nose of the aircraft may also tend to pitch down. Undershoot effect may result from flying into a decreasing headwind, an increasing tailwind, from a headwind into a tailwind, or into a downdraft.

Note that the actual windshear effect depends on:
1. The nature of the windshear.
2. Whether the aeroplane is climbing or descending through that particular windshear.
3. The direction in which the aeroplane is flying.

WINDSHEAR REVERSAL EFFECT

Windshear reversal effect is caused by a windshear which results in the initial effect on the aeroplane being reversed as the aircraft proceeds further along the flightpath. It would be described as overshoot effect followed by undershoot, or undershoot followed by overshoot effect, as appropriate.

Windshear reversal effect is a common phenomenon often experienced on approach to land, when things are usually happening too fast to analyse exactly what is taking place in terms of wind. The pilot can, of course, observe undershoot and overshoot effect and react accordingly with changes in attitude and/or thrust.

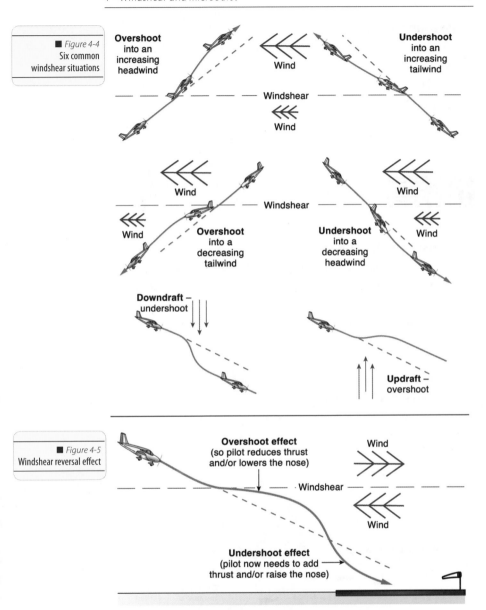

■ *Figure 4-4*
Six common
windshear situations

Overshoot into an increasing headwind

Undershoot into an increasing tailwind

Wind

— — — Windshear — — —

Wind

Wind

— — — Windshear — — —

Wind

Overshoot into a decreasing tailwind

Undershoot into a decreasing headwind

Wind

Downdraft – undershoot

Updraft – overshoot

■ *Figure 4-5*
Windshear reversal effect

Overshoot effect (so pilot reduces thrust and/or lowers the nose)

Wind

— — · Windshear — — —

Wind

Undershoot effect (pilot now needs to add thrust and/or raise the nose)

CROSSWIND EFFECT

Crosswind effect is caused by a windshear which requires a rapid change of aircraft heading to maintain a desired track (not uncommon in a crosswind approach and landing because the crosswind component changes as the ground is neared).

■ Figure 4-6
Crosswind Effect

THE CAUSES OF WINDSHEAR

Causes of windshear include the wind being slowed down by ground surface roughness, abrupt changes in terrain, thunderstorms, cumulonimbus clouds, large cumulus clouds (downbursts and gust fronts), low-level jetstreams, fronts, thermal activity, sea breezes, etc.

Avoid thunderstorms and cumulonimbus clouds as windshear effects near them can be severe. A strong downburst out of the base of one of these clouds will spread out as it nears the ground. The initial effect may be an overshoot effect followed by what may be an extremely severe undershoot.

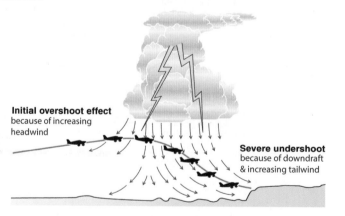

■ Figure 4-7
Avoid thunderstorms
and cumulonimbus
clouds

Initial overshoot effect
because of increasing
headwind

Severe undershoot
because of downdraft
& increasing tailwind

ACTIONS TO AVOID AND ACTIONS TAKEN DURING ENCOUNTER

At the planning stage, study Significant Weather Charts and Terminal Aerodrome Forecasts for the likelihood of thunderstorms and strong gusty winds. The relevant airfield entry in the AIP might indicate that the airfield is prone to low-level windshear when the wind favours a specific direction. In flight listen to the airfield ATIS (if it has one) and contact the ATSU early for the local weather conditions/pilot reports. If you have the ability to obtain satellite weather reports, then do so for your destination and alternate airfield(s).

If it seems likely that you may encounter windshear, ensure that you carry extra fuel for both holding and diversion. The best action to avoid a windshear or microburst encounter is to delay the take-off/landing, or if airborne, to divert to another airfield. However, if you inadvertently experience windshear or a microburst then CAA AIC 84/2008 (Pink 150) gives the following guidance:

- Recognise and execute the escape manoeuvre in the AFM.
- Adopt an appropriate pitch angle and try to hold it; do not 'chase' airspeed.
- Be guided by stall warnings when holding or increasing pitch, easing the back pressure as required to attain or hold a lower pitch attitude if necessary. (In many aircraft types optimum performance is very close to the point of onset of stall warning. It is important, however, not to go beyond the point of onset as it is then not possible for the pilot to know how deeply into the warning the aircraft is).

Please note that the techniques described above are aimed at commercial aircraft, which have more power available to escape the windshear or microburst.

Following recovery from a windshear encounter, report it to ATC as reports of windshear encounters are important sources of information to warn other pilots of the danger. The UK AIP (GEN 3-5-21) contains guidance on windshear reporting. AIC 84/2008 (Pink 150) concludes with the following:

Recognise – that windshear is a hazard and the signs that may indicate its presence;

Avoid – windshear by delay or diversion;

Prepare – for an inadvertent encounter by a 'speed margin' if 'energy loss' is expected;

Recover – know the techniques recommended for your aircraft and use them without hesitation if windshear is encountered;

Report – immediately to ATC controlling the airfield at which the incident occurred and using the Mandatory Occurrence Reporting Scheme, to the Civil Aviation Authority.

Even if windshear has not been reported and there is no weather associated with it in the vicinity, always check the wind before commencing the take-off or landing; either by obtaining the ATIS, or asking for a 'wind check' from the ATSU. Certain localised wind directions may create low-level wind shears close to the ground.

The runway in use will normally be that most closely aligned to the surface wind direction but may vary because of local operational restrictions or procedures. If you are unable to accept the runway in use you should advise ATC, the FISO, or Air/Ground communication service radio station operator, that the crosswind (or tailwind) on that runway is outside your limits and request the use of a more suitable runway. There might be a delay in ATC complying with your request, and in certain cases diversion to an alternate aerodrome with a more suitable runway direction might be the only option.

If you are unable to accept the runway in use inform ATC

FURTHER READING:
The following articles may prove useful when preparing for your exam:

·   AIC P 84/2008.
·   AIC P 062/2012

Windshear and Microburst

1. During an approach the aircraft is subjected to a windshear with a decreasing headwind component; without pilot intervention the aircraft:

   a. Rate of descent increases, indicated airspeed decreases.
   b. Rate of descent decreases, indicated airspeed decreases.
   c. Rate of descent increases, indicated airspeed increases.
   d. All parameters stay the same.

2. During an approach the aircraft is subject to a windshear with an increasing headwind component; without pilot intervention the aircraft:

   a. Rate of descent increases, airspeed decreases.
   b. Rate of descent decreases, airspeed increases.
   c. Rate of descent increases, airspeed increases.
   d. All parameters stay the same.

3. After take-off an aircraft is subject to windshear with an increasing tailwind component; in the absence of pilot intervention:

   a. Nothing happens.
   b. Indicated airspeed reduces, rate of climb decreases.
   c. Indicated airspeed increases, rate of climb decreases.
   d. Indicated airspeed reduces, rate of climb increases.

4. If you see a Thunderstorm overhead the destination airfield, the safest course of action is to:

   a. Hold well clear of the Thunderstorm area, and if necessary divert to a suitable airfield in better weather.
   b. Continue; Thunderstorms are only damaging if an aircraft flies through them.
   c. Let another aircraft attempt an approach first.
   d. Attempt an approach; thunderstorms don't affect light aircraft.

5. You experience windshear on approach to an airfield in the UK, what should you do?

   a. Do not tell anyone.
   b. Inform ATC once safely on the ground and submit a MOR to the UK CAA.
   c. Inform your instructor only.
   d. Inform your family upon return.

Wake Turbulence

Cause

As a wing produces lift, the higher static pressure area beneath it forces an airflow around the wingtip into the lower pressure area above. The greater the pressure differential, the greater is this flow around the wingtips.

At the high angles of attack necessary to produce the required lift force at low speeds, very large and strong trailing vortices are formed. As the aeroplane is moving forward, a trail of wingtip vortices is left behind. This effect was discussed under *Induced Drag* – the drag generated by the production of lift.

■ *Figure 5-1*
Wake Turbulence

Wake turbulence will be strongest behind a heavy aircraft flying with its flaps up

As a large and heavy aircraft is rotated for take-off or flared for landing, the angle of attack is large. The trailing wingtip vortices formed can be strong enough to upset a following aeroplane if it flies into them. They are invisible but real. This effect is known as wake turbulence.

The main danger from wake turbulence is loss of control caused by induced roll

The wake turbulence behind a *Boeing 747* can significantly affect, for example, a *737* or a *DC-9*, and can cause lighter aircraft to become uncontrollable.

To avoid wake turbulence accidents and incidents, Air Traffic Control delays the operation of light aircraft on runways behind heavy jets for up to 3 minutes before take-off (or 8 nm if landing) to allow the vortices to drift away and dissipate.

All pilots must be aware of wake turbulence because even the Air Traffic Control procedures occasionally provide insufficient separation from the wingtip vortices behind another aircraft. Air Traffic Controllers are experts at their job – do not expect them to be experts at yours as well. As pilot you have the ultimate responsibility for the safety of your aeroplane – so learn to visualise the formation and movement of invisible wingtip vortices.

Heavy aircraft will also leave vortices in their wake in flight, especially in the circuit area where they are flying slowly at high angles of attack – make sure that you provide your own separation in the circuit.

The vortices will tend to lose height slowly (drift downwards) and drift downwind. To be able to avoid these invisible danger areas when following heavier aircraft, you must be able to visualise the movement of the vortices and take steps to avoid them.

Light wind

Vortices move apart and drift downwind

Vortices drift down

■ *Figure 5-2*
Wingtip vortices drift downwind (as well as backwards)

- A crosswind will cause the vortices to drift off the downwind side of the runway.

- A headwind or a tailwind will carry them down the runway in the direction of the wind.

- In nil-wind or light and variable conditions, the vortices will 'hang around'. Calm conditions can be very dangerous – delaying your take-off or changing runway is worth considering.

Be extra careful in calm conditions, as the vortices will not be blown away.

List of Relevant Parameters

Wake Vortex categories depend on aircraft weight as shown in the table below:

WAKE TURBULENCE CATEGORIES

Category	ICAO and Flight Plan (Kg)	UK (Kg)
Heavy (H)	136,000	136,0000
Medium (M)	< 136,000 and > 7000	< 136,000 and > 40,000
Small (S)	-	40,000 or less and >17,000
Light (L)	7000 or less	17,000 or less

In the UK pilots shall adhere to the UK minimum distance and time separation requirements published in AIC P001/2015 when taking off or landing whether operating in the UK or not. These criteria are:

WAKE TURBULENCE SEPARATION MINIMA – FINAL APPROACH

Leading Aircraft	Following Aircraft	Minimum Distance (Nm)
A380	Heavy/Medium/Small/Light	6/7/7/8
Heavy	Heavy/Medium/Small/Light	4/5/6/7
Medium	Medium/Small/Light	3/4/6
Small	Medium/Small/Light	3/4

Where the leading medium aircraft is a B757 the minimum distance shall be increased to 4 miles. The minima specified in the above table are to be applied when:

a. An aircraft is operating directly behind another aircraft at the same altitude or less than 1000 ft. below; or

b. An aircraft is crossing behind another aircraft at the same altitude or less than 1000 ft. below; or

c. Both aircraft are using the same runway or parallel runways separated by less than 760 m (2500 ft.).

WAKE TURBULENCE SEPARATION MINIMA – DEPARTURES

LEADING AIRCRAFT	FOLLOWING AIRCRAFT	MINIMUM WAKE TURBULENCE SEPARATION AT THE TIME AIRCRAFT ARE AIRBORNE	
A380	Heavy (including A380)	Departing from the same position or From a parallel runway separated < 760m (2500ft)	2 minutes
A380	Medium (upper and lower)/Small/Light	Departing from the same position or From a parallel runway separated < 760m (2500ft)	3 minutes
Heavy	Medium (upper and lower)/Small/Light	Departing from the same position or From a parallel runway separated < 760m (2500ft)	2 minutes
Medium (upper and lower)/Small	Light	Departing from the same position or From a parallel runway separated < 760m (2500ft)	2 minutes
A380	Heavy (including A380)	Departing from an intermediate point on the same runway or From an intermediate point of a parallel runway separated < 760m (2500ft)	3 minutes
A380	Medium (upper and lower) Small/Light	Departing from an intermediate point on the same runway or From an intermediate point of a parallel runway separated < 760m (2500ft)	4 minutes
Heavy (full-length take-off)	Medium/Small/Light	Departing from an intermediate point on the same runway or From an intermediate point of a parallel runway separated < 760m (2500ft)	3 minutes
Medium/Small	Light	Departing from an intermediate point on the same runway or From an intermediate point of a parallel runway separated < 760m (2500ft)	3 minutes

The minima specified above apply when the aircraft are using:

a. The same runway;

b. Parallel runways separated by less than 760 m (2500 ft.);

c. Crossing runways if the projected flight path of the second aircraft will cross the projected flight path of the first aircraft at the same altitude or less than 300 m (1000 ft.) below;

d. Parallel runways separated by 760 m (2500 ft.) or more, if the projected flight path of the second aircraft will cross the projected flight path of the first aircraft at the same altitude or less than 300 m (1000 ft.) below.

In the event of Wake Turbulence being encountered, *Report Form SRG 1423* should be submitted to:

Wake Turbulence Analysis Team
NATS Corporate and Technical Centre
4000 Parkway
Whiteley
Hampshire
PO15 7FL

Actions taken when crossing traffic, during take-off and landing.

AVOIDING WAKE TURBULENCE

Avoid wake turbulence by flying above and upwind of the path of other aircraft.

The main aim of wake turbulence avoidance is to avoid passing through it at all, especially in flight.

On Take-Off

When taking off behind a large aircraft which has itself just taken off, commence your take-off at the end of the runway so that you will become airborne in an area well before the point where the heavy aircraft rotated or to where its vortices may have drifted. If doubtful, delay your take-off.

Do not use an intersection departure (less than the full length of the runway) behind a heavy aircraft, as this may bring your flightpath closer to its wake turbulence.

Manoeuvre to avoid the vortices in flight by climbing steeply (but not too slowly, as speed is a safety factor if you strike wake turbulence) or turning away from where you think the wake turbulence is.

When taking off after a heavy aircraft has landed, plan to become airborne well past the point where it flared and landed.

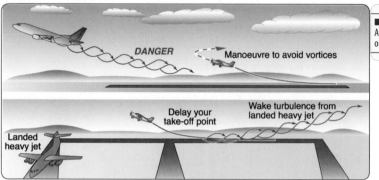

■ Figure 5-3
Avoid wake turbulence on your take-off

If a heavy aircraft has taken off on a different runway and you expect to be airborne prior to the intersection of the runways, observe that the heavy aircraft was still on the ground until well past the intersection, before you commence your take-off.

Always avoid flying through the wake of a heavy aircraft, especially at low speed near the ground.

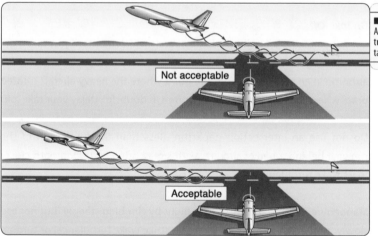

■ Figure 5-4
Awareness of wake turbulence for your take-off

IN THE CIRCUIT

Avoid flying below and behind large aircraft. Fly a few hundred feet above them, a thousand feet below them or to windward of them. Calm days where there is no turbulence to break up the vortices are perhaps the most dangerous.

■ *Figure 5-5*
Avoidance of wake turbulence in the circuit area

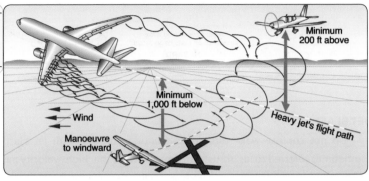

ON APPROACH TO LAND

When following a preceding landing heavy aircraft, fly above its approach path and land well beyond its touchdown point. This is usually possible in a light aircraft landing on a long runway where heavy aircraft are landing.

■ *Figure 5-6*
Avoidance of wake turbulence on your approach

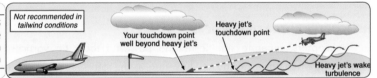

When landing on a runway where a heavy aircraft has just taken off, touchdown well short of its lift-off point or where you think the vortices may have drifted to. The normal touchdown zone will probably ensure this.

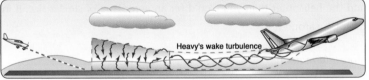
■ *Figure 5-7*
Landing behind a heavy aircraft that has taken off

If a preceding heavy aircraft has discontinued its approach and gone around, its turbulent wake will be a hazard to a following aircraft. You should consider changing your flightpath in these circumstances.

Note: Accentuated wake
turbulence on Heavy's go-around
HAZARD

■ *Figure 5-8*
Making an approach
behind a heavy aircraft
that has gone around

JET BLAST

Do not confuse wake turbulence (wingtip vortices) with jet blast (sometimes referred to as thrust stream), which is the high-velocity air exhausted from a jet engine or a large propeller-driven aircraft, especially a turbo-prop. Jet blast can be dangerous to a light aircraft taxiing on the ground behind a jet or large propeller-driven aircraft. Always position your aeroplane when taxiing or when stopped to avoid any potential jet blast.

■ *Figure 5-9*
Wake turbulence is
different from jet blast

HELICOPTER ROTOR TIP VORTICES

Helicopters generate significant and powerful rotor tip vortices, particularly when hover-taxiing and hovering, as the rotors are supporting the full weight of the helicopter.

> Avoid helicopters by a wide margin, especially if they are hover-taxiing

Take extra care when taking off and landing near air-taxiing helicopters, as their rotor tip vortices will drift downwind, and may drift across your runway. When on final approach, it may not be apparent to you at which stage of flight the helicopter is – so allow a larger space between yourself and the helicopter than you would for an aeroplane of similar size. If in doubt, go around.

More Information

Read the CAA's *General Aviation Safety Sense leaflet No. 15* – it contains excellent practical information on wake turbulence and rotor tip vortices.

Pilots of light aircraft should avoid operating within three rotor diameters of any helicopter in a slow hover taxi or stationary hover. As a visual indicator: if the skids / wheels of the helicopter are resting on the surface then the helicopter will be producing a much reduced downwash. Caution should be exercised however since the helicopter may lift into the hover with little or no notice, thus increasing downwash significantly.

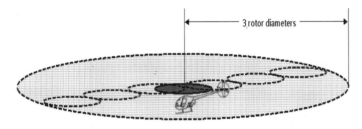

FURTHER READING:

The following material may provide useful when preparing for your exam:

- AIC P001/2015.

INTENTIONALLY BLANK

Wake Turbulence

1. Which scenario from the answers below, is likely to create the largest amount of wake turbulence:

   a. Large aeroplane, flying slowly, flaps retracted in light winds.
   b. Small aeroplane, flying slowly, flaps retracted in light winds.
   c. Large aeroplane, flying fast, flaps retracted.
   d. Small aeroplane, flying fast, flaps retracted.

2. A light aircraft following an Airbus A380 requires a minimum separation of how many nautical miles?

   a. 4 NM
   b. 5 NM
   c. 7 NM
   d. 8 NM

3. Wake turbulence:

   a. Only occurs when an aircraft is in the cruise phase of flight.
   b. Is confined to helicopters.
   c. Is produced by all lighter than air vessels.
   d. Is produced when an aircraft generates lift or when a helicopter hovers.

4. Wake turbulence:

   a. Is produced by an aircraft's jet engine.
   b. Is a hazard to a light aircraft taxiing within 3 rotor dimensions of a hovering helicopter.
   c. Is produced by an aircraft when it is on the ground.
   d. Is an aircraft only phenomenon.

5. In which of the following scenarios could a wake turbulence encounter occur?

   a. Departing from a crossing runway after another aircraft rotated beyond the intersection.
   b. Upwind of an aircraft that has executed a missed approach.
   c. Crossing behind a 'Heavy' aircraft 1000ft above, on an approach.
   d. Landing on a crossing runway after another aircraft rotated prior to the intersection.

Emergency & Precautionary Landings

Definition

ICAO Annex 12 defines two types of emergencies:

Distress – A condition of being threatened by serious and/or imminent danger and of requiring immediate assistance.

Urgency – A condition concerning the safety of an aircraft or other vehicle, or of some person on board or within sight, but which does not require immediate assistance.

When an aircraft declares an emergency, the state's Rescue Coordination Centre will allocate one of three emergency phases:

Uncertainty Phase: A situation wherein uncertainty exists as to the safety of an aircraft and its occupants.

Alert Phase: A situation wherein apprehension exists as to the safety of an aircraft and its occupants.

Distress Phase: A situation wherein there is a reasonable certainty that an aircraft and its occupants are threatened by grave and imminent danger and require immediate assistance.

A **Rescue Coordination Centre (RCC)** is a unit responsible for promoting efficient organisation of search and rescue services and for coordinating the conduct of search and rescue operations within a search and rescue region.

■ *Figure 6-1*
Rescue Coordination
Centre

When a pilot transmits a distress call on the international distress frequencies of 121.500 or 243 MHz the RCC will be notified and co-ordinate the appropriate response.

Cause

It is impossible to describe every possible scenario which may constitute an emergency and this depends on numerous factors such as type of aircraft, pilot experience, weather conditions, severity of event, time, and system redundancy, etc. Indeed the pilot-in-command can declare an emergency for any condition, which he/she feels puts the aircraft and its occupants in danger. If in doubt, it is wise to ask for help early, before the situation gets critical; you can always downgrade a 'MAYDAY' to a 'PAN' once you have a better grasp of the situation.

As a guide only, the following situations may warrant declaring an emergency using the radio phrase '**MAYDAY, MAYDAY, MAYDAY**' in a light aircraft:

- Engine Failure
- Emergency descent
- Fire or Smoke
- Mid-air collision
- Loss of control
- Hijack
- Fuel leak
- Undercarriage failure
- Any time-critical non-normal event

As a guide only, the following situations may warrant declaring an emergency using the radio phrase '**PAN PAN, PAN PAN, PAN PAN**' in a light aircraft:

- Alternator failure
- Cracked windscreen
- Landing on a flat tyre
- Sick passenger
- Any non-normal event which is not time-critical

The important thing to do in any non-normal event is to fly the aircraft first, navigate to a point of safety, complete the appropriate checklist, and communicate to both ATC and the passengers. The most common time-critical emergency that affects light aircraft is an engine failure, which can be avoided through proper fuel planning and conducting regular carburettor ice checks. Initial actions following an engine failure/rough running engine are to:

- Trim for the best glide speed (range if overwater)
- Plan forced landing pattern
- Declare a 'MAYDAY' call to ATC and set transponder code 7700
- Complete the following generic fault finding checks:

1. Fuel Selector...........................Tank containing fuel
2. Electric fuel pump.....................ON
3. Mixture................................Check RICH
4. Carburettor heat......................ON
5. Engine gauges........................Check for indication of power loss
6. Primer................................Check locked

If no fuel pressure is indicated, check tank selector position is on a tank containing fuel. Attempt restart, if power is restored:

7. Carburettor heat......................OFF
8. Electric fuel pump....................OFF
9. If power is not restored, prepare for a power off landing
   – Trim for best glide speed.

If time permits consider turning the magnetos to 'L' then 'R' then back to '**BOTH**' to isolate a faulty magneto. Move the throttle and mixture controls smoothly to different settings to see if there is a fuel restriction, linkage failure, or too rich/leaner mixture being supplied to the engine. If fuel contamination/starvation is suspected changing tanks will provide an alternate supply.

Note. — that in the case of contaminated fuel, pressure indications will be normal.

Once you have transmitted either a '**MAYDAY**' or '**PAN**' call, enter one of following the transponder codes, unless instructed to do otherwise by ATC:

7700 – General Emergency
7600 – Loss of Communication
7500 – Unlawful interference

EMERG
AFS001↑ U
A025↑
M327
GOTT LJ45

■ *Figure 6-2*
A radar screen shot of an aircraft squawking 7700

Once the situation has been contained and only if time permits, consider supplying ATC with more information regarding the effect the problem will have on the approach and landing; although more appropriate to larger aircraft, the following mnemonic may help and is often used by commercial pilots (sometimes referred to as a '**NITS**' briefing):

Nature of Problem
Intentions
Time to handle the situation
Special Instructions

FOR EXAMPLE: *Farnborough Radar G-AB, I have suffered an alternator failure, I am diverting to Shoreham airport, I require 5 minutes in my present position to complete the checklist, I will then require a radar heading to Shoreham airport and inform Shoreham ATC that I want to complete an overhead join which may be executed non-radio.*

Passenger Information

The pilot-in-command (PIC) is required by law to complete a safety briefing before departure to all passengers on board the aircraft; however, as the PIC you may have to give them further, more specific instructions in the event of an emergency. There are two categories of emergencies:

1. **PLANNED** – Time available to brief passengers, secure the cockpit/ seating area, ready emergency equipment.
2. **UNPLANNED** – No warning given, normally occurs at a critical phase of flight such as the take-off or landing, actions have to be specific and direct.

Items that should be covered during the initial safety brief should include:
- Emergency exit locations and use.
- Operation of seat belts.
- Location and use of both the fire extinguisher and first aid kit.
- Correct seating position and adjustment.
- Instruction to remain clear of the controls.
- Brace position.

The **NITS** briefing described earlier, may serve as a framework to inform the passengers of the situation and what you require them to do. What you tell them, and specifically how to position them for landing will depend on the type of emergency, time available, aircraft type, survival equipment on board, and the landing surface.

In the event of a planned emergency on land instruct passengers:
- To remove all sharp objects, dentures and high-heeled shoes – stow in passenger compartments or under the seat.
- Location of the emergency exit(s) and alternatives.
- How to fasten, tighten seat belts and when and how to release them.
- How to get into the brace position and how long to maintain it for.
- Location and operation of Emergency Locator Transmitter and/or Personal Locator Beacons.

In addition to those points above, in the event of a ditching instruct passengers:

■ *Figure 6-3*
Inflate the life jackets and raft once outside the aircraft

- To don life jackets and inflate them only once outside the aircraft, but before entering the water, or life raft.
- On the location and operation of the life raft, inflate only once outside the aircraft.
- The location of the grab bag (if applicable).

Approximately 15 seconds before impact inform passengers to adopt the Brace position by shouting loudly '**BRACE BRACE, BRACE BRACE, BRACE BRACE**'.

Some modern aircraft such as the Cirrus SR20 and SR22 are fitted with a ballistic parachute recovery system that fires a parachute from the rear fuselage and allows the aircraft to drift down. The operation of this system and different BRACE position should be specifically briefed on the ground, and the PIC should read the applicable entry in the Aircraft Flight Manual regarding its use. Consideration should be given to the type of scenarios in which it will be deployed.

■ *Figure 6-4*
Cirrus SR20 and SR22 aircraft have a parachute system which requires a specific passenger briefing and brace position.

Evacuation

Touchdown should normally be made at the lowest possible airspeed. When committed to a landing, close the throttle control and turn "OFF" the master and ignition switches. Flaps may be used as desired. Turn the fuel selector valve to "OFF" and move the mixture to idle cut-off. The seat belts and shoulder harness (if installed) should be tightened.

Once the aircraft comes to rest, gather information and assess the situation, if an evacuation is required (following an engine failure for example) complete the evacuation checklist, or equivalent. Once the evacuation checklist is complete, instruct passengers to evacuate the aircraft by shouting '**EVACUATE EVACUATE UNDO YOUR SEAT BELTS AND GET OUT**'. Instruct passengers to use the nearest emergency exit; in the case of a light aircraft with only one door this is pretty obvious, however, larger aircraft may have more. Gather any suitable emergency equipment as time permits.

ACTION AFTER LANDING

Post evacuation on land, you should:

- Direct passengers upwind of the aircraft.
- Administer first aid as required.
- Conduct a head count.
- Contact the emergency services.
- Activate Personal Locator Beacons if in a remote location.
- Reassure passengers.
- Do not return to the aircraft unless there is no fire present and it is absolutely necessary for survival.

Post evacuation on water you should:

- Instruct passengers not to inflate their life jackets until outside the aircraft, but before entering the life raft/dinghy or the water if no life raft/dinghy is available.
- Locate the grab bag and life raft – inflate the life raft once outside the aircraft.
- Group passengers together, remain inside the life raft and hold on to any grasp handles fitted.
- Administer first aid as required.
- Activate Personal Locator Beacons.

Ditching in Water

AIM: *To alight on water as successfully as possible, if ditching is the only available option.*

Note. – This exercise is not part of the EASA Part-FCL syllabus.

Being forced to ditch in the ocean is a remote possibility; however, it is worthwhile having a suitable procedure in the back of your mind.

Try to land near a ship or in a shipping lane if possible. Make a Mayday radio call before too much height is lost to ensure the best chance of reception by ground stations.

LANDING DIRECTION

If the water is smooth, or smooth with a very long swell, then land into wind.

If there is a large swell or rough sea, then land along the swell, even if you have to accept a crosswind. This avoids the danger of nosing into a big wave. Waves generally move downwind except near a shoreline or in fast-moving estuaries, but swells may not bear any relationship to surface wind direction.

Clues to wind direction include:
- Wave direction;
- Wind lanes (the streaked effect being more apparent when viewed downwind);
- Gust ripples on the water surface;
- Aeroplane drift.

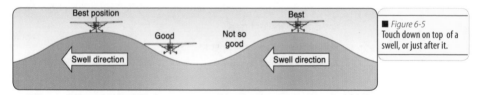

■ *Figure 6-5*
Touch down on top of a swell, or just after it.

FLYING THE MANOEUVRE

If your engine is running, use a powered approach for ditching. From altitude, water generally appears to be calmer than it is. Fly low and study the water surface before ditching.

Generally ditch with an early stage of flap set, using a low speed, a high nose attitude (tail-down) and a low rate of descent controlled by power (if available). Power gives you a lot more control over the touchdown point, so avoid running out of fuel prior to ditching.

Touch down with as low a flying speed as possible, but do not stall in.

ALERT THE PASSENGERS

Warn the passengers. Buckle up and don life-jackets, if available, but do not inflate them until in the water, as they may restrict the evacuation. Remove headsets and anything else that may get in the way during the evacuation.

Be prepared for a double impact – the first when the tail strikes the water, the second (and greater) when the nose hits the water. The aircraft may also slew to one side.

Evacuation (if possible) should be carried out as calmly as possible, life-jackets being inflated outside the cabin. The PIC should supervise.

INTENTIONALLY BLANK

Emergency & Precautionary Landings

1. What is the definition of distress?

   a. A condition of being threatened by serious and/or imminent danger and of requiring immediate assistance.

   b. A condition concerning the safety of an aircraft or other vehicle, or of some person on board or within sight, but which does not require immediate assistance.

   c. Any time the Pilot-in-Command is apprehensive.

   d. A condition of being stressed by serious and/or imminent danger and of requiring immediate assistance.

2. What is the definition of urgency?

   a. A condition concerning the safety of an aircraft or other vehicle.

   b. A condition concerning the safety of an aircraft or other vehicle, or of some person on board or within sight, but which does not require immediate assistance.

   c. A condition where the Pilot-in-Command wants to a get home quickly.

   d. A condition of being threatened by serious and/or imminent danger and of requiring immediate assistance.

3. If an engine fails in flight in a single engine aircraft which is over land, what are the correct generic actions?

   a. Trim for the best glide speed, plan a forced landing pattern, declare a 'MAYDAY', check fuel selector ON and change fuel tanks, mixture rich, carburettor heat on, check engine gauges, primer locked, magnetos on both – attempt restart.

   b. Declare a MAYDAY and if you have a parachute abandon the aircraft immediately.

   c. Trim for the best glide speed, plan a forced landing pattern, declare a 'MAYDAY', throttle closed, mixture ICO, fuel selector off, magnetos off, battery master off.

   d. Do nothing; the engine will come back to life in its own time.

4. What is the emergency transponder code?

   a. 7500.

   b. 7600.

   c. 7700.

   d. 7000.

5.   Regarding life jackets:

    a.   The Pilot-in-Command should inflate his life jacket before exiting the aircraft and instruct the passengers to do the same.

    b.   The passengers should inflate their jackets before ditching, however the Pilot-in-Command should wait until after exiting the aircraft.

    c.   Both the Pilot-in-Command and passengers should inflate their life jackets once outside the aircraft.

    d.   It doesn't matter.

6.   When ditching the pilot should:

    a.   Land as slowly as possible into a rising swell, with a strong headwind.

    b.   Land as slowly as possible, declare a 'MAYDAY', and squawk 7700 as early as possible.

    c.   Glide at best range speed to allow the longest time airborne.

    d.   Glide at best range speed, squawk 7600, and turn away from any shipping.

7.   In a ditching scenario, the pilot should instruct passengers to don life jackets and inflate them:

    a.   In the aircraft.

    b.   Once in the dinghy, or if no dinghy is available once in the water.

    c.   Outside the aircraft but before entering the water, or dinghy if one is available.

    d.   Once in the water.

8.   In a ditching situation best practice is to:

    a.   Inflate a life jacket before ditching to give crash protection.

    b.   Inflate a life jacket using the manual inflation tube once in the water.

    c.   Inflate a life jacket before completing a running jump off the fuselage.

    d.   Inflate a life jacket after leaving the aircraft but before entering the dinghy or the water if no dinghy is available.

9.   In the event of a planned emergency on land instruct passengers:

    a.   To remove all sharp objects, dentures and high-heeled shoes – stow in passenger compartments or under the seat.

    b.   Not to panic.

    c.   Turn on all mobile phones.

    d.   Loosen seat belts ready for evacuation.

10.   When should the command 'BRACE BRACE' be given?

    a.   15 minutes before impact.

    b.   15 seconds before impact.

    c.   25 seconds before impact.

    d.   5 seconds before impact.

11. In the event of an evacuation what are the generic actions to shut down the aircraft and limit the risk of a fire?

   a. Battery master off, fuel on, ignition 'OFF', run.

   b. Throttle closed, master switch 'OFF', fuel selector 'OFF', mixture ICO.

   c. Throttle closed, master switch 'ON', fuel selector 'ON', mixture ICO.

   d. Getting out of the aircraft is the most important action, you can always return.

Contaminated Runways

Kinds of Contamination

Take-off and landing performance is affected by, amongst other things, runway surface condition; for example performance calculations on a grass runway will be greater than those on an equivalent tarmac one. A tarmac runway is designed and built to allow precipitation to drain away from the surface, however, when the amount exceeds a natural run off point it will remain on the runway. On a grass runway, or unprepared strip (and to a certain extent a tarmac one too), the drainage depends on local geology, climatology, type of surface, and slope. Matting can be laid on the surface to improve drainage and reduce runway closure periods. When a runway has precipitation on it, it reduces the braking coefficient, which is a measure of the amount of friction available on the runway between the tyre and the surface. The depth and type of precipitation determines the braking coefficient. The more severe the precipitation, the smaller the coefficient and less grip the wheel has on the runway; therefore, the less effective the brakes are at stopping the aircraft.

■ *Figure 7-1*
Take-off and landing performance depends greatly on the runway surface and condition

The following definition of a contaminated runway is the one found in EASA Opinion No 04/2011 Annex 1 (Definitions) and has been adopted by the CAA:

A runway is considered to be contaminated when more than 25% of the runway surface area (whether in isolated areas or not) within the required length and width being used is covered by the following:

a. Surface water more than 3 mm deep, or by slush or loose snow equivalent to more than 3 mm of water;

b. Snow which has been compressed into a solid mass which resists further compression and will hold together or break into lumps if picked up (compacted snow); or

c. Ice, including wet ice.

A typical example of a contaminated runway, that a private pilot may face, is when a small grass airfield's runway becomes FLOODED after a heavy period of prolonged rainfall. It even happens at the larger ones as the picture below shows:

■ *Figure 7-2*
Flooded runway

The presence of water on a runway will be reported to the pilot using the following descriptions:

REPORTING TERM	SURFACE CONDITION
DRY	The surface is not affected by water, slush, snow, or ice. *NOTE: Reports that the runway is dry are not normally passed to pilots. If no runway surface report is passed, the runway can be assumed to be dry.*
DAMP	The surface shows a change of colour due to moisture. *NOTE: If there is sufficient moisture to produce a surface film or the surface appears reflective, the runway will be reported as WET.*
WET	The surface is soaked but no significant patches of standing water are visible. *NOTE: Standing water is considered to exist when water on the runway surface is deeper than 3 mm. Patches of standing water covering more than 25% of the assessed area will be reported as WATER PATCHES and should be considered as CONTAMINATED.*
WATER PATCHES	Significant patches of standing water are visible. *NOTE: Water patches will be reported when more than 25% of the assessed area is covered by water more than 3 mm deep.*
FLOODED	Extensive patches of standing water are visible. *NOTE: Flooded will be reported when more than 50% of the assessed area is covered by water more than 3 mm deep.*

For EU-OPS performance, runways reported as DRY, DAMP or WET should be considered as NOT CONTAMINATED. Runways reported as WATER PATCHES or FLOODED should be considered as CONTAMINATED.

In the picture above the runway is contaminated with snow; in the UK operators of small airfields (and sometimes large ones too!) do not have the necessary equipment to clear the runway from contaminants and often close the airfield.

Light aircraft are not designed to operate from them so the best advice is to delay take-off or landing, and if necessary, divert to an airfield that has better weather conditions.

Estimated Surface Friction & Friction Coefficient

Historically runway surface condition reports have been made using any combination of the following methods:

a. Measuring type and depth of contamination;

b. Readings from runway friction measuring devices; and

c. Pilot braking action reports (PIREPs).

There is no universally accepted method to measure the surface friction of a runway and this has led to standardisation issues across the world. The CAA publishes CAP 683 'The Assessment of Runway Surface Friction Characteristics' which describes in great detail the procedures that airfields must adopt when measuring the surface friction of a runway, however, it only applies to paved runways with an Accelerate Stop Distance Available (ASDA) of 1,200 metres or greater in length and used for public transport operations by aeroplanes with a maximum take-off weight (MTOW) in excess of 2730 kg. It is not applicable to grass runways, helicopter landing sites or waterdromes. On paved runways where prescribed public transport operations are not carried out, the application of the procedures is at the discretion of the aerodrome operator.

Therefore, if you operate from an airfield that doesn't meet the criteria above, you have no way of knowing how the brakes will react with precipitation on the runway surface; this is often referred to as the 'braking action'.

For the purpose of a runway surface friction assessment the following definitions apply:

CFME – Continuous Friction Measuring Equipment.

Runway Surface Friction Assessment – The assessment of friction carried out under conditions of self- wetting using a CFME.

Airport operators must periodically assess the runway friction in order to confirm that aircraft will stop safely on a **WET** runway. Runway Surface Friction Assessment only applies to runways that are **NOT** contaminated because of the potential for unreliable readings.

■ *Figure 7-4*
A Continuous Friction
Measuring Unit

A Runway Surface Friction Assessment is achieved by conducting 'Runs' which is where a vehicle drives up and down a runway several times. On each 'Run' the vehicle tows a machine called a Continuous Friction Measuring Unit (CFMU) which has the ability to assess the friction available if the runway were wet. All the results are recorded and then analysed to assess whether any maintenance action is required to improve the surface condition.

In the UK, friction coefficients used to be reported as a two-digit number obtained from measuring friction characteristics on contaminated runways using Continuous Friction Measuring Equipment (CFME). This was stopped a number of years ago and since then UK runway surface condition reports have been given for each third of a runway in the form of type and depth of contaminant together with percentage coverage.

A contaminated runway will have a SNOWTAM issued by the airport operator. A SNOWTAM is a special series NOTAM notifying the presence or removal of hazardous conditions caused by snow, ice, slush, or standing water associated with snow, slush, and ice on the movement area, by means of a specific format.

Essentially, it is informing the pilot of the type of contamination, depth, length of runway available, and braking action (if provided by the airport operator). A SNOWTAM is not easy to decode as you can see from the example below, so reference to the UK AIP, or suitable flight guide, will be required.

GG EGZZSBLL EGZZSLHR
070645 EGLLZGZX
SWEG0149 EGLL 11070620
SNOWTAM 0149
A) EGLL B) 11070620 C) 05 D) . . . P)
C) 09L D) . . . P)
C) 09R D) . . . P)
R) NO S) 11070920 T) DEICING

Where:

A. AERODROME IDENTIFIER
B. DATE/TIME OF OBSERVATION (UTC)
C. RUNWAY DESIGNATOR
D. CLEARED RUNWAY LENGTH (if less than published length)
E. CLEARED RUNWAY WIDTH (if less than published width)
F. DEPOSITS OVER TOTAL RUNWAY LENGTH (Observed on each third of the runway)

G. MEAN DEPTH OF DEPOSITS (mm) (for each third of total runway length)
H. FRICTION MEASUREMENTS OR ESTIMATES (for each third of runway length)
I. Not used
J. CRITICAL SNOWBANKS (if present)
K. RUNWAY LIGHTS (if obscured)
L. FURTHER CLEARING OPERATIONS (if planned)
M. FURTHER CLEARANCE EXPECTED TO BE COMPLETED BY . . . (UTC)
N. TAXIWAY
O. Not used
P. TAXIWAY SNOWBANKS
Q. Not used
R. APRON
S. NEXT PLANNED OBSERVATION/MEASUREMENT
T. PLAIN LANGUAGE REMARKS

Operating on a contaminated runway presents the following problems to **ALL** aircraft:

- Reduced braking action.
- Reduced ground control authority.
- Reduced traffic flow rates.
- Restrictive crosswind limits.
- Reduced operating weights.
- Potential damage to airframe and engines due to ingestion of contaminant.
- Greater potential for runway overrun.

In conclusion, contaminated runway operations in the UK are rare, however, light aircraft are not designed, nor equipped, to operate on contaminated runways, therefore delay departure or arrival, and if airborne divert to the nearest suitable airfield.

FURTHER READING:
The following articles and AICs have further guidance and a more in-depth description of operating on contaminated runways, which you may find useful when preparing for your exam:

- AIC P 86/2007
- CAP 683

INTENTIONALLY BLANK

Contaminated Runways

1.   What is the definition of a 'WET' runway?

   a.   The surface is soaked but no significant patches of standing water are visible.
   b.   Significant patches of standing water are visible.
   c.   It is damp to touch.
   d.   Extensive patches of standing water are visible.

2.   Which of the following statements is correct regarding operations on a contaminated runway?

   a.   Operations by all aircraft classes and types should be avoided whenever possible.
   b.   Whenever a departure from a contaminated runway is unavoidable, adopt the short field take-off technique.
   c.   Whenever a departure from a contaminated runway is unavoidable, use the full length of the runway available, the lowest take-off flap setting possible and maximum take-off power.
   d.   Operations from contaminated runways require little risk assessment by the Pilot-in-Command.

3.   A runway is classed as contaminated if it is:

   a.   'DRY'.
   b.   Notified as 'WET'.
   c.   Notified as having 'WATER PATCHES'.
   d.   Notified as 'DAMP'.

4.   ATC report to you that the runway is 'FLOODED', this means that:

   a.   Extensive patches of standing water are visible.
   b.   The runway is safe to use.
   c.   Significant patches of standing water are visible.
   d.   This term only applies to large aeroplanes.

5.   With regard to contaminated runway operations which of the following statements is true?

   a.   The friction coefficient increases with the amount of precipitation on the runway.
   b.   The friction coefficient on ice increases therefore the landing distance reduces.
   c.   Both departure and arrival on a contaminated runway by any aircraft should be avoided if possible.
   d.   A pilot should use a reduced power setting for take-off on a contaminated runway.

6.   ATC report to you that the runway is 'WET', is the runway contaminated?

    a.   No.

    b.   Yes.

    c.   This term only applies to large aircraft.

    d.   Only if more than 20% is covered with a depth greater than 2 mm.

7.   A runway is said to be contaminated if it:

    a.   Is 'WET'.

    b.   Has greater than 3 mm of slush over 22% of the surface area.

    c.   Has ice covering more than 25% of the runway surface area within the required width and length.

    d.   Is 'DAMP'.

Abbreviations

A/G	Air to Ground
A320	Airbus A320
AFM	Aircraft Flight Manual
AIC	Aeronautical Information Circular
AIP	Aeronautical Information Publication
ANSV	Agenzia Nazionale per la Sicurezza del Volo
AOM	Aerodrome Operating Minima
APM	Air Pilot Manual
ASDA	Accelerate Stop Distance Available
ATC	Air Traffic Control
ATSU	Air Traffic Service Unit
AVGAS	Aviation Gasoline
BCF	BromoChlorodiFluoromethane
CAA	Civil Aviation Authority
CAT	Category
CFME	Continuous Friction Measuring Equipment
CFMU	Continuous Friction Measuring Unit
CO$_2$	Carbon Dioxide
DA	Decision Altitude
EASA	European Aviation Safety Agency
ECU	Engine Control Unit
ELT	Emergency Locator Transmitter
EU-OPS	European Operations
EVS	Enhanced Vision System
FCL	Flight Crew Licensing
FISO	Flight Information Service Officer
FSTD	Flight Synthetic Training Device
HALON	Halogenated hydrocarbons
HUD	Head Up Display

ICAO	International Civil Aviation Organisation
ICO	Idle Cut Off
ILS	Instrument Landing System
IMC	Instrument Metrological Conditions
LAPL	Light Aircraft Pilots Licence
LVPs	Low Visibility Procedures
MDA	Minimum Descent Altitude
MTOW	Maximum Take-Off Weight
NAP	Noise Abatement Procedure
NOTAM	Notice To Airmen
NPR	Noise Preferential Routing
PIC	Pilot-in-Command
PIREPS	Pilot Reports
POH	Pilot's Operating Handbook
PPL	Private Pilots Licence
RCC	Rescue Coordination Centre
RNAV	Area Navigation
RVR	Runway Visual Range
SA	Situational Awareness
SNOWTAM	Snow Notice To Airmen
TCDSN	Type-Certificate Data Sheet for Noise
VFE	Velocity Flap Extension
VLE	Velocity Leg Extension
VMC	Visual Meteorological Conditions
VNO	Velocity Normal Operation

Index – Operational Procedures

A

Abbreviations 399
Acts of Unlawful Interference 257
Aerial Work 257
Aerodrome Boundary Markers 306
Aerodrome Operating Minima (AOM) 257
Aerodrome Signals & Markings 302
Aircraft Operating Manual 258
Airworthy 258
Alert Phase 375
Alternate Aerodrome 259
Applicability 271
Area Navigation (RNAV) 259
Automatic Deployable ELT (ELT(AD)) 260
Automatic Fixed ELT (ELT(AF)) 260
Automatic Portable ELT (ELT(AP)) 260
AVGAS 340

B

BromoChlorodiFluoromethane (BCF) 341

C

CAP 637 319
Carbon Monoxide 344
Carburettor Fire 335
CAT I, II and III 322
CFME 393
checklist 334
Compliance with Laws,
    Regulations & Procedures 284
Contaminated runways 389
Crosswind Effect 358

D

DAMP 391
Dangerous Goods 260
Definitions 257
Destination Alternate 259
Displaced Threshold Markings 308
Distress 375
Ditching in Water 381
DRY 391

E

Effect of Windshear 351
Emergency Locator
    Transmitter (ELT) 260
Emergency & precautionary
    landings 375
Emergency Use Only 307
Engine Fire 336
Enhanced Vision System (EVS) 260
En-route Alternate 259
Environmental Protection Act 1990 291
Evacuation 380

F

Fire in the Cabin and Cockpit 339
Fire or Smoke 330
Flight crew members
    at duty stations 284
Flight Planning 284
Flight Procedure 293
Flight Recorder 261
Flight Simulation
    Training Device (FSTD) 261
Flight Simulator 261
FLOODED 391
friction coefficient 392
Fuel 333
Fuel based fire 337

G

Gliding 304
green flag 302

H

Halogenated hydrocarbons (Halons) 341
Halon 341
Head-Up Display (HUD) 262
Helicopter Operations 304
Helicopter Rotor Tip Vortices 370
Holding Point on Paved Taxiway 305
Hydrogen Cyanide 344, 345

I

ICAO Annexes 257
Ignition 333
Instrument
  Meteorological Conditions (IMC) 262
International Flights (ICAO Annex 6) 279

L

Land in Emergency Only 307
Landing Dangerous 307
Landing Distance Available (LDA) 270
Light Aircraft Area 306
Light Signals (Rule 61) 310
Low Visibility Procedures (LVPs) 321

M

Markers on Unpaved
  Manoeuvring Areas 306
MAYDAY 338

N

NITS 378
Noise Abatement Procedure 291
Noise Act 1996 291
Noise Certificate 293

O

Overshoot Effect 351, 356
Oxygen 333

P

Parallel yellow lines 305
Passengers 284
Psychoactive Substances 263

R

red flag 303
Rescue Coordination Centre (RCC) 375
Right-Hand Circuit 303
runway hotspot 318
Runway/Stopway Boundary Markers 306
Runway Surface Friction Assessment 393
Runway to be Used 307
Runway Visual Range (RVR) 263

S

Safety Harness 285
Seat Belts 285
Signals Area 309
Signals on Paved
  Runways and Taxiways 304
Situational Awareness (SA) 324
Smoke in the Cockpit and Cabin 344
SNOWTAM 394
Special Precautions 303
surface friction 392
Survival ELT (ELT(S)) 260

T

Take-off Alternate 259
Take-off Clearance 329
Taxi Clearances 327
threshold marking 309
Type-Certificate Data Sheet
  for Noise (TCDSN) 292

U

Uncertainty Phase 375
Undershoot Effect 352, 356
Unlawful seizure 257
Unserviceable Portion 306
Urgency 375

V

Visual Meteorological
  Conditions (VMC) 263

W

Wake turbulence 363
WATER PATCHES 391
WET 391
white dumb-bell 303
Wig Wags 320
Windshear 353
Windshear and Microburst 351
Windshear Reversal Effect 356

Y

yellow cross 304